Day Mark St. Martins I.
Also White Red & White bands
185 f.t above High Water

CW00821425

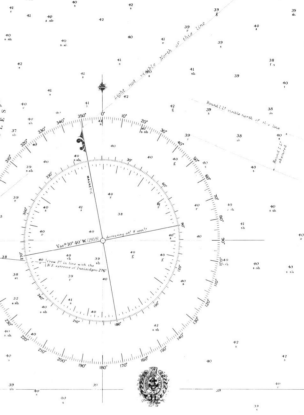

ENGLAND — WEST COAST

THE SCILLY ISLES

CHIEFLY FROM SURVEYS BY STAFF CAPTAIN W.F.MAXWELL,R.N.,1898-1904.

assisted by Staff Commander T.C.Pascoe, R.N. and Sub Lieutenant E.A.Forbes, R.N.R.

The northern part & the outer soundings from a Survey by Captain G.Williams and
Staff Commander J.S.Wells,R.N.,1860-3.

The Topography is taken chiefly from the Ordnance Survey.

St. Agnes Lighthouse. Lat. 49°53′31″N. Long. 6°20′41″W.
(disused.)

Bearings refer to the True Compass and are given from Seaward (thus 126° etc.)
Underlined figures express the Heights, in Feet, of drying banks
or rocks above the datum to which the soundings are reduced.
All other Heights are expressed in Feet above Mean High Water Springs.
For Abbreviations see Admiralty Chart 5011.

SOUNDINGS IN FATHOMS

Natural Scale
Projection - Gnomonic

Metres 1000   500   0   1000   2000 Metres

Feet 1000   0   5000   10,000 Feet

Cables 10   5   0   1 Sea Mile

CHARTS AND SURVEYS

IN PEACE AND WAR

1. 1808

2. 1839

3. 1857

4. 1908

5. 1986

The Development of the Seal of the Hydrographic Office

(1) shows the Seal in 1808, as first introduced - a band with the lettering HYDROGRAPHICAL OFFICE and a star at the bottom, surrounding a fouled anchor. By 1839 (2) the band itself is surrounded by a tight wreath of oak leaves, with a stylised rose at the top and a thistle at the bottom, HYDROGRAPHICAL has become HYDROGRAPHIC, and the Hydrographer's initials have replaced the star. By the 1850s (3) the wreath becomes looser, the acorns project further, the boxy stylised rose becomes a rose on a square box, and shamrocks are added to the thistle at the base. By 1908 (4) the box and rose are bigger, all the acorns round the wreath are doubled, and a ribbon ties the bouquet together at the base, where the shamrocks have become more prominent. In 1934 the Seal was redesigned, tidying it up while retaining the basic features. The example (5) dates from 1986, and shows the author's initials. This design remained standard until the Office became a Defence Support Agency on 1 April 1990.

MINISTRY OF DEFENCE

CHARTS AND SURVEYS
IN PEACE AND WAR

The History of
The Royal Navy's Hydrographic Service
1919–1970

Rear Admiral R O Morris, CB

LONDON: HMSO

First published 1995

ISBN 0 11 772456 4

The front endpaper of this book shows the last 'feet and fathoms' chart of the Scilly Islands and the back endpaper shows the current modern metric chart of the same area.

Contents

ST. JAMES'S PALACE

The Hydrographic Service of the Royal Navy was instituted by an order in Council of my ancestor, King George III, in August 1795. Since then it has served the Navy, the mariners of this nation and of the rest of the world with painstaking attention to detail and exemplary devotion to duty. Without the surveys carried out by its ships, the charts and publications produced at Taunton, and its encouragement of international hydrographic cooperation, the worlds's seas would be very much more dangerous for shipping, both naval and mercantile.

Previous authors have written up the history of the service as far as 1919 and the end of World War I. In the service's bicentenary year it is particularly appropriate that a former Hydrographer of the Navy should bring the story up to its post-World War apogee in 1970, when the chart-making process was concentrated in purpose-built accommodation at Taunton and a new fleet of ships, designed from the start for surveying, had just entered service. The period covers the change from lead-line sounding and fixing by horizontal sextant angles to seabed depiction by echo-sounder and sonar positioned by electronic navaids.

I saw something of the work of the service myself when, in 1973, I spent some time in HMS <u>Fox</u> in the West Indies, just after the period covered by this book but mentioned briefly in Admiral Myres's biography. When we had to do a rapid sketch survey round the bulk carrier <u>Ariadne</u>, aground off Antigua, to enable her to be refloated, I had a vivid practical demonstration of its importance, and when Commander Myres, as he then was, invited me to draw the fair chart of the survey, I realized just how much painstaking care goes into that aspect of the work.

The means by which ships navigate round the world may change, but the need for accurate and up-to-date information for them to do so safely will not diminish. Whether the charts they produce are printed on paper, on floppy disc or CD-ROM, the Hydrographic Service will, I am sure, be surveying and charting well into their third century.

Introduction

The first history of the Royal Navy's Hydrographic Service was Commander L S Dawson's 'Memoirs of Hydrography', published in two volumes in 1885. Dawson followed a biography of each Hydrographer of the Navy with a narrative of the events during his time in office and a series of brief biographies of the officers who had held charge of surveys during the period. When Vice Admiral Sir Archibald Day published his 'The Admiralty Hydrographic Service 1795-1919' in 1967 he followed Dawson's format, adding to it a table of principal surveys carried out for each year. Though he dated his work 1795-1919, Day merely gave an outline of the period before 1880, deeming it sufficiently covered by Dawson.

Though the current work is dated 1919-1970, both Day and Dawson are now long out of print, and even the reprint of Dawson in one volume published by the Cornmarket Press in 1969 is hard to come by. I have therefore followed Day in running briefly through the story of the Hydrographic Service from its foundation in 1795 to 1914 in an opening chapter. For the Kaiser War in the second chapter I have gone into a little more detail, since the war and the preparations for peace merge without a clear break into the post-war years which are where my main story begins.

In the format of my work I have followed the general pattern of Dawson and Day, with the exception that I have grouped some of the Hydrographers who served for shorter periods into single chapters, and in all cases have put their biographies with those of other officers in the sections devoted to them to avoid unduly cluttering the main narrative. They head the biographical sections at the ends of each chapter, surveyors holding charge appointments first during the period covered by the chapter following in alphabetical order.

It is necessary at the outset to explain the terminology within the Hydrographic Service and the conventions I have used. The Hydrographic Service of the Royal Navy includes all the areas within the remit of the Hydrographer of the Navy. It comprises two main parts. The first is the Surveying Service, the ships, officers and men engaged, under the Hydrographer's direction but not always under his direct command, in carrying out hydrographic surveys and other marine scientific observations at sea. Second, and no less important, is the Hydrographic Department, the shore organisation, mainly civilian manned, which takes the observations from our own ships and from other sources and compiles them into the world-wide Admiralty charts and publications which are then distributed to the world over the Hydrographer's imprint. The Navy's navigation specialists and its meteorological services have from time to time come under Hydrographer's aegis, but neither, in the long term, form part of the Hydrographic Service.

When writing about the Admiralty and the Hydrographic Department, I have used the word 'Department', capitalised, to mean the Hydrographic Department, and given all other divisions or government departments their full titles.

In referring collectively to the ships of the surveying service I have used the term 'fleet', the word in common use up to the formation of the Surveying Flotilla in 1984. This is always given with a small 'f', to distinguish the surveying fleet from the Fleet with a capital 'F', the totality of the ships of the seagoing Navy. On the rare occasions where one of the fleets under a local Commander in Chief is written about, this should be obvious from the context.

There are many views and conventions about when it is correct to insist on prefacing ships' names with HMS, and when to insert or omit the definite article. In this book I have been unashamedly idiosyncratic, using the formal preface only where it is neccesary for clarity, but more often omitting it. With officers' styles and titles I use the same cavalier lack of convention in the main text. In general if I mention in the text an officer whose biography is given I use simply his surname. In the chapter headings I give the respective Hydrographers' ranks and decorations as they bore them when they ceased to be Hydrographer (or in the case of Edgell which he reached by the end of the period covered by the chapter). Their biographies, as with the other officers, are headed by the highest rank and decorations which they achieved at any time. Where names are mentioned whose biographies do not appear, I give them their rank and, where appropriate, decorations as they were at the time of the mention, only mentioning any later eminence if it serves to clarify who I am writing about and to avoid confusion. Where no service is given, RN should be implied. In a book about a branch of the Navy this, I believe, is reasonable, and to add the postnominal initials wherever rank is given would add several pages in total to the size of the volume. For the Navy itself I follow the heraldic rule that the senior branch of a line needs no difference, and leave the noun unadorned except where it needs a 'Royal' or 'British' for clarity.

I had hoped to include the biographies of the principal professional cartographers as well as those of the naval charge surveyors. In the event there were two reasons why I decided, reluctantly, against this. The first is that I found no source for those who were no longer alive when I started this work, since Day did not give them in his continuation and none appeared to have rated an obituary in any of the major journals. The second is that they spent all their working lives in the Department, and though this was of vital importance for the office and for the safety of the mariners who used its products, it does not make an interesting story for the general reader.

With place names I give the name as in use at the time about which I am writing. Though various euphemisms are nowadays used to avoid giving offence to the countries on either side of the Gulf, for the whole of the period of my story and beyond it was known as the Persian Gulf, and that is what I have used. Similarly the groups of Pacific islands had not then gained the euphonious, but to European eyes exotic, names they have adopted since independence, and I have retained the name in use at the time. The modern names will be found cross-referenced to the names used in the main text in Appendix 6.

Though the book treats formally of the period from 1919 to 1970, in biographies and in the details of surveying ships I carry the story, at least in outline, up to the time of completing the manuscript draft. This means that 'now' indicates early 1994.

The fundamental source for this work is the series of Annual Reports by the Hydrographer, and the bound annual volumes of survey details held at Taunton. Unfortunately, for the years between 1926 and 1957 the Annual Reports give only statistical details of ships and surveys. Day prepared a continuation of his History, running from 1919 to 1960, including biographies, which I have found most useful, but it contains several inaccuracies, and deals almost exclusively with the afloat side of the Service.

For the Second World War the primary source is the manuscript 'The Admiralty Hydrographic Department and the Royal Naval Surveying Service 1939-1945', prepared under Wyatt's direction in 1948. To augment the skeleton that these works provide, individual papers in both the Hydrographic Department archives and the collections of the Naval Historical Branch have been used. For the design histories of the ships the Ship Covers held at the National Maritime Museum have been used, while for the tortuous history of the pay and conditions of the cartographers the comprehensive book published in support of the 1938 claim and the files of the magazine of the Institution of Professional Civil Servants 'State Servant' have been used. A very large number of officers, serving and retired, naval and civilian, have sent me their biographies, memoirs and recollections, and have responded willingly to my requests for amplification of points of detail.

Illustrations are drawn mainly from the Hydrographic Department's archives. Where this is not the case an appropriate credit is printed in the caption.

Of the very large number of people whose assistance I have to acknowledge, my first thanks must go to His Royal Highness the Prince of Wales, who has graciously written the foreword.

I began collecting material for this history in the last year or so of my time in office as Hydrographer, and my next acknowledgement must go to my two secretaries, Mrs Marilyn Horsfall at Taunton and Mrs Daphne Guildford in London, who collated lists, typed letters and replies, and generally kept the growing mounds of papers in order. In retirement I missed them both sadly. Next I must thank my successor, Rear Admiral J A L Myres, CB for his encouragement and interest throughout the work's gestation. To his people, and in particular to the Curator of the archives at Taunton, Mr Ken Atherton, and to Helen Breeze of his staff, I am deeply indebted for their patience and services. Without Mr J D Brown and his staff in the Naval Historical Branch the aspects outside the narrow fields of surveying and charting would be even thinner than they are. Mr L N Pascoe, Chief Civil Hydrographic Officer and then Assistant Director (Professional) from 1962 to 1972, has read the whole of the main text, and has put me right on matters cartographic and civil service. Rear Admiral Ritchie, Hydrographer from 1966 to 1971, sent me a pre-publication draft of his biography 'No Day Too Long', and answered many questions in a long correspondence. To them, and to all those officers, serving and retired, Naval and civilian, who have replied to my importunate queries I am most grateful, and assure them that the use to which I have put their information is entirely my responsibility.

Lastly, but by no means least in importance, I must thank Carol Wardle and the production team at HMSO, without whose unstinting efforts this book would not have appeared.

CHAPTER ONE

Origins
1795–1914

The first official hydrographic survey of British waters was begun in 1683, when King Charles II charged Captain Greenville Collins with carrying out a survey of the coast and waters of his kingdoms, and placed the Royal Yacht *Merlin* at his disposal for the work. He took ten years over this task, and his surveys were published as ' Great Britain's Coasting Pilot' in 1693. However, these results of his labours had to be published at Collins' own expense, and the captains of His Majesty's ships of war had to find their own charts and navigational publications, and pay for them themselves.

Throughout the eighteenth century Naval officers were enjoined to carry out, and some were specially tasked with, hydrographic surveys. Among the most distinguished of these may be counted James Cook, George Vancouver and William Bligh. In every case, though, they still had to publish the result themselves, and to recoup the costs through sales. Captains and masters of ships had to provide themselves with such charts as were available, and which they could afford, though occasionally charts or atlases would be provided for special operations from official sources. In the wars against France more ships were lost through faulty navigational information than from enemy action, and senior Naval officers long agitated for steps to be taken to improve the situation.

Finally, in August 1795, King George III issued an Order in Council setting up the office of Hydrographer to the Board of Admiralty, and Alexander Dalrymple was appointed to fill it.

Dalrymple was a distinguished geographer and surveyor, a Fellow of the Royal Society and Hydrographer to the Honourable East India Company. He had been passed over in favour of Cook for the Royal Society's expedition to Tahiti to observe the Transit of Venus in 1769, and was dismissive and resentful of the policy of preferring naval officers to men of science for command of any such expeditions, which had prevailed since the troubles between Edmond Halley and his officers in the *Paramore* pink at the beginning of the century.

Unlike the French Hydrographic Office, which had been set up under Colbert in 1720 with powers of oversight of all published navigational information within the realms of His Most Christian Majesty, the British Hydrographer was solely concerned with providing charts and sailing directions for the Royal Navy. The opening paragraph of the Order in Council made this plain :

'The great inconvenience which has constantly been felt by the Officers in Your Majesty's Fleet, especially when ordered abroad, from the want of sufficient information respecting the navigation of those parts of the world to which their services may be directed, and with which they are sometimes totally unacquainted, has led us to consider of the means most adviseable to be adopted for furnishing such information, and for preventing, as much as possible, the difficulties and dangers to which Your Majesty's Fleet must consequently be exposed from any defect on this head.'

Dalrymple was charged with the duty of selecting and compiling all the existing information, and making it available to the commanders of His Majesty's ships. The expenses of his entire establishment were limited to £650 per annum, £500 for his own salary, with £100 for an assistant and £50 for one draughtsman. It did not take him long to expand upon this, and by 1797 he had one John Walker, the first of a line of Walkers who were to serve successive Hydrographers until 1865, as his assistant, as well as a draughtsman, three copper plate engravers and a printer. All were accomodated in two rooms in the Old Admiralty Building, and the total wage bill was now £1400.

It took Dalrymple and his people some time to sort through the miscellaneous collection of information which had accumulated in the attics of the Admiralty through the century. It was not until November 1800 that he published the first Admiralty chart, 'Sketch of the Road on the NE side of the Island Houat in Quiberon Bay'. In 1801 ten charts were published, 4 of locations in the Mediterranean, 3 in South Africa, 2 on the coast of the Netherlands and one on the north coast of Spain. For a period in 1804 when Dalrymple was away from the Hydrographic Office due to ill health, Captain William Bligh took charge of the office, and was then or later consulted by Dalrymple for his scheme of producing a series of charts covering both sides of the English Channel, most of which finally came out under the imprint of Dalrymple's successor, Hurd.

The compilation of such a series of charts required the collation of various surveys and charts of different scales and in some cases of great complexity and detail. It was a much more taxing work than the publication, virtually in facsimile, of plans of harbours and anchorages surveyed by officers of the Fleet or of the Honourable Company, which had been Dalrymple's work so far both at the Admiralty and with the East India Company. The process was slow and laborious. In 1807 the Admiralty Board instructed Dalrymple to purchase a complete set of the charts published in England and to make a selection of those suitable for issue to His Majesty's ships. He made the purchases, amounting to over one thousand charts, but pleaded that he was not qualified to select the most suitable from them, and suggested that a committee of experienced officers be formed to do the sifting.

The Committee was duly appointed. It comprised Captains E N Columbine, T Hurd and Sir Home Popham. It found Dalrymple difficult to deal with. He was fiercely resistant to any suggestion of change, and dilatory in producing evidence which they requested. A major bone of contention was Dalrymple's treatment of the data from D'Entrecasteaux's Pacific surveys which had been captured from the French. He asserted that under the convention which exempted scientific research from the process of war he held the surveys as a sacred trust, and that they could not be used until the French had themselves published them. He was overruled. Further, in May 1808 he was told that there were new plans for the Hydrographic Office requiring 'great and continued exertion on the part of the Hydrographer', and that since at his advanced period of life (he was then seventy one) he could not be expected to make this exertion he was dismissed. Deeply mortified, he died three weeks later.

After his death the copper plates of his East Indian charts were acquired by the Admiralty, and impressions of them may be found with the Hydrographic Office seal, though with the original imprint and date. He was not involved with the issuing of surveying instructions to Naval vessels, and so cannot be considered the founder of the Royal Naval Hydrographic Service, but Dalrymple certainly merits the credit for having founded the Admiralty chart. To him are due the meticulous care for accuracy and detail, and also the clear, crisp style of lettering and engraving, which have remained since his day the hallmarks of the series.

1808–1823

Captain Thomas Hurd, one of the members of the Chart Committee, was appointed to supercede Dalrymple in May 1808. He had carried out surveys of his own before being appointed to the Chart Committee, notably one of Bermuda in the 1790s and work in the approaches to Brest in 1804. He also had personal knowledge of the working of the Office from having been attached to it while preparing his surveys of Bermuda for the engraver.

It is not apparent from either the Order in Council setting up the office of Hydrographer or from any action of Dalrymple's that any connection had been intended between the office and the naval service other than the former providing the latter with navigational information. Any interference in Naval affairs by Dalrymple, a geographer rather than a seaman, and a civilian to boot, would in any case have been resented and deplored. Hurd, though, was himself a naval officer and a seaman, and the results of this were not long in coming. Early in his tenure we find him actively seeking information with which to improve his publications, and before long ships were being commissioned to carry out his instructions. In 1809 William Chapman, Master, was sent in the *Sorlings*, brig, to survey the dangers and banks off the Thames and the East Coast. In 1811, when the *Investigator* was built and commissioned for surveying under George Thomas, her master, Mr Triskey, asked who was in command. He was told to 'obey Thomas in all things', thus establishing the precedent of surveying officers in command of their own ships.

At the start of Hurd's time surveys on foreign stations were initiated by the local

Commander in Chief or senior officer. It was the Commander in Chief in the Mediterranean who ordered the survey of the south coast of Asia Minor by Beaufort in the *Fredericksteen* between 1810 and 1812. By 1821, and the start of W F Owen's great African survey, ships were being sent from home for major foreign surveys on the instructions of the Hydrographer. In this case Owen was given command of the *Leven* and the *Barracouta*, for a voyage which lasted five years during which 30,000 miles of coastline were surveyed and over 90 chart sheets forwarded to the Hydrographer.

With the run-down of flotilla craft in the Mediterranean in 1816, Admiral Penrose was ordered to allocate a vessel to Commander W H Smyth, who had already distinguished himself surveying with the Fleet, specially for survey work. In 1817 the *Aid*, renamed *Adventure* in 1821, was sent out from England for this purpose.

Also in 1816, Their Lordships instructed the Navy Board to fit two gunbrigs for surveying in the North Sea and the English Channel, ordering them to 'take care to have a proper cabin for the use of the surveyors', and to communicate with the Hydrographer on the subject.

The long-established co-operation between the Royal Navy and the Royal Society in the search for knowledge also continued. Sir Joseph Banks, who had been with Cook on his first voyage in 1768 and who was now President of the Royal Society, instigated in 1816 an expedition to explore the River Congo. The ship specially built for this task, HMS *Congo*, was to have been an early steam paddler, but on trials she was found to be so underpowered that her machinery was removed and she was commissioned as a vessel powered solely by sail. The expedition was not wholly successful, most of its company dying of fever, but the ship was found to be seaworthy and staunch, and was employed for some years after the return of the expedition on surveys in home waters.

In fact Hurd took the opportunity of the peace following the end of the Napoleonic Wars to press for an active surveying policy both at home and abroad. In his letter to the Secretary of the Admiralty of 12 October 1816, of which only the Secretary's digest survives, he proposed two further steps towards the Hydrographic Service as it exists today. He suggested 'with a view to the defraying a part of the expenses of the Department, that after a plate has been engraved and a sufficient number of charts struck off it for Naval uses, that the remaining impressions be disposed of at a moderate price for the benefit of the Trading Interest.' This proposal was eventually agreed in a Board minute of November 1819, though the first sales were not brought to account until 1823, when the princely sum of £72 is recorded as having been received.

Hurd's second proposal was the 'selecting of a certain number of officers well acquainted with the science of maritime surveying, and forming them into a distinct and separate corps something similar to that of the Engineers of the Army'. This bore more immediate fruit. In a Board minute of 7 January 1817 special pay rates for officers in the surveying service were established - twenty shillings for a commander, fifteen shillings for lieutenants and masters, all in addition to the pay of their rank in the vessel in which they were employed. In March of the same year the Navy Board was instructed to keep a separate list of surveying vessels, and to consult the Hydrographer before appointing a master or second master to them.

One of the proposals of the Committee on Charts which Hurd took up on his appointment as Hydrographer was that sets of charts should be made up in boxes for issue to ships of the Fleet, and that spare boxes should be held by the commissioners at Portsmouth, Plymouth and Chatham Dockyards. Issue of charts by this method was started in Hurd's first months in office. It was formalised in the Naval Regulations and Instructions promulgated in 1813. A suggestion by the Navy Board in 1815 that there should be chart depots at Malta and on other foreign stations was turned down as unnecessary by Their Lordships.

Thus by Hurd's death in office in May 1823, the main elements of the Navy's Hydrographic Service as it has endured to this day were in place. A world-wide series of charts, printed and published by the Hydrographer in house, was being issued to the Fleet in pre-packed boxes (the forerunner of the folio system) from chart depots in the main naval bases and were on sale to the general public. And surveys ordered by the Hydrographer were being made by a corps of specialised seaman Naval officers commanding their own ships which were themselves specially fitted out for surveying. If Dalrymple is the father of the Admiralty Chart, Hurd is undoubtedly the father of the Hydrographic Service.

1823–1829

W E Parry was appointed Hydrographer on 1 December 1823, some months after Hurd's death. He was already a noted Arctic explorer. He pioneered the practice of wintering in the ice, successfully keeping his crews' morale and physique up during the long night of inactivity with entertainments and instruction. He had only returned in October 1823 in the *Fury* from an expedition north of Hudson's Bay, and accepted the appointment as Hydrographer only on condition that he could go back to the North West Passage in 1824. In fact he was away from office in the Canadian Arctic from May 1824 to November 1825, and again from April to October in 1827. Despite this record as an absentee Hydrographer, there was considerable progress in the evolution of the Hydrographic Service in Parry's reign.

Administratively it was a difficult time. The Admiralty was in the grip of the Secretary, J W Croker. This archtype of the dominant bureaucrat held office for twenty two years from 1809, and was always determined to keep everything under his own control and to limit expenditure. Fortunately his iron grip on the Hydrographic Office was to some extent ameliorated by the Second Secretary, John Barrow, a widely travelled and broad-minded man who was a good friend to successive Hydrographers. In Parry's absence the Office was run by Walker, the Hydrographer's Assistant, and sometimes by A B Becher, a naval officer appointed to the Office in 1823 to catalogue and sort the holdings of original documents and who remained there, except for two brief periods at sea, for forty-three years.

One major development instituted by Parry was the provision of 'Sailing Directions' to accompany the charts. This led to the appointment in 1828 of two more Naval Assistants (making four in all). That Croker consented to this shows that he was not totally impervious to proposals requiring additional expenditure if he could be convinced that they were in the public interest.

Parry had previously prepared a 'Notice respecting the establishment of the Hydrographical Office' which strikes a note which every chief of a hydrographic office will recognise.

He began: 'The slowness with which our hydrographic materials are rendered available by publication arises entirely, I conceive, from the small number of individuals employed in this Department, for it so happens, altho' I believe unintentionally, that almost in proportion as the surveying work has increased (as it has done since the Peace) so has this establishment been diminished; there being three individuals less belonging to it at this time than in the year 1823.'

In 1827 His Royal Highness the Duke of Clarence, later to become King William IV, became Lord High Admiral, and took a personal interest in the Hydrographic Office. On 7 June he directed that six extra draughtsmen should be employed on temporary weekly pay until the arrears of work had been cleared; that weekly reports of their work and a monthly report from the engravers should be made to him; that Becher should compile Sailing Directions for publication, and that a clerk should be added for chart supplies.

Experiments were also made with the use of lithography for printing charts. Croker was in favour, since it was said to be cheaper than engraving. Parry was less enthusiastic, citing the problems of correcting stones and preserving them from injury.

Besides Sailing Directions, the first 'Light Lists' were also published under Parry. The first chart catalogue was published in 1825, listing 643 charts or surveys, and 98 views. Boxes had now been abandoned for stiff, marbled covers, and charts were sold either as series in these folios or separately. Chart sales were through agents, the agency fee being twenty five per cent.

More detailed instructions began to be given to the surveyors afloat, with standard scales at which the surveys were to be conducted being laid down, and reports on the methods used during the survey being called for.

The restrictions of a desk-bound office could not contain so active a man as Parry, though, and he resigned in May 1829 after less than six years in office, having been knighted earlier in the year.

1829–1855

Francis Beaufort, Parry's successor, was certainly the longest-serving, and probably the greatest, of all the Hydrographers to date. When he was appointed in May 1829 he already had twenty-five years of sea service behind him, including surveying in the River Plate and his great work of hydrography and archaeology on the coast of Karamania.

His twenty-five years in office saw a great expansion of the Hydrographic Service both afloat and ashore. By the end of them his authority in fields far beyond his official responsibilites was unparalleled. His advice was sought on such disparate matters as pilotage, harbours of refuge, the siting of lighthouses, the building of harbour works, the equipment to be carried on expeditions to unexplored Africa; he was even consulted on behalf of Queen Victoria to ascertain where on the Isle of Wight Her Majesty could land to reach Osborne without passing under the scrutiny of the inquisitive crowds at Cowes.

Beaufort's authority was increased by two moves early in his time as Hydrographer. In 1831 a Scientific Branch of the Admiralty was instituted, comprising the Hydrographic Department, the Royal Observatory at Greenwich, the Cape Observatory, the Nautical Almanac Office and the Chronometer Office. The estimates for this branch were prepared by the Hydrographer, who thus bcame its *de facto* head. And Secretary Croker retired. His successor, Captain the Hon. George Elliot, was a nonentity. Power within the administration lay with the Second Secretary, Barrow, already a good friend to science in general and hydrography in particular.

The estimates for the Hydrographic Department for 1831 show the organisation as it had developed so far. The Assistant Hydrographer was Michael Walker, who had succeded his father, John, on his death that year. There were four draughtsmen and three Naval Assistants, with one clerk helping with tidal information. The manually drawn charts were sent for engraving to Walkers of Castle Street, Holborn, a firm run by two more of old John Walker's sons. Once the plates were engraved they were sent back to the Admiralty, where one or two printers ran off copies as required. Twenty-four years later the assistants and draughtsmen had risen to six of each, including among the former the tidal computer, with a total office expenditure of £26,000.

With such a small staff much of Beaufort's own time was taken up with checking and approving each new chart before publication. Though this did cause delays, it resulted in the standardisation of symbols and conventions, which were promulgated in the first edition of a sheet of 'Abbreviations used in Admiralty Charts' in 1835, setting the 'house style' which lasted until the complete restyling introduced with the modernisation and metrication programme in 1968.

Afloat there was a similar expansion. The first use of steam in surveying is recorded by Day as being by Richard Owen in the paddle gunboat *African* on the Gambia in 1828. With the appointment of Sir Edward Parry as Comptroller of Steam

Machinery in 1837 the Hydrographer had a powerful friend at court, and in 1841 six paddle steamers, *Blazer, Dasher, Firefly, Lucifer, Porcupine* and *Shearwater,* were appropriated for surveying round the United Kingdom. The standard of surveying rose appreciably, and the small paddle steamer was found to be ideal for this work. However, in 1848 all six were diverted to famine relief work on the west coasts of Ireland and Scotland, and surveying work had once again to be carried out from hired vessels. It was the efficiency of surveying which suffered, though, not the number of units, as by 1853 there were no less than twelve surveys in hand round the coasts of the United Kingdom.

In 1853 this expansion was brought to an abrupt halt. Beaufort was directed to reduce the cost of home surveys, which had risen to £17,000, to no more than £7,000. This resulted in the forced resignation of four captains and one master.

Foreign surveys were not affected by this edict. They had been progressing world-wide, serving the interests of both defence and trade. They were not confined to the British Empire, many foreign governments being requested, and giving, permission for British vessels to survey their waters. A rare case of refusal came when the Emperor of Morocco required the *Hecla* to break off her survey of his coast.

Polar exploration continued. John Ross and his nephew James Clark Ross made important voyages in both north and south polar regions. When a new search for the North West Passage was to be mounted in 1845 James Ross, knighted and newly married, declined the command and Beaufort was instrumental in procuring the post for Sir John Franklin, now sixty years old. The loss without trace of the Franklin expedition led to a series of expeditions to search for him in the course of which knowledge of the Canadian Arctic was greatly enhanced. Taking personal responsibility for the original expedition, Beaufort also personally directed the plans for those searching for it.

In the various expeditions and wars in the Far East surveying ships were often called to explore paths for safe navigation ahead of the major war vessels, and were never found wanting. Some, indeed, exceeded their instructions. Belcher, a brilliant surveyor though a tyrannical commander of his officers, became heavily embroiled with the petty sultanates of the Eastern Archipelago. After one of his reports Beaufort wrote to him :

> 'Your last letter of April 8 is really all Hebrew to me; ransoms and dollars, queens, treaties and negotiations? What have I to do with these awful things; they far transcend my limited chart-making faculties, however well suited they may be to Admiralty Lords, the Commanders-in-Chief, to Governors of Colonies and to you..... That you may have been doing good service to the country I will not deny, but the harvest I look for at your hands does not stretch beyond the reach of a deep sea line and all the credit I crave for you, and through you for myself, must be won in the kingdoms of science and reaped in hydrographic fields'.

Nevertheless Beaufort was well aware of the military applications of his work, and when the Russian War broke out he attached Brock and Sulivan to the Commanders in Chief in the Mediterranean and Baltic respectively. In 1854 he suggested that the Fleet should have a lithographic press on board to supply charts for war operations - a suggestion finally put into effect in 1915!

So far there was no way of promulgating to the mariner new information which affected his charts, short of publishing a new edition of the chart. In 1832 Beaufort published the first issue of the *Nautical Magazine*, principally to promulgate to the subscriber information of navigational significance before it was incorporated in new charts - necessarily a slow and lengthy process. The *Magazine* soon became both popular and full of general marine matters, and in November 1834 the chart correcting information was removed and published separately as *Notices to Mariners*. For the surveying service Beaufort issued the first edition of the *General Instructions for Hydrographic Surveyors*, setting out the procedures to be followed in every kind of survey, and how the results were to be rendered.

The policy, fostered by Parry, of international co-operation in hydrography was furthered by Beaufort. A friendship with the Spanish hydrographer Don Felipe Bauza during his exile in London guaranteed good relations with the Hydrographic Office in Cadiz when Bauza returned there. Relations were equally good with both the American and French offices, the latter writing to Beaufort in 1848 hoping that France's becoming a republic would not interfere with the free exchange of data. Many Admiralty charts drawn from Russian surveys attest to the cordial relations with St Petersburg, though by 1850 these had cooled.

In March 1854 Beaufort, now eighty and in failing health, asked to resign. With the Russian War breaking out Their Lordships refused to spare him, and he soldiered on for a further nine months, finally being relieved in January 1855. By the time of his departure the Royal Navy was recognised as pre-eminent in hydrographic matters in Europe and throughout the world.

1855-1874

Captain John Washington succeeded Beaufort as Hydrographer. He had been actively employed in the hydrographic service since 1841. He had recently, just before the outbreak of the war, visited Denmark, Sweden and Russia ostensibly in connection with the lifeboat service, but had taken the opportunity to gather intelligence about the Russian Baltic Fleet and their coastal defences.

This intelligence was followed up and augmented by the efforts of Sulivan in H.M. Paddle Surveying Vessel *Lightning*, first in the approaches to Bomarsund, and then at Sveaborg and Kronstadt. In the Mediterranean and the Black Sea Spratt in the *Spitfire*, another of the handy steam paddlers, provided equally important service on both the Black Sea and Sea of Azov coasts of the Crimea. Spratt was employed and consulted constantly by the Commander in Chief, Admiral Lyon, during the war, and at the peace was awarded the CB and promoted to captain.

Developments in the colonies led to surveying and charting arrangements with the India Office which were still-borne on account of the abolition of the Indian Navy in 1862, and with the governments of the various states of Australia. For surveys along the coasts of New South Wales, Victoria, South Australia, Tasmania and Queensland the governments would provide for local expenses, while the Admiralty would pay the salaries of the staff engaged on them, provide instruments for surveying, and carry the production costs of the charts arising from the work.

The advent of the trans-oceanic submarine telegraph cable led to a call for deep sea soundings along possible routes. Washington appreciated that knowledge of the depths of the open ocean was not only desireable for itself, but that it could help to eliminate some of the numerous reported dangers ('vigias') with which oceanic charts were encumbered.

In the office Washington decentralised more than Beaufort had done, and some of the back-log of material which had built up was cleared into publication. The office staff grew, and additional accomodation was built on in the form of another set of attics to the Admiralty Building. In November 1855 printing of charts in house was stopped, and Messrs Malby took over this task, though the copper plates were still kept in the basement of the Admiralty in Hydrographer's charge when not in use. In 1860 the Stationery Office took over responsibilty for the sale of charts, but within a very few months found it too onerous, and returned the task to the Hydrographic Office, where it has remained ever since.

A number of cases of the loss of ships were attributed to shortcomings in the charts in the early 1860s. Though in most of these blaming the Hydrographer did not stand up to close examination, they nevertheless preyed on Washington's mind and his health suffered. He was still in office when he died, in May 1863. He was then a Rear Admiral, and was aged sixty-three.

A successor was not appointed until January 1864. He was Captain George Henry Richards. He had started surveying as a midshipman in the *Sulphur* under Beechey in 1835, had survived two commissions with Belcher, and had most recently commanded *Hecate* off British Columbia.

Richards was to be Hydrographer for ten years, during which the emphasis of the department's work was more on the support of commercial than military navigation at a time when no major conflicts disturbed the peace. This naturally increased international co-operation. After the opening of the Suez Canal the surveying and lighting of the Red Sea was agreed between Richards and the French Hydrographer, Admiral Paris, while the agreement of the Chilean government was given to a survey of the Magellan Straits by the *Nassau*.

Scientific interest in the oceans increased, and the Hydrographer and his ships played their part in investigating them. A botanist and marine biologist was carried on board the *Nassau* in South America. The Royal Society sponsored Dr Carpenter on cruises in the *Lightning* and the *Porcupine* in 1868 and 1870 respectively. This led directly to the proposal for the world oceanographic voyage of the *Challenger* from 1872 to 1876, from which the science of oceanography can be said to have emerged.

In home waters the effort put into surveying reduced. Only the *Porcupine* and *Lightning*, both with hired crews, were in service in 1866, together with one survey party working in the Channel Islands. Personnel matters also claimed Richards' concern, both the overall number of hydrographic specialists and the problems of getting his senior officers promoted to commander and captain. In 1864 a requirement was introduced for captains of surveying ships to render to Hydrographer a report of their proceedings, half-yearly for home ships and quarterly for ships on foreign stations. One year later a 'memoir' on fair sheets, setting out details of the method of construction and surveying, was introduced.

Richards retired in January 1874 at the age of fifty-four, a Rear Admiral and a CB. He was a fellow of the Royal Society and of the Royal Geographical Society. He was knighted in 1877 and advanced to Vice Admiral on the retired list in the same year.

1874–1884

Richards was immediately succeeded by Captain F J O Evans. His first surveying appointment had been in 1833 under Richard Owen in the *Thunder*. After war service in the Baltic he had, in 1855, been appointed in charge of the Compass Department, where he had made notable contributions to the science of adjusting magnetic compasses in iron and steel ships.

During Evans' ten and a half years as Hydrographer the service's commitments steadily increased. Surveys in Japan, Korea and China, in the Pacific Islands, in the Eastern Archipelago, on both coasts of Africa, as well as in the Mediterranean and the West Indies, all attested to the greater mobility of steam vessels. Many of the ships employed, though, were composite sloops or gunboats, ill suited to their work and more or less worn out before they were given to Hydrographer.

A major source of information from 1879 on is the annual report of the Hydrographer to Parliament. In November 1882 the Board of Admiralty appointed a committee to investigate the Department. This comprised the Hydrographer himself with representatives of the Secretary and the Accountant-General. It reported in March 1883. It lists the establishment at the time : Hydrographer, an Assistant Hydrographer, seven Naval Assistants, a Chief Civil Assistant with an assistant and one or two clerks for accounts and secretarial business, and a Chief Draughtsman and six draughtsmen. Engraving was still done outside the department by contract, as was printing. Sales of charts and books in 1881-82 had brought in £7,400 and £606 respectively, to be set against a total cost of the Department of around £21,000. The Committee thought that the working power of the department was near its limit, but that it could continue for some years at its present level.

Sales arrangements were under frequent discussion with the Treasury and HMSO, and gave rise to Parliamentary questions. Evans, like his predecessors, successfully defended the organisation of a single agent and sub-agents. When J D Potter died in 1882 the agreement was reviewed again, but eventually confirmed to Potter's son, though the contract was not signed until Wharton's time.

Evans was made KCB in 1881, even then an extraordinary honour for a captain, and retired in August 1884. He had been a Fellow of the Royal Society since 1862.

1884–1904

W J L Wharton's first experience of surveying was as a lieutenant in the *Gannet* under Chimmo in the West Indies from 1865 to 1868. From 1872 he was employed continuously in command of surveying ships until he was ordered home from South America in March of 1884 to succeed Evans as Hydrographer. He was then forty-one, and was to hold office for the next twenty years, a tenure only exceeded by Beaufort.

By the later 1880s the long Victorian peace was being increasingly broken by tension in the Far East, in the scramble for colonies in Africa, in the Balkans, and by the Russian advances in central Asia which were seen as threatening India. Military interests began to take a more prominent part in hydrographic plans and employment.

The first comprehensive Instructions for the Hydrographer were issued by the Board in 1889. Within three years of their introduction Wharton had to explain to the First Lord why the surveying service and the Hydrographic Department should be part of the Navy. The expansion of the Fleet beginning with the Naval Defence Act of 1889 was putting extreme pressure on naval manpower, and not for the last time the Hydrographic Service was being put under review to save manpower and cost. There was an ongoing battle with the Treasury on numbers and grades of civilian staff, and for suitable accommodation.

In 1889 the last of the paddle-wheelers, the *Research*, was completed. Built specially for home waters surveying at Chatham, she was an efficient and economical unit who gave good service until she was paid off in 1914 at the outbreak of war. Her earlier near sister, the *Triton*, though also paid off from surveying service in 1914, survived as a training ship until 1961. The last purely sailing surveying vessels were paid off early in Wharton's period in office, the *Lark* on the Australia station in 1887 and the *Sparrowhawk* in the West Indies in 1889.

Surveying in Canada was carried on under the orders of the Dominion government after 1883, with Naval surveyors still doing a decreasing proportion of the work. Newfoundland and Labrador did not come into the Dominion until much later, and here the Hydrographer remained fully responsible, having surveys carried out from the hired steamer *Gulnare* until 1902 and then the *Ellinor* until 1914.

In Australia the co-operative arrangements with the state governments continued, Queensland even making one of their gunboats, the *Paluma*, available for nine years from 1885 to 1894. India now had its own hydrographic service, the Marine Survey of India, with its own purpose-built paddle steamer, the *Investigator*. Successive commanders of the survey, often retired or seconded Naval surveyors, kept in close touch with the Hydrographer at home.

Elsewhere surveying was still carried on in a varying collection of old vessels. When in 1897 Wharton reported on the unsatisfactory nature of the converted sloops, and asked for specially designed ships, he was told that 'for the present some existing ship must be prepared and utilised for the service'.

In his supervision of the surveyors Wharton revised the *General Instructions for Hydrographic Surveyors* twice, bringing out new editions in 1888 and 1902. They were supplemented by *Instructions to Officers in Charge of Admiralty Surveys*, and by a book which Wharton had himself written while he was in the *Sylvia* in 1882, *Hydrographical Surveying*, a manual of surveying so comprehensive and so useful that it ran into four editions and was only replaced by the *Admiralty Manual of Hydrographic Surveying* in 1938.

Wharton was retired as a Rear Admiral on 1 January 1895, being made CB the same year and KCB two years later. He relinquished office at the age of sixty-one in August 1904 and went out to South Africa, where he died a year later.

1904–1914

Arthur Mostyn Field, the next Hydrographer, began surveying as a lieutenant in the *Fawn* in 1876 under Wharton. He spent the next twenty-five years almost continually on foreign service, the last twelve in command. His last years before taking over as Hydrographer were spent in the *Research*, where he was involved in experiments with the Thomson Sounding Machine, later to become the Kelvin machine.

During his time in office Field concerned himself with the status of Chart Branch staff, arguing successfully for the name of cartographer as more descriptive of the duties of the graduate chart compilers than simply draughtsmen. Afloat, he introduced the specialisation of surveying recorder for ratings, with a specialist allowance to go with it.

With the storm-clouds of war gathering, the Hydrographic Department was heavily involved in defence measures. A war organisation for chart depots was set up. Issues Branch instituted special chart sets for destroyers and small craft in home waters which were first sent out for the Grand Manoeuvres of 1906. Resurveys were put in hand of likely Fleet bases and anchorages. Hydrographer was consulted on the building of the new harbours at Dover and Rosyth.

Within three months of taking office Field was required to report 'on the Hydrographical Service of the Admiralty with the possible changes and economies which might be effected'. A very full report was submitted on 25 November 1904 which once again confirmed the case for the close connection between the

Hydrographic Service and the Navy. The requirement for surveys, their increasing detail and hence the time taken on them, and thus the need to maintain if not to increase the number of ships engaged, were all stated strongly. Apart from adjustments to chart prices and agents' discounts, Field's main recommendation for change was that the Board of Trade should include the sum of £50,000 per annum in their Estimates to go towards the cost of maintaining surveying ships, which was said to be about half the annual cost. This does not appear to have been taken up or even discussed at any length, though it was to bear belated fruit in the 1970s.

As a result of Field's report another committee to examine the organisation of the department was set up, which reported in January 1906. This broadly endorsed Field's remarks, particularly on the need for more staff. It noted that only by the increasing use of Notices to Mariners was information got out to the seafarer in a timely fashion, but that this was less economic for the department than issuing new charts or new editions with a fuller account of the new information. Only in January 1909 did the Treasury approve an increase in draughtsmen from 14 to 19, as well as the new title of 'cartographer'. Charts were still printed by Malbys, and engraved by two firms, Davies and Weller.

Field was elected a Fellow of the Royal Society in 1905, and promoted to Rear Admiral in 1906. On his retirement in August 1909 he became the Admiralty representative on the Port of London Authority, where he served until 1925. He was also Acting Conservator of the River Mersey from 1910 to 1930. He was made a Vice Admiral on the retired list, and a KCB in 1911, and made Admiral on the retired list in 1913. he died on 3 July 1950, six days after his ninety-fifth birthday.

Field was succeeded as Hydrographer by Captain H E Purey-Cust. He had started surveying in 1881 in the *Fawn*, working in the Red Sea and on the east coast of Africa. Much of his time was spent in the Far East, and it was in the Pacific that he obtained his first command, the *Dart*, in 1892. From 1895 to 1897 he was in the Department as a naval assistant.

During his time as Hydrographer Purey-Cust was greatly concerned with the approaching war. A new survey of the southern North Sea was put in hand, and the *Hearty*, a former salvage tug, was converted for this task. Initially a series of old cruisers were provided to act as floating beacons for her, but in 1912 two trawler-type vessels, the *Daisy* and *Esther*, were completed as surveying ships and commissioned to assist in the work. The first purpose-built surveying ship since the old paddler *Research* was also commissioned in 1912. The *Endeavour* had a handsome, if even by those days' standards antiquated, yacht-like profile. She was well equipped, but with only one screw was less manoeuvrable than Hydrographer would have wished. Purey-Cust introduced the Hydrographer's annual visits to ships in home waters, the first of these being made in 1912 when he embarked in *Endeavour* to visit both *Hearty*'s group at Lowestoft and *Research* at Cromarty.

Ashore the Compass Branch was separated from the Hydrographic Department in 1911, and transferred to the Controller of the Navy. Increasing dissatisfaction with the performance of Malbys, and with their resistance to change, resulted in a recommendation to bring chart printing under Hydrographer's direct control. The war intervened, and it was not until 1919 that approval was given to set up an Admiralty Chart Establishment.

An International Maritime Conference was held at St Petersburg in 1912, but the United Kingdom was not represented. Purey-Cust was concerned, but on seeing the report of its proceedings noted that a special conference to address international hydrography was planned. With the demise of the Imperial Russian regime in 1917 this hydrographic conference was eventually held in London in 1919.

A month after war broke out Purey-Cust handed over to J F Parry. He had been promoted to Rear Admiral in 1910 and made CB in 1911. Throughout the war he served as a commodore, RNR. He was promoted to Vice Admiral on the retired list in 1915 and to Admiral in 1919, in which year he was made KCB. He died in November 1938 at the age of eighty-one.

CHAPTER TWO

The First World War
1914–1919

Admiral Sir John Parry, KCB

J F Parry succeeded Purey-Cust one month after the outbreak of war, on 1 September 1914. He was the grandson of the third Hydrographer, Admiral Sir Edward Parry. He started surveying as a sublieutenant in 1884, gained his first command, the *Dart*, on the Australia station in 1897, and was promoted commander in 1899. He served in the Department under Wharton from 1900 to 1903, and then after more sea service returned to Whitehall in 1910 as Assistant Hydrographer. In this post he represented the Admiralty at the conference on an Atlantic ice patrol after the *Titanic* disaster, and was the British delegate to a conference held in Paris on the use of wireless telegraphy for time and weather signals. He was also chairman of the committee set up to inquire into the organisation of Admiralty charts in 1912.

He was thus well fitted both by professional competence and by extra-departmental experience to head the Department through the war. Those who knew him testify to his genius for organisation, his breadth of vision, and his genial yet commanding personality. He gained the affection and loyalty of his subordinates. He and Hall, the Director of Naval Intelligence, were personally instrumental in bringing women to work in the Admiralty during the war, and their choice was such that the women were known as 'Parry's peaches' and 'Blinker's beauties'.

The Department saw an enormous expansion during the war, the personnel employed rising from 62 in August 1914 to a peak of 367 in December 1918. The increase consisted in large part of temporary draughtswomen and clerks. The work had to be re-organised to meet the demands placed on it. All extant publications were kept under revision as far as possible, but their distribution was strictly controlled, and the promulgation of corrections to them limited to items not of value to the enemy.

A wide range of charts and diagrams were produced for the use of the Fleet and of others over and above the normal world series of Admiralty Charts. Fleet charts, showing information which it was not wished to make public, had been started in 1886, but their number rose from 56 in 1914 to 118 in 1918. Another series of charts and diagrams, the 'X' series, covered so wide a range of information, both in importance and in sensitivity, that in 1917 it was divided into 'X' charts, those of a non-confidential nature, 'Y' charts, of a confidential nature issued to various authorities for official purposes, and 'Z' charts, secret charts kept under stringent precautions and issued in very limited quantities to recipients on an approved list only. 345 'X' charts, 80 in the 'Y' series and 118 in the 'Z' series were in the catalogue in 1918. Two sets of 'OXO' charts were produced for the Intelligence Department, one in 1915 and one in 1918, from information captured from enemy units. Air charts were also produced, first for the Royal Naval Air Service and later for the Royal Air Force. A special series was also produced for submarines. Classified charts were at first printed by the Ordnance Survey, but in October 1917 a Secret Press was set up in the Admiralty which took over the bulk of this work.

The promulgation of Notices to Mariners was likewise affected by the needs of war. To avoid confusion with the various notices produced by the Board of Trade, Trinity House, harbour authorities and so on, the title Admiralty Notices to Mariners was introduced in July 1915, and has continued ever since. The number of these unclassified notices diminished during the war from 2,030 in 1913 to as low as 1,345 in 1915, though it rose again slightly thereafter. This, though, was more than offset by a great increase in Fleet Notices, correcting the Fleet charts and also placing classified information on the other charts for official users. These rose from 43 in 1913 to no less than 855 in 1918. There was also a series of Fleet Auxiliary Notices, extracts from the full Fleet series removing those more highly classified notices which it was not desired to release to minor war vessels and auxiliaries.

The Hydrographer was also responsible, in his role as superintendent of the Royal Observatory, for the issue of chronometers to ships. The upsurge in demand following the expansion of the Fleet and the need for more precise navigation by merchant ships soon outstripped the ability of the manufacturers of these precision instruments to meet it. Restrictions were placed on the export of chronometers and chronometer watches, and when this proved inadequate a census was demanded of all instruments in the United Kingdom, and dealing in them controlled. From an annual purchase of 26 chronometers and 53 watches in 1913 procurement orders rose in 1918 to 176 new chronometers and 349 new watches, with an additional 464 second-hand chronometers and 7 watches being bought in.

During the war years only surveying judged to be essential for Fleet and other operations was carried on. In August 1914 the old paddlers *Triton* and *Research* were paid off, as were the converted sloops surveying abroad, *Fantome*, *Merlin* and *Mutine*. The first of these was soon armed and recommissioned by the Royal Australian Navy as a patrol vessel. The trawlers *Daisy* and *Esther* were transferred to minesweeping work, though they both reverted to surveying in 1916. Only the *Hearty* and *Endeavour* continued surveying.

In September 1915 *Endeavour* was sent out to the eastern Mediterranean to support the Dardanelles operation. She carried printing equipment to allow the results of her work to be promulgated directly to the Fleet without the delay of having to send it home for compilation and printing. After a short time the presses were disembarked, first to Imbros, then later to Mudros and last to Malta. After the army was withdrawn from Gallipoli the ship was engaged in surveys elsewhere in the

Aegean, then on the Egyptian coast and off Malta. Two hired vessels, the *Enterprise* and the *Imogene*, were employed in the Red Sea under Haselfoot, only paying off in 1919 when relieved by the recommissioned *Merlin*.

Surveying officers distinguished themselves in many other fields during the war: in fixing the positions of bombarding ships off the Belgian coast, in minelaying operations, and as navigators of ships wherever precise positioning was needed.

In April 1917 the first consideration was given to the organisation required after the war. In September an attempt to define the Admiralty's departmental organisation led to a memorandum setting out the current system within the Department. When the Admiralty Reconstruction Committee was set up in April 1918 Parry provided it with a list of hydrographic problems for consideration. They included a revival of the proposal to acquire Malby's business and to print charts in house, to take over sales from Potters, and to acquire a building on the outskirts of London to house these activities. Afloat there was the reconstitution of the surveying service and the arrangements to be followed for colonial surveys.

In his statements to the various Admiralty and other committees determining the shape of the post-war Navy Parry stressed the need to reduce the backlog of chart work, which had been a concern even before the war, but which had become very much worse as Chart Branch effort had been diverted from the world series of Admiralty charts to operational charting. He considered that a bigger staff than that during the war would be needed indefinitely, and that only Issues Branch's numbers could be reduced during the reconstruction period. However, Navy Estimates for 1919-20 only made provision for fourteen naval officers where Parry has wanted nineteen.

The total provision in the Estimates for the Hydrographic Service was £149,407, nearly double that of pre-war. This was broken down as follows: Hydrographer £2,100; Assistant Hydrographer £1,434; Superintendents of Sailing Directions £1,144, of Charts £988, of Tidal Work £925; nine naval assistants £7,794. Naval assistants received the full pay of their rank plus a lodging allowance of £160, and the superintendents' allowances were £100.

The civil staff figures were: one chief cartographer first grade, with the title of Assistant Superintendent of Charts, £600; two chief cartographers second grade £500; thirteen cartographers £400, of which four were borne in lieu of eight draughtsmen; one Chief Civil Assistant, £700 plus £200 for acting as Admiralty Director of Malby's; three staff clerks £450; and a total of 320 subordinate professional and technical grades, clerical staff, packers and messengers. For the revisers of Sailing Directions £1,800 was allowed.

The preparation of charts was broken down into: drawing and engraving £15,000; printing and, for HM ships, mounting, £64,000; Ordnance Survey services £17,000. For the repair of instruments and chart boxes, and their carriage, £6,300 was allowed, for chronometers £7,500, and for the Nautical Almanac Office £4,523.

The extra pay of surveyors came to £4,700; and for lodging allowances, the hire of vessels and the purchase of stores £9,200 was allowed.

During the war all shipping under the control of the Ministry of Shipping was supplied with charts and publications on loan by the Hydrographer. At Parry's request the Admiralty approved a scheme, which started operation in February 1919, whereby owners and masters of merchant ships released from Government control could continue to receive charts in folios, with an automatic supply directly from the Department of new charts, new editions, Notices to Mariners etc. Charts would be sold at published prices, with a small charge for folio covers. Some sixty-five shipping firms accepted the scheme, and soon a thousand ships were being supplied under it. One substantial advantage to the Hydrographer was that charts which were on loan to ships at the Armistice could be used.

It meant that all the wartime chart depots remained in being. These were, at home, London, Sheerness, Portsmouth, Plymouth, Cardiff, Pembroke Dock, Rosyth, Haulbowline and Newcastle; and abroad at Gibraltar, Malta, Port Said, Aden, Bombay, Colombo, Hong Kong, Simonstown and Bermuda. It was also necessary to add Liverpool at home, and Kingston (Jamaica) and Trinidad abroad.

Before long protests were received from the chart agents, and questions were asked in Parliament. Hydrographer in response regretted the loss of trade, but disclaimed any responsibility to the agents, and said that they would still sell loose charts and have the benefit of advertisement. He also emphasized that there was no cost to the taxpayer, if anything the reverse. Discussion continued, and in August 1919 Hydrographer had to admit that any full and accurate financial assessment of the benefits was difficult, not least because of the problems of assessing the costs of the depots, some of which were on Government property and others not. The Deputy Chief of Naval Staff, Vice Admiral Sir Osmond Brock, was not in favour of the scheme, and in February 1921 it was dropped, and the sales organisation reverted to supply through Potters as Principal Admiralty Chart Agent.

The Hydrographer continued to handle the Astronomer Royal's administration, and personnel were lent from the Royal Observatory during the war to help the Department in producing certain charts and diagrams. In June 1918 Parry wrote a minute to the Board arguing the need for uniformity in timekeeping. Civil time was reckoned in two twelve-hour periods for each day. The Fleet had already adopted a twenty-four hour clock starting from midnight. The twenty-four hour system was to be used in the Admiralty Tide tables from 1920 and it was used in the new French abridged Nautical Almanac, which might adversely affect the sales of the British Nautical Almanac which still used the astronomical day running from noon to noon.

Parry chaired a conference convened by the Admiralty in June 1918, attended by the Astronomer Royal and representatives from the Board of Trade, the General Post Office, the Home Office, the Meteorological Office, the Ordnance Survey, the War Office, the Royal Society, the Royal Astronomical Society, the Royal Geographical Society and the Eastern Telegraph Company. The French Hydrographer, Ingenieur General Hydrographique Renaud, also attended. The conference found that the world-wide use of Greenwich time at sea was not practicable, and recommended the adoption of a series of time zones in hours ahead of or behind Greenwich. It also recommended that the astronomical day should start at midnight. The Superintendent of the Nautical Almanac Office was directed to make the change from the 1925 edition, and letters informing the scientific world of this change were widely circulated.

On 28 November 1918 Parry submitted a memorandum on the measures to be taken to survey the waters of the colonies of the Empire. His starting point was a 1914 paper by Purey-Cust on the state of hydrographic knowledge. He then explained the pre-war arrangements, which were that the Royal Navy undertook such work if a ship could be spared and if the colony undertook to pay half the cost of maintaining the vessel and paying her ship's company. This had not proved satisfactory to either party, as the Admiralty had to place the emphasis on Naval requirements which were not always those of the colonial government, while much work was of Imperial importance and had to be done whether the colony paid its share or not. Only Canada had set up its own hydrographic service, starting by using retired Royal Naval hydrographic surveyors. This example could not now be followed elsewhere because of a general lack of such personnel.

Parry contended that in the interests of trade a new initiative must be taken by the Imperial government, making sufficient ships available for both Imperial and colonial needs. The large number of vessels suitable for conversion, and the probable redundancy of officers in the Navy, made the time favourable for such a plan. An Imperial surveying service, headed by the Hydrographer whose office would publish and distribute the resulting charts, would be more efficient and economical than a series of small surveying services run by individual colonies, even if trained staff could be found and all the colonies could afford the expense.

The amount of work required was enormous, and was in addition to a very large amount necessary in home waters and on the sea routes to the home country. Nine ships would be needed over a long period to work in both Imperial and colonial interests in Australia, New Zealand, the Pacific Islands, the south, east and west coasts of Africa, the West Indies, the Straits Settlements and Egypt. The cost would be £160,000 a year (£100,000 more than pre-war), a part of which would be recouped from the sale of charts. Of the need for the work there could be no doubt, the only questions were where the costs should fall, and the rate of accomplishment of the task. Parry argued strongly that the whole cost should be borne by the Imperial government, and that the time was ripe for a special effort to reduce the size of the task.

The memorandum was adopted by the Admiralty Reconstruction Committee in January 1919, and the self- governing Dominions asked for their views in March. In reply, the South African government suggested a monetary contribution, or assistance by their land surveyors; the New Zealand government wanted the task carried out by the Admiralty with half the cost borne by the Dominion government; while the Australian Commonwealth government said that they would be glad if the Admiralty would continue, halving the cost with them, until they could establish their own surveying service. Unfortunately, this imaginative plan foundered on the severe retrenchment forced on the Admiralty by the post-war pressure for economy.

For the immediate prosecution of the surveying task, the *Hearty, Daisy, Esther,* and the hired yacht *Melisande* were kept in commission for home waters surveys, and the *Fantome, Merlin* and *Mutine* recommissioned for surveys abroad, with the *Endeavour* continuing to work in the Mediterranean.

The *Melisande* gave nothing but trouble in her eighteen months in naval service. If her machinery was not unserviceable her upper deck was opening up under the strain of hoisting and lowering the boats fitted for surveying. Little useful work was achieved with her, and she was returned to her owners in August 1919. *Hearty* and the two little trawlers were also less than fully satisfactory for modern surveying.

Parry therefore secured six *Aberdare* class minesweepers surplus to the Fleet's post-war requirements for conversion to home waters surveying ships. They were useful little vessels, twin screw coal-burners of 800 tons with a speed of 16 knots, disarmed on conversion and fitted with a chartroom and a full outfit of boats for surveying. *Ambleside, Amersham, Portreath, Radley, Uppingham* and *Ventnor* were renamed respectively *Beaufort, Collinson, Fitzroy, Flinders, Kellett* and *Crozier*, and taken in hand for conversion to be completed by June 1919. The post-war cutbacks soon hit even this programme, and neither the *Collinson* nor the *Crozier* were ever commissioned with Royal Naval crews except for brief trials. Manpower was not available for the Hydrographer to operate them, and they were offered to colonial governments. *Crozier* was taken up by the South African Naval Service and became the first of a line of *Proteas. Collinson*, after trials, was laid up at Harwich from November 1919, and sold as surplus to naval requirements in 1922.

Thus by the end of 1919 there were four new ships surveying in home waters and four older but larger ones overseas, working in the West Indies, the Mediterranean, the Red Sea and on the Australian east coast. By an Admiralty Weekly Order of 1 March 1919 surveying ships were again to be painted white.

Like the Royal Naval Air Service, the Royal Naval Meteorological Service was transferred to the Air Ministry on the formation of the Royal Air Force in 1918. It was, however, recognised that a supplementary organisation dealing with the forecasting, and the promulgation of forecasts, for purely naval purposes would still be required. An Admiralty Meteorological Service was set up in August 1918 as a branch of the Hydrographic Department. With the advent of peace reports from sea could be received, and the system of weather reporting from volunteer ships which has endured to this day was set up. The pattern of broadcast forecasts to the Fleet was also re-organised to fit peacetime patterns, and promulgated in an Admiralty Weekly Order in 1919.

One of Parry's last acts as Hydrographer was to chair the International Hydrographic Conference held in London in June and July 1919. After the 1912 St Petersburg International Maritime Conference, which dealt mainly with navigational and commercial matters, it had been generally agreed that there was a need for a conference to address specifically hydrographic questions. Various suggestions were made both before and during the war, and the very experience of the war itself emphasized both the world-wide need for hydrographic information and the charts that cannot be produced without it, and the very wide divergence both in the methods of production of charts and in the symbology used on them within the international hydrographic community.

The question of holding an international conference was discussed between the British and French Hydrographers, and after the Armistice it was decided between them that the time was ripe to call such a gathering. At the particular urging of the French Hydrographer London was selected as the most suitable place to hold the conference, and Parry obtained the Board's approval for the project. All maritime states with any form of hydrographic office or organisation were invited to send delegates to a conference to be held in London in June 1919, and in view of his particular interest in oceanography a special invitation was sent to His Serene Highness Prince Albert I of Monaco.

The invitations were accepted, and at the opening of the Conference on 24 June twenty two states* were represented, to be joined by two more a few days later. The delegates of a twenty-fifth, Uruguay, did not reach London until after the Conference was over, but expressed the support of their government for its work and conclusions.

The Conference was mounted by Parry and the Admiralty with considerable style. Delegates were accommodated at the Savoy and Carlton Hotels, with the meetings being held at the Office of Works in Westminster. They were received in audience by King George V, and were taken to visit the Royal Observatory at Greenwich, the Admiralty Compass Department at Slough, the Ordnance Survey at Southampton, the Port of London and Trinity House, and the University of Oxford. They went to Chatham to see the newly converted surveying ship *Kellett* fitting out. Entertainment was provided with visits to the Royal Opera House, Covent Garden for 'Faust' and to His Majesty's Theatre for 'Chu Chin Chow', and at weekends cars were placed at their disposal to take them to places of interest in the countryside outside London.

The Conference was opened by the First Sea Lord, Admiral Sir Rosslyn Wemyss. At the first session Parry was elected president of the Conference, with Ingenieur General Hydrographique Renaud, the French Hydrographer, as vice-president and W D Barber, Chief Civil Assistant to the British Hydrographer, as secretary-general. In preparation for the Conference the Department had prepared a long list of points to be discussed and, if possible, standardised, with the British practice in each case appended. These points were divided into ten headings, and committees were set up to deal with each.

From the outset it was agreed that an International Hydrographic Bureau was needed to push forward international co-operation in the hydrographic field, and to encourage the standardisation of charts and nautical publications. With some

---

*Argentine, Australia, Belgian Congo, Belgium, Brazil, Chile, China, Denmark, Egypt, France, Great Britain, Greece, India, Italy, Japan, Monaco, Netherlands, Norway, Peru, Portugal, Siam, Spain, Sweden, United States of America.

reservations it was also agreed that it should be set up under the auspices of the League of Nations, a view encouraged by a letter from the Acting Secretary-General of the League pointing out that under the League's Covenant any international bureau set up after the League itself was instituted should come under the direction of the League. The reservations about the Bureau being under the wing of the League mainly arose from fears that it might become politicised, and it was repeatedly emphasized that the Bureau should be composed of professional hydrographers and not of politicians. The non-political nature of the Bureau, and of the International Hydrographic Organisation which grew from it, has been maintained to this day.

Another question which exercised the delegates was the seat of the Bureau. London was at first suggested, but Parry resisted this as he saw that a Bureau in Britain would be seen as being under the control of the United Kingdom Hydrographer, a perception which would be to the advantage neither of the Bureau nor of the Hydrographer. Geneva was suggested as being the seat of the United Nations, the parent body, but was thought by many to be too remote from the sea for a body concerned with marine matters. Eventually, in 1921, Prince Albert offered the Bureau a home in Monaco. This, as a seaside location in a state too small to be accused of trying to bring improper influence on any other member state, was seen as ideal, and the Prince's generous offer was accepted.

It was also agreed that the Bureau should operate by concensus and advice, rather than have any coercive power over member states, and this too has stood the test of time.

A committee was elected to take the formation of the Bureau forward at the conclusion of the Conference, comprising Parry, Renaud and Captain E.Simpson, USN, Hydrographer of the United States of America.

The Conference held its final sitting on 16 July, having put in place the organisation for the formation of the International Hydrographic Bureau. Parry's presidency was acclaimed at this final session, as was the organisation by his Department which made the Conference run smoothly and achieve so positive a result. A very full report of the Conference was published by His Majesty's Stationery Office in 1920.

Just over a month later, on 1 September 1919, Parry, who had been knighted by the King during the Conference, handed over to Learmonth and retired. He was promoted vice admiral on the retired list in 1920, and to admiral in 1925. He remained active on the committee setting up the International Hydrographic Bureau, and was elected the first Presiding Director in 1921, a post which he continued to fill until his death in 1926 at the age of sixty-one.

CHAPTER THREE

Between the Wars
1919–1932

Vice Admiral F C Learmonth, CB, CBE, 1919-1924

Vice Admiral H P Douglas, CB, CMG, 1924-1932

When F C Learmonth succeeded Parry as Hydrographer in September 1919 he had already been serving in the Admiralty for the whole of the war, following a career spent at sea in surveying ships since 1890. Whereas Parry had prepared the plans for the Hydrographic Service, both ashore and afloat, to return to peace routine, it fell to Learmonth to implement them in the prevailing climate of financial stringency which followed.

He was in his turn succeeded in October 1924 by H P Douglas. Serving until 1932, Douglas became the first Hydrographer since Wharton to serve more than five years in the post. He had been the Director of the Naval Meteorological Service for much of its brief life, and had given a practical demonstration of the value of observation and forecasting when, in command of the *Mutine* at Bermuda during the passage of a hurricane in 1921, his observations and his deduction from them enabled the ships and naval establishments there to be warned and given time to prepare and so to minimise the damage caused by the weather. He was of a scientific and inventive bent, and it was largely due to his enthusiasm that echo-sounders were introduced and accepted so quickly. From the historian's point of view it is unfortunate that he also introduced an extremely abbreviated format for the Annual Reports, which under him became no more than a list of the ships in commission and a table of their surveying achievements.

In home waters the four *Aberdare* class conversions all commissioned in March 1920 and were at sea and surveying by the middle of May. All spent their entire surveying career in home waters. On commissioning *Kellett* was fitted with experimental sound ranging gear. Though the technique appeared promising it was not, in the event, developed. In the following year she was fitted with echo-sounder equipment, which was more successful. The *Aberdares* were useful little ships, though they remained coal-burning until their last days, with all the aggravation in frequent coaling smothering the ship with black dust which that entailed. Another limitation on coal-fired vessels appeared at the time of the miners' strike in 1925, when three of the four home ships had to be immobilised for most of the season to reduce coal consumption. Work was carried on from the sounding boats in inshore waters while the ships were kept alongside in dockyard ports.

Abroad all was less well. *Fantome*, *Merlin* and *Mutine* had all recommissioned either late in 1918 or early in 1919. *Fantome*'s work was in the far north of Queensland, surveying the Torres Strait and the Barrier Reef Inner Route. *Merlin* was brought back from Singapore to operate in the Red Sea, where work on the survey of Loheiya had to be broken off in June 1919 owing to the excessive heat. She refitted at Gibraltar in the winter of 1919-1920, and after working off Malta and in the Straits of Messina returned to Singapore in November 1919 to start work in the Johore Strait, surveying possible sites for the projected Naval Base. As well as simply surveying, Edgell, her captain, conducted the Admiralty committee looking into the area round the sites. For his work he received Their Lordships' appreciation.

Mutine, meanwhile, under first Glennie and then Douglas, was working in the West Indies, mainly round Bermuda and in the Bahamas.

These old conversions had been obsolete when they were built at the turn of the century as masted sloops. In the post-war Navy living conditions on board were intolerable, particularly in the heat of the Red Sea or northern Queensland. Reports speak of 'crowded messdecks, inadequate sanitary arrangements, with very poor washing facilities and inferior ventilation'. Both in the surveying ships, and in their general service sisters* who had also been run on after the war, representations were made by their ship's companies about conditions on board. In at least *Fantome* and *Mutine* there were cases of insubordination which were attributed to a combination of the uncomfortable conditions on board and the remoteness of the survey grounds with no opportunities for shore leave.

It was quickly agreed that replacements were needed, and needed quickly. Learmonth argued for specially built vessels though it must be confessed that he did not strengthen his case by listing in his statement of requirements such niceties as 'a clipper bow'. In any event, with the volume of surplus craft available and the stringent financial situation it was not likely that new construction would be sanctioned. After some discussion of alternatives four of the '24'† class Fleet Sweeping Sloops were selected for conversion. The planned work included adding a superstructure containing chart and instrument rooms, and davits and surveying boats. To counteract the topweight a substantial amount of ballast was required, additions and ballast together increasing the displacement by some 350 tons.

Clio, *Espiegle*, *Odin* and *Shearwater* were all recommissioned after the War for the East Indies station, as it was not considered that the war-built sloops of the Flower and 24 classes had sufficient range for the distances involved.
†The class of 24 vessels were named after famous racehorses, but were known as the "24" class to avoid confusion with the paddle minesweepers of the Racecourse class.

Whereas the *Aberdares* as converted for surveying retained very much the appearance they had as minesweepers apart from their white paint, the '24's were unrecognisable, changing from gawky double-enders to very seemly ships.

In the interim some steps were taken to improve conditions in the older sloops. Ventilation was upgraded, and refrigerators were fitted to improve the food supply. Learmonth also wrote to all commanding officers instructing them not to remain for too long away from recreational ports, and assuring them that interference with the output of survey work would be accepted. Once the '24's entered service the old sloops were paid off and scrapped.

The four new vessels were taken in hand in 1921 and 1922. *Iroquois*, the first to enter service in November 1923, went to replace the *Merlin* on the China station, starting work in the approaches to Singapore early in 1924. *Herald* (formerly *Merry Hampton*) sailed from England on 9 January 1924 for Australia to relieve the *Fantome*. *Ormonde* commissioned in March 1924 and sailed in the same month for the West Indies to take over from *Mutine*. The fourth, *Silvio*, was transferred to the Royal Australian Navy and renamed *Moresby*. She sailed for her new homeland in June 1925, with a largely RN crew and with an RN commanding officer, Edgell. Unlike her Royal Naval sisters, who remained coal-burning throughout their service, *Moresby* was converted to oil-burning in 1931.

The new ships quickly took up the routines established by their predecessors. *Iroquois* divided her time between the Malay peninsula and British Borneo (including work in Sarawak waters, though that state was officially independent under the Brooke rajahs.) In the winter she visited Hong Kong, both to do necessary work in the colony and its approaches and to give her people a break from the humid equatorial climate of Malaya and the Archipelago. *Ormonde* worked in the West Indies until 1926, when she went east under Rice to survey in the Indian Ocean. In 1927 she joined *Iroquois* on a detailed survey of the Malacca Strait, returning west in 1929 to Aden. By 1930 she had begun work in the Persian Gulf, withdrawing to the Mediterranean in the heat of the Gulf summers. *Herald* worked in Australian waters until the arrival of *Moresby* in 1926, then moved north to take over the surveys of Sarawak and British North Borneo from *Iroquois*, leaving her to concentrate her efforts on the Malay peninsula.

Endeavour started the post-war period surveying the Mediterranean coast of Egypt, with some work in the approaches to Malta. From 1922 to 1924 she spent part of each year on the west coast of Africa, surveying the Sierra Leone coast and the approaches to the colony. By 1926 she was working in the Red Sea, withdrawing to the Mediterranean for the hottest part of the year.

The Royal Australian Navy established its own surveying branch in 1921, at first using the sloop *Geranium*. For some time it relied heavily on Royal Naval personnel while a corps of Australian surveyors was built up. Even since the Australian service has grown more or less fully up to strength, a regular series of exchanges of personnel with the RN surveying service has been maintained to the mutual benefit of both services. When *Moresby* arrived on station *Herald,* as we have seen, moved north to work off Malaya and Borneo, leaving Australian waters to the new ship, at first with *Geranium* as well.

For a long time the results of Australian surveys were sent to the Department in London to be compiled and printed. The first Australian chart was not published until 1941. This was a classified Fleet chart, and a sales version was produced in 1949. From this time on the RAN Hydrographer took complete responsibility for producing charts from his own people's surveys, the charts being compiled by his office and printed by the Australian Military Survey.

The interest in oceanography which had always been present came to the fore towards the end of this period with a close liaison with the Ministry of Agriculture and Fisheries. In 1929 and 1930 HMS *Rosemary* was employed during the summer months making oceanographic observations to the north west of Scotland. This was so successful that it was proposed to build a special oceanographical surveying vessel, to be operated by Hydrographer on behalf of the fishing industry. Douglas chaired a conference in January 1930 to determine the ship's characteristics, and it is evident from the resulting specification that he, like Learmonth before him, had some notions which seem strange today, and may have seemed so even then to non-surveyors. The hull form, with a straight stem and a cruiser stern, was modern; a staysail and gaff sails can be argued as sensible for laying to while taking observations, but to say that no gyro compass is required because it is little use above 65° latitude was to deprive the ship of not only a modern compass but of the repeaters and ancilliary equipment which depend on it, on the assumption that she would seldom if ever work in any but high latitudes. Fortunately this last omission was not implemented.

The Board approved the legend and drawings in May 1930, and the name *Challenger* was allocated, after her illustrious oceanographic predecessor. She was laid down in a dry dock at Chatham, 'launched' on 1 June 1931, and completed in November 1931. By this time the great slump had struck, and national finances were even more constrained than in the early 20's. The Ministry of Agriculture and Fisheries had to cut the ship from their budget, and she was taken over fully by Hydrographer, at the cost of bringing *Iroquois* home from the Far East and paying her off.

Experimental echo-sounders had been built and operated by scientists before the First World War. After the war Admiralty scientists, first at Shandon and then at Teddington, worked to produce a practical echo-sounder for use in ships. B S Smith's was chosen as the preferred from four possible designs, and a set was fitted in the *Kellett* in 1921. This early echo-sounder was a diaphragm sounder, working at a frequency of 1250 cycles per second with an electromagnetically operated hammer striking a 5-inch steel diaphragm on the ship's bottom as the sound source and the echoes being received by a simple carbon hydrophone. The operator listened for the echo on earphones, and read the depth off a graduated scale the moment the echo was heard. The initial trials in the *Kellett* were promising, but the trouble experience with the set fitted in 1923 in *Ormonde* showed the importance of the precise positioning of the transmitter and hydrophone on the hull. Nevertheless both scientists and surveyors persisted, and slowly more refined sets were fitted in other ships. The replacement of the unreliable electro-magnetic hammer by magneto-striction oscillators was a breakthough, as was the development in 1929 of an automatic recorder which traced the depths on a paper roll, removing the need for an operator to listen and to write down the soundings. Further development and volume production of the magneto-striction echo-sounders were beyond the capacity of the Admiralty Research Laboratory, and in 1931 Henry Hughes & Co were given a licence to manufacture the Admiralty echo-sounder. Full marketing by Hughes began in 1934, and by the end of 1935 they had sold 500 world-wide.

By 1927 Douglas was able to assure the surveying fleet that there was no reason against the use of the echo-sounder for definitive surveys, but it was ordered that to distinguish soundings obtained by echo from those taken by lead-line, echo-soundings were to be inked in on fair sheets in burnt sienna, as opposed to the normal black ink for lead-line soundings. In his 1928 Annual Report Douglas stated that the satisfactory increase in the number of square miles sounded was mainly due to the use of echo-sounders.

However, the early sets were not reliable either in very shallow water, where the returning echo arrived too soon after the transmission for the ear to measure the time interval, nor in water over about 150 fathoms, where the returning echo was simply too weak. So the lead line and the wire sounding machine were not totally discarded yet. After surveying in the South China Sea *Herald* reported on the modifications she had made to the standard Somerville deep sounding rig, and in 1927 these were promulgated to the fleet.

On the naval personnel front the specialist Surveying Recorder ratings were re-organised, with three classes attracting specialist pay of 1s 6d, 1s, and 6d respectively per diem. The sleeve badge of a quadrant was introduced, and a roster for advancement established at Chatham. There was a shortage of surveying officers after the war, and in an attempt to alleviate this volunteers from qualified navigating officers were encouraged to serve a commission in a surveying ship. By 1929 the normal period for which surveying officers should serve in each grade was being laid down, though it was emphasised that advancement would remain subject to the commanding officer's recommendation.

Ashore, the personnel of the Department were successively reduced from the 367 of December 1918 to no more than 118 by the end of 1923. This, with the backlog of information to be inserted on charts on which Parry had reported, placed a very great strain on the cartographers and draughtsmen of Chart Branch. It was increased by the problems in connection with cartographers' pay which Learmonth now had to face.

The pay of the cartographer grade had not been increased since 1883. In the reorganisation of 1909 which transferred some of the routine work of the cartographers to the draughtsman grade there had been some adjustments to increments, and in that year the pay on entry had in fact been reduced from £120 per annum to £100. Draughtsmen, being part of a wider class, received increments to their pay from time to time. The cartographers, though, were a small class employed only within the Hydrographic Department, and they saw the differential between them and those they supervised being eroded.

The pay of the administrative, executive and clerical grades (or, more correctly, the classes which became these grades) was reviewed in 1920, and substantial increases awarded. An Admiralty Composite Grades Committee was set up to consider the professional and technical classes, but this body expired before it could report, being absorbed into the National Committees for the professional classes set up in 1921. Cartographers had no place in these National Committees, and it was not until 1923 that a committee of the Admiralty Administrative Whitley Council was set up to consider the duties of the cartographer grade and to make recommendations on their pay. The financial situation of the country was very different in 1923 from that which had prevailed in 1920. While the Committee was sympathetic to the cartographers' case, their recommendations are full of phrases like 'a good case could be made out for a higher rate of pay throughout the scale, had financial conditions been less abnormal than they are now'.

In spite of these caveats the Committee recommended a starting rate of £150, rising to a maximum of £450 for cartographers, with Chief Cartographers starting at £500 and rising to £600 and the Superintending Cartographer starting at £650 and rising to £800. Even this modest increase fell under the axe of the Treasury, who while they allowed the higher starting rate would not permit the old maximum of £400 to be exceeded. The Chief Cartographers (who had been known up until this time as Chief Cartographers 2nd class) received their £500 to £600 in full, but the Superintending Cartographer (old Chief Cartographer 1st class) received a single rate of £700. To some extent the Admiralty ameliorated the worst effect of this blow by providing six £50 allowances for senior Cartographers, but the mood of the cartographic class was one of resentment at being singled out for, as they saw it, sacrifice on the altar of economic expediency.

At this stage it might be appropriate to give a brief outline of the processes involved in compiling and producing an Admiralty chart. Once it had been decided to produce a chart of a particular area on a particular scale the cartographer or cartographic draughtsman allocated to the work would obtain from the archives all the data held on the area. This would, except in the case of a large scale harbour chart being drawn from a single modern survey, invariably include a number of surveys of different scales and ages. All these would be examined, compared where they overlapped, differences reconciled, and from them all a 'compilation drawing' would be made. This would be in the nature of a shorthand sketch of the finished chart, with the positioning of each item of detail from sounding figures to place names precisely indicated, and the styles of lettering and so on shown. The work would be checked by a senior cartographer before being approved for reproduction. The engraver would then take the compilation drawing, transfer the detail in reverse onto his copper plate, and engrave it so that a master printing plate was the result. When any correction was required, the area of the old detail would be hammered up from behind, the plate smoothed clean, and the whole of the area re-engraved with the new material included. From the engraved copper the finished chart would be printed by direct impression on a flat-bed printer.

Parry's recommendation to the Reconstruction Committee that printing should be brought under Admiralty control came to fruition with the setting up of an Admiralty Chart Establishment at Cricklewood in 1922*. At first this was operated by His Majesty's Stationery Office on Hydrographer's behalf, but in 1929 it was transferred to Hydrographer's direct control.

Working conditions for the cartographers improved in 1924 when the whole of Chart Branch moved out of the Admiralty building into Cornwall House, at the southern end of Waterloo Bridge. This move, undertaken to make more room for the Naval Staff in the Admiralty, at last gave the people of Chart Branch space and light far better than they had ever enjoyed in the attics of the Admiralty. Tides also moved to Cornwall House at this time.

The war had shown the need for a gazetteer of names appearing on charts. There were a number of occasions where a ship had made a report using a name taken from the chart she was navigating on, and the location could not be discovered in the shore headquarters to which she had reported. A start had been made in 1917 on an 'Index Nauticus'. A first edition was published in 1920 covering the British Isles only, and listing some 100,000 names. In the squeeze on personnel in the early '20s this was one project which could not be sustained, and no further editions were published. The need was to some extent filled by a deliberate policy of listing and indexing minor names in the various volumes of the Sailing Directions.

Not only the listing of names was needed; their spelling also needed standardisation, particularly where transcription from a different alphabet or writing system was involved. At Admiralty instance a Permanent Commission on Geographic Names was set up in 1920, with representatives of the Admiralty (Hydrographer and Intelligence Division), the War Office, the Foreign Office, the Colonial Office and the Royal Geographical Society. This provided an authoritative set of systems for transliteration into the Roman script, and also acted, for the first time, as an approving and co-ordinating authority to accept new names given by explorers or geographers to features hitherto un-named, mainly in the polar regions. It has indeed justified its name of 'Permanent', enduring to this day based at the Royal Geographical Society in Kensington, though an Antarctic Placenames Committee, based in Cambridge, has been set up to take over responsibility for the south polar region.

The Admiralty Meteorological Service set up in 1918 had a very short life. In August 1920 all weather services were brought together under the Air Ministry's Meteorological Office. However, a Navy Services Division within the Meteorological

---

*Day and some other authorities give 1923 as the date for the starting of printing at Cricklewood, but Learmonth's Annual Report for 1922 states that the ACE 'has been completed and is now in operation'

Office remained responsible, under Hydrographer, for supervising the meteorological work of the Fleet, and for providing the weather forecasts and other services the Fleet required.

The committee set up at the conclusion of the International Hydrographic Conference pressed ahead devising the organisation necessary to set up the International Hydrographic Bureau under Parry's energetic chairmanship. A Convention setting out the rules under which the Bureau would operate was drawn up and approved. The salient points, most of which had already been foreshadowed in the Conference, were that the Bureau would operate by concensus with no coercive authority, that it would be financed by contributions weighted in proportion to the shipping tonnage of member nations and that voting rights would be similarly weighted, that the Bureau would be managed by three Directors, one of whom would be elected as Presiding Director and who would be *primus inter pares* among the three, that the seat of the Bureau would be in Monaco by invitation of HSH Prince Albert I, and that member states would meet in conference every five years to review the work of the Bureau.

In May 1921 nineteen member states elected the first Directors: Parry, Captain I M Pfaff, Royal Netherlands Navy, and Captain S H Muller, Royal Norwegian Navy. Commander G B Spicer-Simson, DSO, RN was appointed Secretary. These officers took up residence in the Principality and set up the Bureau in a rented building in Monaco in July 1921.

The Second International Hydrographic Conference (they are always numbered from the 1919 conference as the First) was held at Monaco in the autumn of 1926, in the Oceanographic Museum founded by Prince Albert on the Rock of Monaco. Parry had died earlier in the year, and the presidency of the Directing Committee had been assumed by Pfaff. 21 member states sent representatives, Siam being the only member state not represented. Also attending were observers from British India and from the Kingdom of the Serbs, Croats and Slovenes. A new Directing Committee was elected without a British member, the Directors being Rear Admiral A P Niblack, DSM from the United States of America, Ingenieur General P de Vanssay de Blavous of France and Captain L Tonta from Italy.

By the time of the Conference Prince Albert had also died, and at it Spain offered a site in Malaga as the permanent home of the Bureau. The offer was remitted to a committee, to report at an intermediate conference called for the spring of 1929, two and a half years after the last regular one. When the Monaco government offered to build a permanent home for the Bureau and to maintain it free of charge, Spain gracefully withdrew, and the conference voted to waive Monaco's statutory contribution to the Bureau in consideration of its generosity. It was indeed generous, since Monaco's total tonnage of shipping was and is such that its contribution would be far less than any commercial rent for a building on the waterfront of the port of Monaco, to say nothing of the costs of repairs and renovation which the building has undergone from time to time. The foundation stone of the building was laid by HSH Prince Louis II during the 1929 conference.

The first arguments about the scale of contributions occurred soon after the foundation of the Bureau, with Belgium first trying to limit its contribution to 6000 gold francs, and then when that was not allowed withdrawing from the organisation. This resignation was balanced by the accession to the Bureau in 1926 of Germany and Poland. It was, though, to be the forerunner of a flow of resignations during the slump at the end of the decade and in the early '30s.

From the start Learmonth reported on the benefits to the British Hydrographic Service from the IHB. As a world charting authority, closer co-operation between nations engaged in hydrography and standardisation of practices could only help to reduce the load on Great Britain in maintaining world chart cover. From the outset this was fostered by the IHB. Standardisation of the symbols and conventions of nautical cartography was pressed vigorously by the Directing Committee, and agreement on a number of matters reached in the early years. It was not, though, until the 1970s that a full International Chart Specification was published.

The Principal Surveys of 1919

HOME

Daisy	Harvey	England, South Coast	Dover Harbour and off-lying wrecks.
		Scotland, West Coast	Gareloch.
Esther	Knowles	Scotland, West Coast	Inverness.
		North Sea	The Northern Barrage.
Hearty	Chearnley, Gibson	England, East Coast	The Wash; Thames Estuary.
		Scotland, East Coast	Moray Firth.
Melisande	Maxwell	England, East Coast	Rivers Colne and Blackwater approaches.
	Combe	Scotland, East Coast	Rosyth and Granton.
	Lanyon	England, South Coast	Portsmouth.

ABROAD

Endeavour	Reyne	Mediterranean	N Coast of Egypt.
Merlin	Nares	Red Sea	Loheiya; Hurghada; Strait of Jubal.
Mutine	Glennie	West Indies.	Bermuda, Hamilton Harbour; St George's Harbour; Ship Channel.
Fantome	Scott	Australia, East Coast	Sydney; Port Jackson; Port Stephens.

The Principal Surveys of 1920

HOME

Beaufort	Knowles	Shetland Isles	Sullom Voe; Yell Sound.
Fitzroy	Gibson	England, East Coast	Winterton Ness to Yarmouth Haven; Cockle Gatway; Ship to Race Bank.
Flinders	Maxwell	Ireland, East Coast	Approaches to Wexford.
		Scotland, West Coast	Sound of Islay.
Kellett	Harvey,	England, East Coast	Thames Estuary.
	Lanyon,	England, South Coast	Portsmouth; Portland;
	May		Plymouth.

ABROAD

Endeavour	Reyne	Mediterranean	N Coast of Egypt.
Fantome	Scott	Australia, East Coast	Port Stephens.
		Australia, North Coast	Torres Strait.
Merlin	Nares,	Mediterranean	Hurd Bank; Straits of Messina.
	Garbett	Malay Peninsula	Singapore Old Strait.
Mutine	Glennie	West Indies	Bahamas, Crooked Island Passage; Bermuda, Great Sound; Port Royal Bay; Hamilton Harbour.

The Principal Surveys of 1921

HOME

Beaufort	Knowles	England, South Coast	Start Bay, Skerries Bank.
		Wales, West Coast	Milford Haven.
		Shetland Isles	Mid Yell Voe; BastaVoe; Hascosay Sound.
Flinders	Jackson	England, South Coast	S Approaches to Isle of Wight; Needles Channel.
		Scotland, West Coast	Sound of Islay.
Fitzroy	Viney	England, East Coast	River Medway; Approaches to the Wash (Race Bank); Yarmouth Roads.
Kellett	Harvey	England, East Coast	Thames Estuary; Galloper Shoal; Approaches to Orfordness.
		England, South Coast	Royal Sovereign.
	May	England, South Coast	Devonport; Portland; Portsmouth.

ABROAD

Endeavour	Reyne, Geary-Hill	Mediterranean	Hurd Bank; N Coast of Egypt.
Fantome	Scott, Maxwell	Australia, North Coast	Torres Strait.
		Australia, East Coast	Passages inside Great Barrier Reef.
Merlin	Edgell	Malay Peninsula	Singapore Old Strait.
Mutine	Glennie, Douglas	West Indies	Jamaica, Port Antonio; Approaches to Belize; Bermuda, St George's and Hamilton Harbours.

The Principal Surveys of 1922

HOME

Beaufort	Knowles	Wales, West Coast	Approaches to Milford Haven.
		Shetland Isles	Mid Yell and Basta Voes; Yell Sound.
Fitzroy	Silk, Woodhouse	England, East Coast	Yarmouth and Lowestoft Roads; Race Bank.
Flinders	Jackson	Scotland, West Coast	Sound of Islay.
		England, West Coast	Bristol Channel.
		England, South Coast	Portland, Shambles.
Kellett	Haselfoot	England, East Coast	Thames Estuary; Southwold to Harwich.
		England, South Coast	Beachy Head to Bexhill.
	May	England, South Coast	Portsmouth; Portland; Plymouth.

ABROAD

Endeavour	Geary-Hill	Mediterranean	N Coast of Egypt.
		Africa, West Coast	Sierra Leone: Cape Ann Shoals
Fantome	Maxwell	Australia, North Coast	W Approaches to Prince of Wales Channel; Thursday Island harbour.
		Australia, East Coast	North Barnard Is to Dunk Island.
Merlin	Edgell	Malay Peninsula	Singapore Old and Main Straits.
		China, South Coast	Hong Kong.
Mutine	Douglas	West Indies	Bermuda, Hamilton and St George Harbours; Approaches to Belize; Jamaica, Portland Bight.

Merlin paid off for sale at Hong Kong 6 December.
Iroquois commissioned 30 November for service in Far East

The Principal Surveys of 1923

HOME

Beaufort	Rice	Shetland Islands	Yell Sound; Gossaborough Ness to Hoaf Gurney I.
		Scotland, East Coast	Firth of Forth.
Fitzroy	Woodhouse	England, East Coast	Blakeney to Brancaster; Cromer Knoll to Sheringham Shoal; Lowestoft Roads
Flinders	Jackson, Henderson	England, West Coast	Bristol Channel.
Kellett	Haselfoot	England, East Coast	Thames Estuary.
		England, South Coast	Beachy Head toBexhill; Dover harbour.
	May	England, South Coast	Portsmouth; Plymouth

ABROAD

Endeavour	Geary-Hill, Nares	Africa, West Coast	Sierra Leone: Cape Ann Shoals.
Fantome	Maxwell	Australia, North Coast	W. Approaches to Torres Strait; Argan Bay: Badu I.
		Australia, East Coast	Ellison Reef to Beaver Reef.
Iroquois	Tinson	Malay Peninsula	Johore River; Singapore Main Strait.
		Borneo, North Coast	Lebam River; Miri and approaches.
Mutine	Douglas	West Indies	Jamaica, Portland Bight; Bermuda, Hamilton Harbour.

Endeavour also carried out a survey of Falmouth Harbour after refit in England in the summer.
Mutine paid off to disposal 11 October, to be replaced by *Ormonde*, then fitting out.
Herald commissioned 17 December for the Australia Station to replace *Fantome*.

The Principal Surveys of 1924

HOME

Beaufort	Rice	Shetland Islands	Blue Mull Sound; Bixter and Weisdale Voes; Scalloway.
		Scotland, West Coast	Loch Goil; Loch Shieldaig.
Fitzroy	Woodhouse,	England, East Coast	Harwich harbour; Great Yarmouth approaches; Cromer Knoll to Sheringham Shoal; Approaches to the River Tyne.
Flinders	Henderson	England, South Coast	Poole Harbour.
		Bristol Channel	Cardiff and Barry Roads; River Severn.
		Scotland, West Coast	Loch Fyne.
Kellett	Haselfoot	England, East Coast	Thames Estuary; River Medway.
		England, South Coast	Bexhill to Fairlight.
	May	England, South Coast	Portsmouth; the Solent; Plymouth.

ABROAD

Endeavour	Nares, Geary-Hill	Africa, West Coast	Sierra Leone: Cape Ann Shoals; Freetown.
Herald	Harvey	Australia, North Coast	Endeavour Strait; Western Approaches to Torres Strait.
		Australia, East Coast	Barrier Reef to S of Beaver Reef.
Iroquois	Tinson	Malay Peninsula	Singapore Main Strait; E Coast of Johore.
		China, South Coast	S Approaches to Hong Kong.
Ormonde	Douglas,	West Indies	Trinidad, Port of Knowles Spain & Approaches; San Fernando & Approaches; W.Coast of Trinidad; Virgin Is, Gorda Sound; Virgin Sound.

Endeavour also carried out a survey of Fowey Harbour, Cornwall, after refit in England in the summer.

The Principal Surveys of 1925

HOME

Beaufort	Rice	Scotland, West Coast	Loch Torridon.
		Shetlands Islands	Scalloway and Approaches; Lerwick Harbour.
		England, South Coast	Approaches to Falmouth.
Fitzroy	Silk	England, East Coast	River Orwell; Cromer Knoll to Sheringham; Donna Nook to Trusthorpe; North Scroby Sand; River Stour.
		England, South Coast	Spithead & E. approaches.
Flinders	Henderson	England, South Coast	Fowey Harbour.
		Bristol Channel	Cardiff & Barry Roads; Watchet to Bairnbach Island.
		Wales, West Coast	River Cleddau.
Kellett	Maxwell	England, East Coast	Thames Estuary; River Medway.
	May	England, South Coast	Portsmouth; Eastern Approaches to Spithead; Plymouth.

ABROAD

Endeavour	Geary-Hill	Africa, West Coast	Sierra Leone: Cape Ann Shoals; Freetown; Cockerill Bay; False Cape to Cape Shilling.
Herald	Harvey	Australia, North Coast	Endeavour Strait; Alpha Rock to Prince of Wales Channel.
Ormonde	Knowles	West Indies	Bermuda, Great Sound and Port Royal Bay; Challenger Bank; Virgin Is; Approaches to Virgin Gorda; Road Harbour & Approaches;. Trinidad, Gulf of Paria; St Kitts, Belletete to Brimstone Hill.
Iroquois	Jackson	China, South Coast	Approaches to Hong Kong.
		Malay Peninsula	Singapore Main Strait; E. Coast of Johore.
		Borneo, N.E.Coast	Cape Sirik; Acis Shoal.

Endeavour returned to England at the end of June, and left for the Red Sea early in November, starting surveys at the end of the year.

The Principal Surveys of 1926

HOME

Beaufort	Rice	Scotland, West Coast	Loch Fyne.
		England, South Coast	Falmouth harbour; Fowey harbour.
		England, West Coast	River Mersey approaches.
Fitzroy	Harvey, Lockhart	England, East Coast	Lincolnshire Coast.
Flinders	Law	England, South Coast	Approaches to Spithead; Portland.
		Bristol Channel	Watchet to Bairnbach Island.
Kellett	Maxwell	England, East Coast	Thames Estuary; The Downs.
	May	England, South Coast	Portsmouth; Plymouth.
	Henderson	Bristol Channel	River Severn.

ABROAD

Endeavour	Geary-Hill	Red Sea	Kamaran and Approaches; Arabian coast S of Jiddah.
Herald	Silk	Australia, East Coast	Inside Barrier Reef.
		Borneo, N.W.Coast	Approaches to Miri.
Iroquois	Jackson	China, South Coast	Approaches to Hong Kong; North Danger Reef.
		Malay Peninsula	Singapore Main Strait; E Coast of Johore.
Ormonde	Knowles	West Indies	Bermuda.
		British Guiana	Georgetown; Demerara and Essequibo Rivers.

Home ships movements were limited to conserve coal stocks during the miners' strike. Most surveys were carried out by boat parties.

Principal Surveys of 1927

HOME

Beaufort	Wyatt	Scotland, West Coast	Loch Fyne.
		England, West Coast	River Dee.
		England, South Coast	Salcombe.
Fitzroy	Harvey	England, East Coast	Lincolnshire coast.
Flinders	Law, Cary	England, South Coast	Approaches to Spithead; Portland.
		Bristol Channel	Watchet to Bairnbach Island.
		Scotland, West Coast	Ballachulish.
Kellett	Cary, Silk	England, East Coast	Thames Estuary; The Downs.
	May	England, South Coast	Portsmouth to Southampton Water.
	Henderson	Bristol Channel	River Severn.

ABROAD

Endeavour	Geary-Hill,	Mediterranean	Malta
	Law	Red Sea	Kamaran; Approaches to Port Sudan.
Herald	Silk,	Borneo	Cape Sirik to Tanjong Baram;
	Haselfoot		Approaches to Brunei.
		South China Sea	South Luconia Shoals.
Iroquois	Jackson	China, South Coast	Approaches to Hong Kong;
	Malay Peninsula	Malacca Strait.	
Ormonde	Rice	Indian Ocean	Cape Guardafui to Socotra; Maldive Islands.
		Malay Peninsula	Malacca Strait.

Principal Surveys of 1928

HOME			
Beaufort	Wyatt	England, South Coast	Penzance Bay.
		England, West Coast	Isle of Man.
		Scotland, West Coast	Loch Fyne.
		Ireland, North Coast	Portrush and Skerries Roadstead.
Fitzroy	Harvey	England, East Coast	Lincolnshire Coast; Yarmouth & Lowestoft Roads.
Flinders	Cary	Bristol Channel	Watchet to Bairnbach Island.
		England, South Coast	Off Portland.
Kellett	Silk	England, East Coast	Thames Estuary; The Downs; Dover.
	May	England, South Coast	Littlehampton; Portsmouth; Plymouth.

ABROAD			
Endeavour	Law	Mediterranean	E Approach to Port Said.
		Red Sea	Approaches to Kamaran.
Herald	Haselfoot	Borneo	Cape Sirik to Tanjong Baram.
Iroquois	Nares	South China Sea	Paracel Islands, Crescent Group.
		Malay Peninsula	Malacca Strait.
Ormonde	Rice	Malay Peninsula	Malacca Strait.
		Indian Ocean	Maldive Islands.

Principal Surveys of 1929

HOME

Beaufort	Wyatt, Rice	Scotland, West Coast	Sound of Gigha.
		England, South Coast	Approaches to Falmouth.
		Irish Sea	N Approach to the Menai Strait; Isle of Man: Douglas.
Fitzroy	Fryer	England, East Coast	Lowestoft Road; Bridlington Bay; Seaham Harbour; Dogger Bank.
Flinders	Cary	England, South Coast	West Solent; Yarmouth Roads.
		Scotland, West Coast	Approaches to Lochinvar.
Kellett	Hardy, Cowan	England, East Coast	Thames Estuary; Dover Harbour.
		England, South Coast	Portsmouth; Plymouth; Shoreham harbour.

ABROAD

Endeavour	Law	Red Sea	Kamaran Approaches; Towila Island; Shadwan Channel.
Herald	Maxwell	Borneo	N.W.Coast; Sarawak River.
		China, South Coast	Approaches to Hong Kong.
Iroquois	Nares	Malay Peninsula	Malacca Strait; Penang Shoals.
Ormonde	Rice, Wyatt	Arabia, South Coast	Gulf of Aden; W. Approaches to Aden.
		Mediterranean	Malta.

In addition to regular surveying ships, the sloop *Rosemary* (Commander G F W Wilson, DSO) was employed for four months making oceanographic observations on the Rockall bank and between Iceland and the Faeroe Islands. This work was mainly for the fishing industry.

Principal Surveys of 1930

HOME

Beaufort	Rice	England, West Coast	St Ives Harbour.
		Scotland, West Coast	Sound of Gigha.
Fitzroy	Fryer	England, East Coast	Tees Bay; Farne Islands.
		North Sea	Devil's Hole.
Flinders	Cary	Scotland, West Coast	Approaches to Edrachillis Bay.
		England, South Coast	West Solent.
Kellett	Hardy	England, East Coast	Thames Estuary.
		England, South Coast	Folkestone to Hastings.
	Cowan	England, South Coast	Portsmouth; Plymouth.

ABROAD

Endeavour	Law,	Red Sea	Kamaran approaches; Trinkitat.
	Edgell	Mediterranean	Haifa and approaches.
Herald	Maxwell	Borneo	N.W.Coast; Sarawak River.
		China, South Coast	Approaches to Hong Kong.
Iroquois	Law	Malay Peninsula	Malacca Strait; Dindings Channel; Johore Strait.
Ormonde	Wyatt	Persian Gulf	Qatar to Oman.
		Mediterranean	Cyprus, Approaches to Famagusta.

Rosemary (Wilson) carried out another season of oceanographic observations near Rockall and off the east coast of Ireland.

Principal Surveys of 1931

HOME

Beaufort	Turner	England, West Coast	Padstow and approaches.
		Scotland, West Coast	Loch Long; West Loch Tarbert
Fitzroy	Fryer,	Scotland, East Coast	Fraserburgh.
	Wyatt	England, East Coast	Berwick to Holy Island; Yarmouth & Lowestoft Roads.
Flinders	Simpson	Wales, South Coast	Burry Inlet; Caldy Roads.
		Scotland, West Coast	W.Coast of Sutherland.
Kellett	Southern	England, East Coast	Thames Estuary; North Foreland.
	Cowan	England, South Coast	Sandown Bay; Portsmouth; Plymouth.

ABROAD

Endeavour	Edgell,	Red Sea	Trinkitat.
	Rice	Mediterranean	Palestine Coast; Jaffa Anchorage.
Herald	Hardy	Borneo	Coast of Sarawak.
		China, South Coast	Approaches to Hong Kong.
Iroquois	Jackson	Malay Peninsula	Malacca Strait; Dindings, Perak River.
Ormonde	Wyatt	Persian Gulf	Qatar to Oman.
		Mediterranean	Cyprus, Approaches to Famagusta.

Iroquois returned to England to pay off, to be replaced (but not in the Far East) by *Challenger*.

Biographies

1919–1932

Admiral Sir Frederick C Learmonth, KBE, CB
Hydrographer 1919–1924

Frederick Charles Learmonth was born in 1866, the younger son of Colonel Alexander Learmonth, MP. He entered the Navy as a cadet in 1879, was made a midshipman in 1881, commissioned as a sub-lieutenant in 1885, and promoted lieutenant in 1887 while serving in the Royal Yacht *Victoria and Albert*.

He began surveying in 1890 in the *Egeria*, Field, working for three and a half years in Borneo and the Anamba Islands. In 1894 he was sent to the *Rambler*, Richards, first on the west coast of Africa and then in North America and the West Indies. In 1896 he returned to *Egeria*, Smyth, in British Columbia, from where he was invalided in 1899. On his recovery he went to the *Research*, Moore and later Field, in home waters, and while there was promoted commander. In August 1901 he began fitting out the old gunboat *Goldfinch* for surveying, and in 1902 commissioned her for service on the west coast of Africa and the Mediterranean. Further service abroad followed, first in *Egeria* in British Columbia 1905-07, then in the *Merlin* in Borneo 1909-11. Immediately before the First World War he was engaged in surveys of the North Sea banks, first in *Hearty*, then in *Endeavour*.

Throughout the war Learmonth served in the Admiralty, first as Captain Superintendent Submarine Defences and later as Director of Fixed Defences. His work in the production of net defences was recognised as being of inestimable value both to Britain and her allies. He was successively awarded the CBE and CB. In September 1919 he succeeded Parry as Hydrographer. In 1921 he was absent from office for six months to visit Singapore in company with the Civil Engineer in Chief to report on the project to build a naval base there. He was promoted vice admiral in 1923.

Learmonth was succeeded as Hydrographer in October 1924 by Douglas, and was made KBE in the following year. On retirement he became the Admiralty representative on the Port of London Authority and also the Acting Conservator of the River Mersey. He was promoted admiral on the retired list in 1927, and died in London in 1941.

Vice Admiral Sir Henry P Douglas, KCB, CMG
Hydrographer 1924–1932

Henry Percy Douglas was born in 1876, the second son of Admiral Sholto Douglas, CB. He entered the Navy as a cadet in 1890, being made midshipman in 1892 and commissioned sub-lieutenant in 1896.

He specialised in surveying in 1897, joining the *Stork*, Gedge, and working for three years in Mauritius, the Mediterranean and the Red Sea, being promoted lieutenant in 1898.

In 1900 he served in home waters in the *Research*, Field, and the following year joined the *Rambler*, Smyth for three years on the China station. After another season at home in *Research*, Smyth, he joined the *Goldfinch*, Walter, for a year in the Mediterranean and on the west coast of Africa. In 1906 he joined the *Merlin*, Parry, for service again on the China station, but a month later was invalided and sent home to join the Hydrographic Department as a naval assistant. In mid 1907, now fully recovered, he went to the *Egeria*, Learmonth, in British Columbia, and in June 1908 was appointed in command of the *Waterwitch*, where for two years he was mainly employed on surveys in Malayan waters. From 1910 for five years he was Superintendant of Charts, being promoted commander at the end of 1910.

In February 1915 he was appointed to the staff of the Vice Admiral, Mediterranean to supervise the surveys carried out by the navigating officers of the fleet. He was involved in the reconnaisance of the Gallipoli beaches prior to the landings there, and during the campaign applied his surveying knowledge to assist the gunnery officers of the Fleet in bombarding enemy positions by indirect fire. As an acting captain from September 1915 he was in charge of all surveying operations in the war area including those of the *Endeavour*, Edgell, and was confirmed captain at the end of 1915.

On his return from the Dardanelles in June 1916 he was appointed to the Admiralty War Staff, and directed the employment of surveying techniques to bombardment again, this time on the Belgian coast. He also worked on the design of range-finding instruments for anti- aircraft gunnery. For a year from April 1917 he was Director of the newly formed Naval Meteorological Service, then joined the staff of Vice Admiral Dover, where he was involved in the planning of the operations to block Zeebrugge and Ostend, for which he was awarded the CMG and made an Officer of the Belgian Order of Leopold.

Early in 1919 he returned to the Department as Assistant Hydrographer for two years, then commanded the *Mutine* in the West Indies, later transferring to the *Ormonde* on the same station.

In October 1924 Douglas succeeded Learmonth as Hydrographer, serving in the post until 1932. He was promoted rear admiral in 1927, and after being placed on the retired list in 1929 was promoted vice admiral in 1931. He was awarded the CB in 1929, and advanced to KCB in 1933.

After retiring from the post of Hydrographer he was in 1933 appointed an assessor to the House of Lords and Acting Conservator of the River Mersey. In 1934 he became Chairman of Dover Harbour Board, and on the outbreak of war in 1939 was appointed as Commodore Superintendent. He died suddenly on 4th November 1939.

Commander C A Bamford, DSC

Cyril Assafrey Bamford won a DSC as a midshipman RNR in 1916 before joining the surveying service in 1923 as a lieutenant of three years seniority in the *Fitzroy*, Woodhouse, working on the east coast of England. Next year he was one of the officers of the newly commissioned *Herald*, Harvey, later Silk, which proceeded to the Australian station for surveys of the Endeavour Strait and off the Queensland coast. In 1926 he joined the *Kellett*, Harvey, on the east coast of England, and a year later moved to the *Flinders*, Cary, on the south coast of England and the west coast of Scotland. He went back overseas from 1928 to 1931 to the *Herald* again, this time under Maxwell, working on the north coast of Borneo. Returning home in 1932 Bamford went to the *Kellett*, Southern, and soon took over command, carrying out surveys on the east coast of England.

Bamford came ashore in 1934 to serve as naval assistant in the Department until 1941, when he was retired as a commander. In 1937 he was detached to make tidal observations for the projected Severn Barrage. During the war years 1941 to 1944 he was attached to the Inter-Services Topographical Division, planning for commando raids on the Norwegian coast. Bamford returned to the Department for two years in charge of the Light List Branch from 1945 to 1946. For some years after his retirement from direct employment in the Office he continued to work as a reviser of Sailing Directions. He died in Torquay in 1970.

Commander J P Cary

John Pitt Cary joined the surveying service in 1912 when he was appointed to the newly commissioned *Endeavour*, Hardy, as a sublieutenant. She and the ship he transferred to the following year, the trawler *Daisy*, Geary-Hill, were both engaged on North Sea surveys.

1914 saw Cary in the *Fantome*, Reyne, on the Australia station. When war broke out the ship was armed at Sydney, and searched for the German surveying ship *Komet* before being paid off at the end of 1914. By now a lieutenant, Cary was then appointed to SS *Berrima*, which was to tow the Australian submarine AE 2 to England. She was diverted to Port Said, and the submarine commissioned for service in the Mediterranean. With Cary borne as an additional officer AE 2 penetrated the Sea of Marmora, only to be sunk by the Turks. Cary was a prisoner of war in Turkish hands for the remainder of hostilities.

In 1919 he went again to the *Fantome*, Scott, for two years on the Australian station, much of it in the Torres Strait. This was followed by a year in the *Merlin*, Edgell, working mainly in Singapore waters. In 1922 he came home to serve for a season in the *Beaufort*, Knowles, on Shetland Islands surveys, then went abroad again to the *Endeavour*, Nares and later Geary-Hill, working mainly in West African waters.

Returning to England at the end of 1925, Cary joined the *Kellett*, Maxwell, in the Thames Estuary, succeeding to the command early in 1927. From the end of 1927 to 1931 he commanded the *Flinders*, spending much time in Scottish waters.

From 1931 to 1935 he served in the Department assisting the Notices to Mariners Officer. He retired with the rank of commander in 1935. On the outbreak of war in 1939 Cary returned to the Department as instrument officer and Duty Commander (H). In 1944 he went out to Colombo as Assistant Fleet Hydrographic Officer. In 1945 he retired for a second time to live in Chard, Somerset.

Commander C P Chearnley

Cecil Philip Chearnley's first experience of surveying was as a lieutenant in the *Egeria*, Parry, from 1908 for about eighteen months on the Canadian west coast. He was invalided home, then on his recovery joined the *Triton*, Penfold, and served for two years in home waters before going abroad again to the *Merlin*, Pasco, later Gibson, on the China station.

From the outbreak of war until 1916 Chearnley served first in *Rosario* and then in *Pyramus* before returning to surveying to the *Hearty*, Reyne, working in home waters. From August 1918 until early 1919 he temporarily commanded the *Hearty*, and then continued in her under Gibson until he was retired medically unfit in 1920. He went to live in Cork, where he was advanced to commander on the retired list in 1925.

Captain J W Combe, CMG

James William Combe began surveying as a sublieutenant in 1877 when he joined the *Alacrity*, Moore, spending six years in the Fiji Islands, and being promoted to Lieutenant in 1880. In 1881 G.E.Richards succeeded Moore, and in the following year the *Alacrity* was replaced by the *Renard*, one of the last sailing schooners. The survey was completed in 1883, and Combe returned home.

Towards the end of 1884 Combe went back to the east to join the *Paluma* on the Australia station, and served again under Richards for four and a half years, mainly on surveys of the inner route off Queensland. Leaving the *Paluma* in 1889 he served next in the *Penguin*, Moore, on surveys in Australian waters and on the China station.

In 1893 he returned to England and commissioned the *Waterwitch*, sailing her out to the Australia station for further surveys of the Fiji Islands. He was promoted to commander in 1896.

In 1897 he was back in England, and after six months in the Department he took command of the *Triton* for surveys on the east coast of England. After only one season he went abroad again, commanding the *Penguin* for three years, at first in Australia and then in New Zealand. In 1903, by which time he had returned to England, he was placed on the retired list with the rank of captain, and served for a year in the Department.

During 1905 and 1906 Combe undertook detached surveying work at Sligo, Ireland, and at Platea, Greece, the latter for the Mediterranean Fleet. In 1907 he was in charge of the west coast of England survey using the hired vessel *Argo*. In the following year he succeded Tooker in the *Ellinor* on the Newfoundland survey until it was closed down in 1913.

On his return to England Combe was employed visiting the larger ports round the United Kingdom coasts in order to bring Admiralty charts up to date for the latest harbour improvements. He continued this work when the First World War broke out, and from 1915 until the end of 1919 was continually engaged in surveys of the Firth of Forth. For his war service he was awarded the CMG. He reverted to the retired list in 1920.

Commander D L Cowan, DSC

David Laidlaw Cowan started surveying as a lieutenant of three years seniority after gaining a DSC in the First World War. In 1919 he was appointed to the *Mutine*, Glennie, in the Caribbean. From 1921 he served for four years in the *Fitzroy*, Silk then Woodhouse, on the east coast of England. In 1926 he joined the River Severn Survey, Henderson, working there until 1928, when he spent a brief period in the Department.

From April 1929 for five years Cowan served in charge of the South Coast of England Survey, retiring with the rank of commander in 1933.

After retirement he was employed for two years variously in *Vernon*'s mining department and on a tidal survey of Portsmouth. During the Second World War he served briefly in the loop guard ship *Manchester City*, but indifferent health over some years caused his reversion to the retired list in 1941. He died in September 1946.

Commander D H Fryer, OBE

Douglas Henry Fryer was one of the first volunteers for the surveying service after the end of the First World War. As a lieutenant with one year's seniority he joined the *Endeavour*, Reyne then Geary-Hill, surveying on the north coast of Egypt. 1922 and 1923 were spent in the *Flinders*, Jackson and later Henderson, mainly in the upper part of the Bristol Channel. In February 1924 Fryer took passage in the newly-commissioned *Herald*, Harvey, to join the *Iroquois*, Tinson then Jackson, for surveys on the China station, on the east coast of Johore and in the approaches to Hong Kong.

After a year as a naval assistant in Chart Branch he joined the *Fitzroy*, Harvey, in 1928, and succeeded to the command in January 1929. In her he spent nearly three years on the east coast of England and in the North Sea, surveying and charting for the first time the Devil's Hole though this feature had been long known to fishermen. Next he had command of the *Ormonde* from 1931 to 1933, working mainly in the Persian Gulf. He had the misfortune to ground the ship both in the Gulf and off the coast of Cyprus. At the end of 1933 he went to the *Fitzroy*, surveying in the Shetlands, followed by charge of the South Coast of England Survey until August 1935, when he was appointed to stand by the building of the non-magnetic ship *Research*. To gain experience he sailed to Australia and back in the Finnish barques *L'Avenir* and *Pommern*, and did a long meteorological course.

On the outbreak of war in 1939 Fryer was appointed in command of the *Jason* patrolling the Firth of Clyde until June 1940, when he served on the staff first of the Commander in Chief Plymouth and then of the Director of Combined Operations. From 1941 to 1944 he worked for the Inter Services Topographical Division at Oxford. In 1943 he was detached to the Mediterranean to work on beach intelligence for the Sicilian landings. In the latter months of 1944 he stood by in Istanbul to survey the Danube. After the capitulation of Bulgaria he reached Sofia only to be turned back by the Russians, whereupon he took his vehicles back to Cairo overland. Shortly afterwards he went to Naples as Fleet Hydrographic Officer, Mediterranean, and moved to Malta with the headquarters in 1945. He was awarded the OBE in 1946.

After a short period working as a Reviser of Sailing Directions he became Reader in Surveying at a new Department of Surveying set up in Durham University. He was made an honorary DSc of the university before his retirement in 1962. After this final retirement he came to Somerset and now lives in Taunton.

Captain L G Garbett, CBE

Leonard Gillilan Garbett first went to sea in the Merchant Service. He became a midshipman RNR in 1896 and a sublieutenant in 1903. In 1904 he joined the Newfoundland survey in the *Ellinor*, Tooker, as a civilian assistant surveyor. He became a lieutenant RNR in 1906, and by special Order in Council transferred to the RN in 1909, continuing in the Newfoundland survey, now under Combe, until 1912, when for one season the *Ellinor* worked in the West Indies.

In 1913 Garbett joined the *Triton*, Penfold, later Tinson, and surveyed in home waters until the outbreak of war in August 1914, when he was appointed navigating officer of the river monitor *Mersey*. In this ship he saw a variety of service, including bombardment of the Belgian coast and the destruction of the German cruiser *Königsberg* in the Rufiji river. In 1917 he took command of the *Mersey* as an acting commander and did valuable surveying work on the east coast of Africa. The ship was subsequently in the Mediterranean and on the river Danube, and was finally towed back to England in April 1919 by the *Cyclamen*, which Garbett had commissioned with the *Mersey*'s crew.

In June 1919 he commanded the river gunboat *Moth* in North Russian waters, and in November returned to surveying in the *Merlin*, Nares, on special work in the Mediterranean. In September 1920 Garbett, again as acting commander, sailed the *Merlin* out to Singapore and made preliminary surveys in the Johore Strait for the projected naval base.

Early in 1921 he returned to England and was placed on the retired list as a commander. He became superintendent of the Naval Division of the Meteorological Office at the Air Ministry. In 1937, when this division was transferred to the Admiralty and again came under the Hydrographer, Garbett became Chief Superintendent of the Naval Meteorological Branch. Two years later, when the branch was raised to the status of a directorate, he became Director, Naval Meteorological Service. He joined the Meteorological Research Committee as the Admiralty representative in 1941. He had been promoted acting captain on the retired list in 1936, and confirmed in this rank in 1938.

He led the Naval Meteorological Service throughout the Second World War. By 1944 its expansion was such that two assistant directors, Beatty and Bishop, were appointed. His services were rewarded with the CBE in 1942 and the US Legion of Merit in 1946. He finally retired in 1947.

Captain S A Geary-Hill, DSO

Sydney Arthur Geary-Hill joined the *Penguin*, Pudsey-Dawson, as a sublieutenant in 1902 for three years surveying in New Zealand waters, being promoted to lieutenant in 1903. In 1905 he served for a season in home waters in the *Research*, Smyth, and then joined the *Merlin*, Parry then Walter, for a commission on the China station, mainly spent in Borneo waters. On his return to England in 1909 he was briefly a naval assistant in the Department, and then went to the *Mutine*, Hardy, for surveys chiefly on the Liberian coast, until early in 1912.

Geary-Hill was then given command of the trawler *Daisy*, which with her sister the *Esther* worked as tenders to the *Hearty* and later the *Endeavour* on Learmonth's surveys of the North Sea banks. From the outbreak of war in August 1914 he served for two and a half years in the armed merchant cruiser *Armadale Castle*, latterly in command as an acting commander. He then commanded successively the sloops *Buttercup* and *Jessamine*. In the latter he was promoted commander at the end of 1917, and was awarded the DSO for sinking a U-boat. He was also awarded the Navy Cross for his work with the U.S.Naval forces operating out of Queenstown.

In September 1919 Geary-Hill returned to surveying as a naval assistant in Chart Branch for two years, after which he took command of the *Endeavour* from 1921 to 1923 on surveys of the north coast of Egypt and in West Africa. There followed a year unemployed and then a return to the *Endeavour* for surveys on the west coast of Africa in the approaches to Sierra Leone until 1927 when his sea service ended and he was placed on the retired list with the rank of captain. He then served in the Department, first briefly as instrument officer and then as the officer in charge of Light Lists from 1928 to 1945. He died in 1949.

Captain F J B Gibson, OBE

Frederick John Butler Gibson joined the *Waterwitch*, Hardy, later Glennie, in 1902 for nearly four years surveying on the China station. He was promoted to lieutenant in 1903. In 1906 he served for a season in home waters in the *Research*, Smyth, and then did four years in the *Fantome*, Hardy and later Pasco, working in Australian waters. There followed a short time in the Department, and then in 1911 Gibson joined the *Hearty*, Learmonth and later Hardy, on North Sea surveys.

In 1913 he was appointed to his first command, the *Merlin*, for surveys on the China station. *Merlin* was paid off on the outbreak of war in 1914 and Gibson was placed in charge of the Hong Kong Chart and Chronometer Depot. He served in this appointment for the whole of the war, being promoted commander in 1917 and awarded the OBE. In August 1918 he was appointed to the *Hearty*, and early in 1920 he transferred to her successor the *Fitzroy* for a season in home waters. Returning to the Department at the end of 1920 Gibson was a naval assistant until he retired at his own request in 1922, being advanced to captain's rank on retirement.

In 1923 and 1924 he carried out surveys in the Orinoco delta for the British Controlled Oilfields organisation. In 1925 he was appointed Assistant Conservator of the Port of Calcutta, where he was employed until 1938. During the Second World War Gibson served as a naval assistant in the Department, being jacketting officer from 1943 to 1945. He then became a reviser of Sailing Directions, in which employment he remained until his death in 1960.

Vice Admiral R W Glennie, CMG

Robert Woodyear Glennie took up surveying as a lieutenant in 1894 when he joined the *Paluma*, Heming, surveying the Queensland Inner Route. The ship was replaced by the *Dart* in 1895, and when Heming lost the sight of an eye in an accident Glennie commanded for a season, 'doing far more than could have been expected of so young and inexperienced an officer'. He continued in the *Dart* on the same survey under Howard, and later Parry, until 1898. He came home for a brief period in the *Research*, Moore, in 1898-99, before returning to Australasia in the *Penguin*, Combe and later Pudsey- Dawson, working mainly in New Zealand waters.

Promoted commander in 1903, Glennie spent a year in the Department before taking his first command, the *Waterwitch*, for three years on the China station. Returning to England in 1908 he was Superintendent of Charts for a year, and then went to the *Sealark*, at first in the East Indies and then further east, mainly in the Solomon Islands. Promoted to captain in 1913 he spent another brief period in the Department before being appointed to command the *Mutine* in the West Indies.

On the outbreak of war in 1914 he returned to general service, commanding successively the *Suffolk*, *Marmora* and *Glory*. His services in the last ship gained him the award of the CMG. Early in 1918 Glennie rejoined the Department as Director of the Naval Meteorological Service, and in 1919 he returned to the *Mutine* to resume surveys in the West Indies until 1921, when he became Assistant Hydrographer. He was promoted rear admiral on the retired list in 1923, but served on until the following year. Promoted to vice admiral on the retired list in 1928, Glennie died in Haslar in 1930.

Captain N A C Hardy

Norman Arthur Cyril Hardy began surveying as a lieutenant when in 1920 he joined the *Hearty*, very soon transferring to her successor, the *Fitzroy*, Gibson and later Viney, for two years work on the east coast of England. In 1922 he went to the *Merlin*, Edgell, in Singapore waters, and next year was in the *Iroquois*, Tinson, also on the China station, this time mainly in Borneo waters.

After the 1924 season, which he spent in the *Flinders*, Henderson, on the west coast of England and Scotland, Hardy was lent for two years to the Royal Australian

Navy, and served in the *Moresby*, Edgell. He was next in the *Kellett*, Cary then Silk, succeeding to her command for the 1929 season in the Thames Estuary and on the south coast. From 1931 to 1933 he had command of the *Herald* in the South China Sea and in Malayan waters, being promoted to commander in 1932. He came ashore in 1933 to the Department as Superintendent of Charts until 1935.

For the Abyssinian crisis Hardy briefly took charge of a survey and charting unit at Alexandria. After this he went for another two years to the *Herald* on the China station from 1936 to 1937. He had the 1938 home surveying season in the *Jason* before promotion to captain at the end of the year and another spell in the Department as Superintendent of Charts and, on the outbreak of war, as Assistant Hydrographer.

Hardy volunteered for sea service in 1940, and was given command of the Armed Merchant Cruiser *Forfar* in July. He was lost when she was torpedoed and sunk in December 1940.

Captain J R Harvey, OBE

James Robertson Harvey took up surveying in 1906 just before his promotion to lieutenant, and served for two years in the *Egeria*, Learmonth, in British Columbian waters. In 1908 he did a season in home waters in the *Research*, Simpson, and then was appointed to the *Merlin*, Learmonth, for two and a half years on the China station, chiefly working off Borneo. In 1911 he joined the *Mutine*, Hardy then Edgell, and surveyed on the coasts of Liberia and Natal until 1913, when he returned to home waters and the *Research*, Somerville, for surveys which were broken off at the outbreak of war in August 1914.

He was appointed navigating officer of the *Kent*, taking part in the battle of the Falkland Islands, and in 1917 transferred to the *Sandhurst*. Towards the end of that year he returned to surveying duties on the Admiralty War Staff, and in March 1918 obtained his first command, the *Daisy*. In her he was employed on operational surveys in home waters, including work on the Dover Mine Barrage which earned him the OBE.

He paid off the *Daisy* in February 1920, and took command of the new ship *Kellett*, surveying in the Thames estuary. He was promoted to commander in June 1920. There followed two years as a naval assistant to the Hydrographer, during which he supervised the conversion of the sloops *Herald* and *Ormonde* for surveying.

At the end of 1923 Harvey commissioned the *Herald* and sailed for the Australia station to succeed the *Fantome*, working for two years mainly in the Torres Strait. Returning home early in 1926 he commanded the *Fitzroy* on east coast surveys for two seasons, and at the end of 1928 joined the Department to do no less than fifteen years in charge of Notices to Mariners. During this period, in 1932, he was retired with the rank of captain. He died in August 1952.

Captain F E B Haselfoot, DSO

Francis Edmund Blechynden Haselfoot began surveying in 1907 as a sublieutenant when he joined the *Research*, Smyth, for a season in home waters, being promoted lieutenant at the end of the year. From 1908 to the end of 1913 he served on the China station, first in the *Waterwitch*, Douglas, on surveys at Singapore and in the Malacca Straits, and then from 1910 in the *Merlin*, Davy and later Pasco, mainly in Borneo waters.

In 1914 Haselfoot was in the *Research*, Somerville, until the outbreak of war, when he was appointed navigating officer of the river monitor *Humber*, seeing service on the Belgian coast and later at the Dardanelles. Having made a survey of Mersa Matruh on the north coast of Egypt, he joined the staff of the Commander in Chief, East Indies in 1916 for surveying duties, and with the requisitioned vessels *Enterprise* and *Imogen* under his orders carried out a number of surveys in the Red Sea. Early in 1918 he was appointed to the staff of Vice Admiral Dover, where for his services in the Zeebrugge and Ostend blocking operations he was awarded the DSO and the Belgian Order of the Crown. He was also promoted to commander at the end of the year. He remained at Dover until October 1919, and then went to the Local Defence Division of the Naval Staff.

A year later he returned to the Hydrographic Department as a naval assistant, where he worked on a new Manual of Surveying. Before this was completed he was appointed to his first command, the *Kellett*, where he surveyed for three seasons mainly in the Thames estuary and on the south coast. In 1925 he went back to the Department as Superintendent of Charts, and was promoted to captain at the end of 1926. Early in 1927 he went out to *Herald* on the China station, but after eighteen months mainly working in Borneo waters his health broke down and he was invalided home. Shortly afterwards he was placed on the retired list as medically unfit. He died in Switzerland in 1938.

Commander D A Henderson, OBE

Denys Arthur Henderson joined the surveying service as a lieutenant in 1911 after taking the qualifying course in navigation. After a few months in the *Hearty*, Learmonth, in home waters, he was sent out to the *Mutine*, Hardy and later Edgell, for two years work on coastal surveys of Liberia and Natal. Early in 1914 he reverted to general service, and was navigating officer first of the cruiser *Diamond* for two years, and then of the *Chester*, in which ship he was present at the battle of Jutland.

Henderson returned to surveying after the war, and in 1919-20 served first in the *Melisande*, Maxwell, then the *Daisy*, Harvey, and lastly the *Beaufort*, Knowles, in which he worked for a season in the Shetland Islands. At the end of 1920 he went to the *Merlin*, Edgell, on the China station for two years. In 1923 he was given his first command, the *Flinders*, working for two and a half years mainly in the Bristol

Channel. During the seasons of 1926 and 1927 he was in charge of a special survey of the River Severn which was needed for the projected Severn Barrage. The work was of exceptional difficulty in view of the large range of tide and the great strength of the tidal streams, and Henderson received both the thanks of Their Lordships and the award of the OBE for his efforts.

Towards the end of 1927 he was lent to the Royal Australian Navy for three years to command the *Moresby*, in which he made extensive surveys of the Queensland coast. On return to England in 1930 he was placed on the retired list at his own request with the rank of commander to take up the appointment of Chief Hydrographic Surveyor for the Port of Basrah under the government of Iraq. When this post was abolished for reasons of economy he came home to become Chief Compass Adjuster to the Hull Trawler Owners Mutual Insurance Company.

On the outbreak of war in 1939 he was recalled to the Hydrographic Department. In July 1942 Henderson joined the Ministry of War Transport as Naval Professional Officer, a post he held through the Ministry's peace-time reorganisation as the Ministry of Transport and Civil Aviation until reaching retirement age in 1955. He also served from July 1944 to April 1945 as Acting Conservator of the River Mersey.

Rear Admiral A L Jackson

Arthur Lambert Jackson began surveying as a lieutenant when in 1912 he joined the *Sealark*, Glennie and later Hancock, for two years work in the Solomon Islands and on the Queensland Inner Route. During the First World War he was in the *Endeavour*, Edgell and later Hancock, on operational surveys and chart production in the eastern Mediterranean from 1915 to 1917, and was then attached to the Admiralty War Staff for minelaying work.

In 1920 he was appointed to the *Flinders*, Maxwell, whom he succeeded in command at the end of the year. He remained in the ship until 1923, surveying mainly on the west coasts of England and Scotland and being promoted to commander in December 1922. There followed employment at *Dryad* and on an intelligence course until he went to sea again from 1925 to 1928 commanding the *Iroquois* on the China station. In 1928 he was attached to *Vernon* for guard loop trials in the Firth of Forth, and then came to the Department as Superintendent of Charts, being promoted to captain in June 1930.

He returned to the *Iroquois* at the end of 1930, and in 1931 received Their Lordships' appreciation for surveys in the 'Dangerous Area' in the South China Sea. For the first half of 1932 he commanded the *Challenger* in the North Sea, and later, after revising the *General Instructions for Hydrographic Surveyors*, became Assistant Hydrographer from October 1932 to July 1936. While standing by the building of the *Stork* he contracted diphtheria, but recovered in time to join her at the end of 1936 to survey in her in the Indian Ocean for two years. After another short period of sickness he served as Assistant Hydrographer from March 1939 to January 1942, being involved in the move of the Department to Bath. He was promoted to rear admiral on the retired list in June 1940. In February 1942 further ill health necessitiated his retiring on medical grounds. Despite indifferent health in retirement he worked as a reviser of Sailing Directions until his death in November 1956.

Captain C H Knowles, DSO

Charles Hinton Knowles entered the surveying service in 1908 shortly before his promotion to lieutenant when he was appointed to the *Waterwitch*, Douglas, working at Singapore and in the Malacca Strait. He then went to the *Sealark*, Glennie then Hancock, surveying in the Solomon Islands and on the Queensland coast from 1910 to the outbreak of the First World War. *Sealark's* surveying operations were suspended, and she was sent first to Suva in the Fiji Islands, and then to pay off in Sydney early in 1915.

On arrival in England Knowles joined the *Hearty*, Edgell, with whom in September 1915 he went to the *Endeavour* for operational surveys in the eastern Mediterranean. Here he took part in surveys under fire of the Gallipoli beaches in preparation for the evacuation. He continued in the *Endeavour* until April 1918, the last two years under Hancock. On his return home he assisted in the laying of the Northern Mine Barrage, earning the award of the DSC.

Early in 1919 he was appointed to the command of the *Esther*, surveying for mine clearance in home waters until August, when he went briefly to the Department as a naval assistant. In 1920 he commissioned the new ship *Beaufort* and worked in home waters, mainly in the Shetland Islands, for three years, being promoted to commander in June 1922. After another year in the Department, Knowles commanded the *Ormonde* on the West Indies station, surveying in Trinidad, Bermuda, the Virgin Islands and British Guiana from 1924 to 1926. He then reverted to general service.

He retired with the rank of captain in 1932, and died in 1954.

Captain E F B Law

Edward Francis Bold Law was born in 1891, eldest son of Commander E G F Law, RN, and through his great great grandmother could trace a relationship with Fletcher Christian, one of the chief mutineers of the *Bounty*. He entered the Navy as a cadet in 1904. In 1912, as a sub-lieutenant, he joined the *Hearty*, Learmonth, working on the North Sea Banks. When in 1913 the *Endeavour* took over this work Law, by then a Lieutenant, transferred to the new ship.

During the First World War he served in the *Bacchante*, in small craft in the

Cameroons, and in the destroyers *Sarpedon*, *Garry*, *Scourge* and *Relentless*, commanding the last three.

In August 1919 he returned to surveying, first in the Department and then, in 1920, joining the *Beaufort*, Knowles, for a season in home waters. From 1921 to 1924 he was in the *Fantome*, Maxwell, in Australia, working in the Torres Strait and on the Great Barrier Reef. In 1924 he moved to the *Ormonde*, Knowles, in the West Indies.

In 1926 Law obtained his first surveying command, the *Flinders*, for surveys in home waters. In 1927, after promotion to commander, he took the *Endeavour* for work in the Red Sea and eastern Mediterranean until 1930. From 1931 to 1933 he served in the Department as Superintendent of Charts, receiving early promotion to captain at the end of this time and being appointed to command the *Herald* on the China station.

Returning home early in 1936 Law served as Assistant Hydrographer until the spring of 1939, when he sailed in the newly-converted *Scarborough* for the Far East. On the outbreak of war *Scarborough* was paid off and Law became briefly Chief of Staff to Rear Admiral Malaya. From 1940 to 1942 he was in the Naval Intelligence Division in the School of Geography at Oxford preparing information for combined operations. He next commanded the destroyer depot ship *Hecla*, sailing to join the Eastern Fleet in April 1942 but being mined on the Agulhas bank while on the way out. After the invasion of Madagascar he took charge of the naval base at Diego Suarez until July 1944. There followed a period on the French coast first as NOIC Arromanches and later as SNO British Operated Ports based at Calais. In March 1945 he became Captain of the Dockyard at Portsmouth until his retirement one year later.

From 1951 to 1961 he was Acting Conservator of the River Mersey.

Commander C S Lockhart, DSC

Charles Stewart Lockhart joined the *Mutine*, Edgell then Glennie, just before his promotion to lieutenant, in 1912, for two years surveying on the West African station and in the West Indies. During the First World War he reverted to general service, spending three years in the battlecruiser *Tiger* and seeing action at both the Dogger Bank and Jutland.

Early in 1919 he returned to the *Mutine*, Glennie, and surveyed for two more years in the West Indies before coming home to the *Flinders*, Jackson. In 1923 he commissioned the newly converted *Iroquois*, Tinson, for service on the China station, and early in 1925 he took temporary command for a few months when Tinson was invalided. Lockhart himself returned to England later that year and served as a naval assistant in the Department until the middle of 1926, when he was given command of the *Fitzroy* for home waters surveys.

Early in 1927 he retired at his own request to take up the post of Assistant Port Surveyor at Rangoon, a post which he held for ten years, succeeding as Port Surveyor in 1937. He was promoted commander on the retired list in 1929.

In the Second World War he returned to service with the Navy, first in the Naval Control Service at Rangoon and then in command of the minesweeper *Corbrae*. He continued on minesweeping duties in the Port of London from 1941 to 1943, then transferred to port parties in India until January 1944. From then for six months he became NOIC Anzio, where he earned both the DSC and the appreciation of the U.S. authorities. His last war service was in command of the Braintree naval barracks until he reverted to retirement in 1946. He died in 1962.

Captain P S E Maxwell

Patrick Stewart Erskine Maxwell joined the *Research*, Simpson, as a lieutenant in 1910 for a first surveying season in home waters. He then went to the *Sealark*, Davy and later Glennie, for two and a half years first in the East Indies and then on the Australian station.

Returning home early in 1912, he joined the *Mutine*, Edgell, for surveys mainly on the Liberian coast, and remained in the ship until shortly before the outbreak of war in 1914. Maxwell was then appointed navigating officer of the cruiser *Challenger*, transferring in April 1915 to the *Astraea*, both ships operating off the west coast of Africa. He made useful surveys for the Cameroons operations, receiving the thanks of Their Lordships and being made a Chevalier of the Legion d'Honneur.

From July 1916 to March 1917 he was a naval assistant in the Department, and thereafter he had his first command, the *Esther*, on operational surveys in home waters. In 1918 he fitted out the steam yacht *Melisande* for surveying, but she was never a success and after a year she was returned to her owners. In 1920 Maxwell commissioned the *Flinders* for surveys in home waters. A year later he went to the *Fantome* for two and a half years on the Australia station, chiefly working in the Torres Strait. He was promoted commander in June 1921.

In 1925 and 1926 he commanded the *Kellett* surveying in the Thames Estuary, and in 1927 and 1928 he was Superintendent of Charts. In 1929 he was appointed to the *Herald* on the China station, surveying mainly in Borneo waters for two years, and this was his last sea-going command. From 1931 to his retirement in 1936 with the rank of captain he was a naval assistant in the Department, serving for most of this time as Territorial Waters Officer.

On retirement he went to the National Maritime Museum in charge of the Navigation Room until November 1939. He died in 1945.

Commander F May

Francis May joined the *Dart*, Howard, Parry and Monro in succession, in 1895, and spent five years surveying on the coast of Queensland, being promoted to lieutenant in 1896.

Returning to England in 1901 for a season in the *Research*, Field, he was back on the Australasian station next year, and spent three years surveying in New Zealand waters in the *Penguin*, Pudsey-Dawson. In 1905 May was again in the *Research*, by now under Smyth, and next year transferred to the *Triton*, Purey-Cust and then Pudsey-Dawson, for a second season in home waters.

Early in 1907 he commissioned the *Fantome*, E C Hardy, for the Australian station and a continuation of the Queensland coast survey. When, a year later, Hardy was invalided, May took temporary command with the acting rank of commander for some months until the arrival of Pasco. Leaving the *Fantome* in 1909, he was given charge of the South Coast of England Survey. When this was discontinued in the First World War he reverted to general service until 1916, and then became a naval assistant in the Department.

In 1920 he was placed on the retired list as a commander, and took charge again of the South Coast of England Survey, this time in a civilian capacity. Here he remained until 1929, when he retired from active employment. He died in July 1934.

Vice Admiral J D Nares, DSO

John Dodd Nares was the son of the celebrated surveyor and explorer Admiral Sir George Nares. He took up surveying in 1898 as a sublieutenant when he served for a year in the *Triton*, Combe, in home waters. Next year he accompanied Combe to the *Penguin* on the Australian station for four years surveying on the west coast of Australia and in New Zealand. He was promoted to lieutenant in 1900. In 1902 he transferred to the *Dart*, Pasco, and when she paid off in 1904 Nares returned to the *Penguin*, Pudsey-Dawson and later Simpson, for a further three years in New Zealand and Queensland waters.

Returning to England in 1907 after eight years continuous service on the Australian station he did a season in the *Research*, Smyth, and then joined the *Egeria*, Parry, for three years in British Columbia, obtaining command of the ship in 1910. When the *Egeria* paid off in 1911 Nares took command of the *Fantome* for another two years on the Australian station, this time working mainly in the Buccaneer Archipelago.

In 1913 he joined the Department as a naval assistant, being promoted to commander in that year. In 1915 he became Superintendent of Charts, in which appointment he remained until 1917, when he was sent in command of the *Enterprise* for operational surveys in the Red Sea and the eastern Mediterranean. For his service in the operations at Gaza Nares was awarded the DSO.

At the end of 1918 he recommissioned the *Merlin* at Hong Kong to replace the *Enterprise*, and continued Red Sea surveys for two years, being promoted to captain in mid 1919. He then became Superintendent of Charts again until 1923, when he went to the west coast of Africa in command of the *Endeavour*. From 1925 to 1928 he was Assistant Hydrographer to Douglas, and then went to the *Iroquois* for two years on the China station. This completed his sea service, and from 1930 until his promotion to rear admiral and his retirement in 1931 he was Assistant Hydrographer again. He was promoted to vice admiral on the retired list in 1936.

Shortly after his retirement Nares was elected President of the Directing Committee of the International Hydrographic Bureau at Monaco, holding the position until the collapse of France in 1940, when he returned to England. Volunteering for service he was employed first in the rank of commander and then as a captain as a naval assistant to the Hydrographer, assuming the post of Assistant Hydrographer (2) at Bath from 1942 to 1944.

Nares returned to Monaco in 1945 to resume his service on the directing committee of the International Hydrographic Bureau, where he remained until his death in January 1957.

Captain F A Reyne

Frederick Algernon Reyne joined the *Goldfinch*, Learmonth, as a sublieutenant, being promoted to lieutenant in 1903. After three years on the west coast of Africa and in the Mediterranean he was briefly in the Department as a naval assistant before joining the *Waterwitch*, Glennie, on the China station in 1906. Two years later he was back in England for a season in the *Triton*, Pudsey-Dawson, and in 1909 he joined the *Merlin*, Learmonth, surveying mainly in Borneo waters for two years.

In 1911 Reyne did another season in home waters, in the *Research*, Pasco, and then in 1912 obtained his first command, the *Waterwitch*, on the China station once more. The commission ended abruptly after one season when the ship was rammed and sunk while at anchor in Singapore roads. After a second brief spell in the Department Reyne took command of the *Fantome* and was mainly engaged in a survey of the Buccaneer Archipelago in north west Australia until the outbreak of the First World War. During 1915 he was on the staff of the Flag Officer Commanding the Fourth Battle Squadron in the *Benbow*. On his promotion to commander in 1916 he returned to the surveying service in command of the *Hearty* in home waters.

From 1919 to 1921 Reyne commanded the *Endeavour* surveying on the north coast of Egypt, and this ended his seagoing career. There followed long service in the Department, first in charge of Light Lists and then, from 1928 to 1940, as Superintendent of Sailing Directions. He was promoted captain on the retired list in 1925, and died at Farnham in 1962.

Commander W V Rice, DSO, DSC

William Victor Rice joined the *Research*, Simpson and later Pasco, as a lieutenant in 1910 for two seasons in home waters. In 1912 he went to the *Waterwitch*, Reyne, on the China station, but after the sinking of that ship he accompanied Reyne first to the Department and then to the *Fantome* in Australia. When she was laid up after the outbreak of war Rice was transferred to the minesweeping service, where he made use of his surveying knowledge to good effect and achieved distinction with the award of first the DSC and then the DSO.

After the war he returned to surveying, being appointed to the *Fantome*, C.M.L.Scott and then Maxwell, for two years largely spent in the Torres Strait. In 1921 he served for a season in home waters in the *Beaufort*, Knowles, followed by a year in the Mediterranean in the *Endeavour*, Geary-Hill.

In 1923 he was appointed in command of the *Beaufort*, and for four years worked mainly in Scottish waters, being promoted to commander at the end of 1923. From 1927 to 1929 Rice commanded the *Ormonde*, whose surveys were mainly in the Malacca Strait. There followed another period in home waters, again in the *Beaufort*, after which he went to the *Endeavour* for surveys off the west coast of Africa and on the coast of Palestine. He died in tragic circumstances on board that ship in the Mediterranean in 1932.

Commander C M L Scott

Charles Montague Lawrence Scott took up surveying as a lieutenant in 1907 when he joined the *Fantome*, E.C.Hardy then Pasco, for four and a half years on the Australia station.

In 1912 he did a season in home waters in the *Research*, Somerville, and then joined the *Merlin*, Pasco and later Gibson, on the China station. When the First World War broke out and the *Merlin* was laid up, Scott served first in the armed merchant cruiser *Empress of Asia*, and then in the armed boarding steamer *Lama*, not returning to England until early 1918. He was then given command of the *Esther* as an acting commander, being employed on operational surveys in home waters.

In 1919 Scott went to Australia to recommission the *Fantome* for surveys on that station, retaining his command and his acting rank until his retirement in 1921. He was promoted commander on the retired list in 1922.

After retirement he was for some years Port Surveying Officer at Rangoon. When war broke out again in 1939 he returned to active service, being employed in the Naval Control Service at Cardiff. He died in November 1959.

Commander H V Silk

Horace Victor Silk joined the *Merlin*, Davy, later Pasco, in 1911 as a sublieutenant, being promoted lieutenant at the end of the year. He did two years on the China station, largely in Borneo waters, before returning home to go to the *Hearty*, E.C.Hardy and then Edgell, at the beginning of 1914 for surveys in the North Sea.

On the outbreak of war in August Silk reverted to general service, serving in the battleships *Duncan* and *Commonwealth* before returning to surveying in August 1916 to the *Esther*, Gibbings, Maxwell and then C M L Scott, for operational surveys in home waters until the end of the war. At the end of 1918 he went to the *Merlin*, Nares, for two years surveying mainly in the Red Sea. When he returned home in 1921 he joined the *Fitzroy*, Viney, working on the east coast of England. When Viney went sick Silk took temporary command for several months in 1922. Later that year he went to the *Mutine*, Douglas, on the West Indies station, transferring to her successor, the *Ormonde*, in 1924.

In June 1924 he was appointed in command of the *Fitzroy* and for eighteen months was employed on surveys of the east coast of England. Early in 1926 he went out to Australia to command the *Herald*, which was transferred to the China station at the end of that year. In 1927 her surveys were in Borneo waters, and Silk left her during that year to return home for his last seagoing command, the *Kellett*, working on the south coast of England and in the Thames Estuary.

In 1929 Silk joined the Department as a naval assistant, and when he retired with the rank of commander in 1934 he took up the task of reviser of Sailing Directions. He only gave up that employment in 1967.

Commander C Simpson, DSC

Christopher Simpson began surveying as a lieutnant of one year's seniority in 1920, spending a year in the *Kellett*, Harvey, in the Thames Estuary. In 1921 he joined the *Endeavour*, Geary-Hill, working first in the Mediterranean on the Hurd Bank and on the north coast of Egypt, and then on the Cape Ann Shoals on the west coast of Africa. He next went, in 1924, to the *Herald*, Harvey, surveying on the north and east coasts of Australia. At the end of 1925 he came home to the *Fitzroy*, Harvey, working on the east coast of England.

In 1928-29 Simpson served in the *Ormonde*, Rice, working in the Malacca Strait, the Maldives and the approaches to Aden. He then went to the *Beaufort*, Rice, surveying on the west coasts of England and Scotland, being detached for a short period to take part in Mobile Naval Base exercises.

He was appointed in 1931 to the command of the *Flinders*, and for three years surveyed on the north and west coasts of Scotland and the south and west coasts of England. In 1934, after some months on half pay, he retired at his own request with the rank of lieutenant commander.

Simpson was then employed on the Mersey first in a DSIR investigation into sewage and dredging, and later as Liverpool Officer of the Mersey Conservancy. On the outbreak of the Second World War he was recalled to serve as Commander M/S at Liverpool, being transferred to the Clyde from 1942 to 1943 when, still in the same capacity, he went to the Mediterranean for the Sicily landings and the subsequent advance up the Italian coasts. He was awarded the DSC for his part in the assault on Elba. This work concluded with a minesweeping command and liaison with the Allies on the south coast of France. When mine clearing began after the end of hostilities he had responsibility from Naples to the Spanish frontier.

From 1946 to 1949 he was the British Director of the re-formed Deutsche Hydrographische Institut at Hamburg with the acting rank of captain. On completion of this appointment he reverted to the retired list with the rank of commander. He then became Deputy Conservator of Kandla Port in India from 1950 to 1955. He returned to England on his final retirement.

Captain R M Southern

Richard Meuric Southern (always known to his contemporaries as Sam) began surveying as a lieutenant when he joined the *Mutine*, Douglas, for a commission in the West Indies and Bermuda in 1920. He was next, from 1922 to 1924, in the *Kellett*, Haselfoot, working on the east and south coasts of England. In 1925 he went to the *Endeavour*, Geary-Hill, working on the west coast of Africa, in the Mediterranean and the Red Sea. During this time the ship grounded on a reef off Jeddah, but got off without material damage. From 1927 to 1929 he served in the *Iroquois*, Jackson followed by Nares, in the South China Sea and the Malacca Strait. This was followed by two seasons in the *Beaufort*, Rice, on the west coast of Scotland and the north coast of Wales.

In 1930 Southern came into the Department as naval assistant to the Hydrographer. In the next year he took command of the *Kellett* in the Thames Estuary and on the east coast of England. In 1933 he went to the *Endeavour*, surveying on the west coast of Africa, in Palestine, in the Maldives and on the west coasts of Siam and Malaya. He was promoted commander in 1934. During the Abyssinia crisis of 1935 the ship was held at Aden, with Southern temporarily becoming NOIC. This was repeated during civil disturbances the following year.

In 1937 he was in the Department writing the new *Admiralty Manual of Hydrographic Surveying*, and in 1938 commissioned the new *Gleaner* for work in the English Channel, Isle of Man and the west coast of Scotland. In 1939 he went out to the *Herald* on the east coast of Malaya until she was paid off on the outbreak of the Second World War.

During the war Southern was first Fleet Hydrographic Officer Mediterranean, surveying with auxiliary craft in the Red Sea and the coasts of Egypt and Crete, being promoted captain in January 1942. He came into the Department as Assistant

Hydrographer in 1942, then returned to the Mediterranean as FHO from July 1943 for six months, before becoming Superintendent of Charts at the end of 1943. He went back to the Mediterranean once more as FHO for a few months at the end of 1944 before returning to the post of Assistant Hydrographer again in 1945. Southern went back to sea in 1946 in command of the *Challenger* for surveys in the Persian Gulf, in Cyprus and at Gibraltar. He came ashore finally in 1949 to take up the post of Assistant Hydrographer for the third time.

He retired in August 1950, and from 1951 to 1958 was adviser successively to the Nigerian, Turkish and Canadian governments, besides spending a short time revising supplements to Sailing Directions.

Commander C W Tinson, OBE

Charles Wills Tinson began surveying as a sublieutenant in 1903 and served for two and a half years in the *Egeria*, Parry, in British Columbia, being promoted lieutenant at the end of 1903. In 1906 he spent a season in home waters in the *Triton*, Pudsey-Dawson, and at the end of the year he joined the *Merlin*, Parry then Walter, on the China station surveying largely in Borneo waters. In 1909 he went to the *Mutine*, E C Hardy, for two years on the west African coast, after which he joined the new *Endeavour*, still with E C Hardy and later under Learmonth, at home on North Sea surveys.

In May 1914 Tinson obtained his first command, the *Triton*, also in home waters. She was paid off on the outbreak of war, for the greater part of which Tinson served on the staff of Admiral Sir Cecil Burney, second in command of the Grand Fleet, as hydrographic officer. He was in the *Marlborough* at the Battle of Jutland. At the end of 1916 he was promoted to commander and awarded the OBE.

After the war he fixed the positions of the scuttled German ships in Scapa Flow, and was then a naval assistant in the Hydrographic Department, in charge of surveying instruments. From the end of 1920 he commanded the *Fitzroy* in home waters for three months, but his health broke down and he was sick for the whole of 1921. In 1922 he fitted out the *Iroquois* and commissioned her for service on the China station the following year, but towards the end of 1924 his health began to fail again, and he was invalided home early in 1925.

At the end of 1925 his health was thought to be sufficiently recovered for him to join the Department as a naval assistant, but this lasted only until August 1926. He died in February 1927.

Commander H E Turner

Harold Exton Turner started surveying in 1920 a year after being promoted lieutenant, and joined the *Merlin*, Nares, at Malta. The ship was working on the Hurd bank and making deep minelaying experiments in the Strait of Messina. Turner was taken ill, and when the ship sailed for the Far East he transferred to the *Endeavour*, Reyne and later Geary-Hill, surveying the north coast of Egypt until 1922, and then moving to the west coast of Africa.

In 1924, after a brief spell in the Department, Turner went to the *Flinders*, Henderson, on the south coast and in the Bristol Channel. From there, in 1926, he went to the *Herald*, Silk and later Haselfoot, at first on the east coast of Australia and then in Borneo waters. He took temporary command of the *Herald* when Haselfoot was invalided home in 1928. He came home later in 1928 to the *Flinders*, Cary, working off Portland and on the west coast of Scotland. At the end of 1929 he came ashore to the Department as a naval assistant. In 1930 he was attached to the Royal Marines for exercises, including trials of a prototype landing craft.

In 1931 Turner was appointed in command of the *Beaufort*, where he worked for two years mainly on the west coast of Scotland. After doing a 12 week meteorological course he was lent to the Royal Australian Navy for command of the *Moresby* from 1933 to 1935, working on the Great Barrier Reef and the north coast. Finally from 1936 to 1938 he was at home again in charge of the South Coast of England Survey, retiring in August 1938 with the rank of commander.

Living in Australia the first years of the war saw him in command of the *Moresby*, now an anti-submarine vessel. He then joined the naval staff at Singapore, leaving with it hurriedly for Colombo in 1942 and later moving on to Mombasa. Returning to Australia in 1943 he concluded the war years at Darwin as Chief Staff Officer and later as Naval Officer in Charge. After the war he returned in his retirement to Mitcham, Victoria.

Commander R Viney

Rolf Viney joined the *Sealark*, Somerville and later Davy, as a lieutenant in 1906 for just over three years surveying on the East Indies station. In 1910 he went to the *Mutine*, E.C.Hardy, on the west and south coasts of Africa, and for the season of 1912 he was in the *Research*, Somerville, on the west coast of Scotland. In the 1912-1913 winter he served as a naval assistant in the Department, and then joined the *Fantome*, Reyne, in Australia, surveying the Buccaneer Archipelago.

When the ship was paid off at the outbreak of the First World War Viney spent a few months in the Chart Depot at Sydney before coming home to see action on the Belgian coast operations in the armed trawler *Welbeck*. In September 1915 he returned to surveying and joined the *Endeavour*, Edgell, which sailed for the eastern Mediterranean equipped for chart production as well as surveying. In mid 1916 the production equipment was put ashore first at Mudros then shortly afterwards transferred to Malta. Viney was placed in charge of it, with an appointment on the staff of the Commander in Chief, Mediterranean which continued until 1920. He was promoted to commander in 1919.

On return to England Viney spent some months on special duties in the Department before being appointed in command of the *Fitzroy* surveying in home waters. His career came to an abrupt end when, in April 1922, he died after an internal operation.

Commander A F B Woodhouse

Alfred Frederick Bell Woodhouse joined the *Fantome*, Pasco and later Nares, in 1910 as a lieutenant to see service on the north west coast of Australia. In 1913 he went to the *Research*, Somerville, working in home waters until the outbreak of the First World War. Then he served in general service first in the *King Alfred*, and then in first the *Devonshire* and then the *Inflexible*.

He returned to the surveying service in September 1915 when he joined the *Endeavour*, Edgell, employed on operational surveys in the eastern Mediterranean, in the course of which Woodhouse landed several times on the Gallipoli peninsula under fire to make observations. Leaving the *Endeavour* towards the end of 1916 he joined Haselfoot on the Red Sea surveys being undertaken in the *Enterprise* and the *Imogen*, and in September 1917 was in the *Enterprise*, Nares. During her operations on the Palestine coast Woodhouse was landed as a naval gunfire observation officer for the bombardments which preceded the capture of Gaza, for which he was mentioned in despatches.

He temporarily commanded the *Enterprise* when Nares went to Hong Kong to commission the *Merlin* as her replacement, and when she arrived in the Red Sea served in her until September 1919. On his return to England he went to the *Fitzroy*, Harvey, for a year and a half in home waters, and in 1921 joined the *Mutine*, Douglas, for a year in the West Indies, mainly round Bermuda. In 1922 Woodhouse returned home to command the *Fitzroy*, working on the east coast of England. After two years he was lent to the South African government to command their surveying ship *Protea*. In her, over a period of three and a half years, he made extensive surveys of the coasts of South Africa.

This concluded his seagoing service, and in 1928 he joined the Department as a naval assistant in Chart Branch. He continued in this service after his retirement with the rank of commander in 1932. The later years of the Second World War were spent with the Department in Bath. After retirement on age grounds in 1946 he continued as a reviser of, particularly, 'Ocean Passages of the World'. He died in December 1964.

1 Rear Admiral Sir John Parry, KCB,
Hydrographer from 31 August 1914 to 31
August 1919

2 Vice Admiral Sir Frederick Learmonth, KBE,
CB, Hydrographer from 1 September 1919 to 30
September 1924

3 Rear Admiral Henry P. Douglas, CMG,
Hydrographer from 1 October 1924 to 30
September 1932

4 Vice Admiral Sir John Edgell, KBE, CB, FRS,
Hydrographer from 1 October 1932 to 30 April
1945

5 The *Mutine,* one of the obsolete converted sloops recommissioned after the First World War, under the remains of her sailing rig in the West Indies in 1921.

6 The yacht-like *Endeavour,* designed specially for surveying and built by Fairfield in 1912, seen here in the Suez Canal about 1925. (IMPERIAL WAR MUSEUM)

7   The Fleet Sweeping Sloop *Ormonde* as completed in 1918. These ships were built double-ended to confuse enemy submarines. (IMPERIAL WAR MUSEUM)

8   *Ormonde* as converted into a seemly-looking vessel for surveying. The added topweight necessitated ballasting, and the lower deck scuttles were uncomfortably close to the water. (AUTHOR'S COLL)

9   *Flinders,* one of four *Aberdare* class minesweepers completed after the end of the First World War as surveying ships, seen here entering Portsmouth about 1928.
(National Maritime Museum, London)

10   *Challenger* was completed in 1931 specifically for oceanographic research. Here she is leaving Portsmouth in April 1932 to start her first surveying season.
(Author's coll)

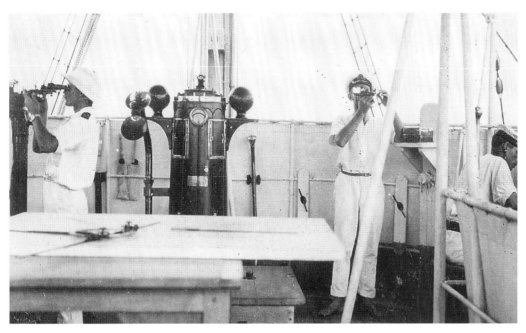

11   The bridge of *Iroquois* in 1925. An officer and a petty officer are taking sextant angles, while a surveying recorder on the right books the readings. Station pointers lie on the chart table for plotting the fix.

12   One of *Iroquois'* surveying motor boats at the davit head ready for lowering. Note the chains rigged for lead line sounding over its starboard side.

13   *Stork* in Plymouth Sound before departure for surveys in the Far East in
September 1936.

14   *Stork* fully armed and camouflaged as a Convoy Escort Sloop in 1942.

15   *Scott*, one of the two *Halcyon* class Small Surveying Ships, as completed in 1939.

16   *Gleaner*, first of two Surveying Minesweeping Sloops, in 1938. The derrick stump
was removed and the standard 4″ gun fitted when rearmed as a minesweeper in
wartime. (J. CLARKSON, LONGTON)

17   The sloop *Scarborough* was converted for surveying in 1938. She is seen her at Plymouth in March 1939, about to sail for the Indian Ocean.

18   The non-magnetic research vessel *Research*, just before being towed to the breakers incomplete in 1952.

CHAPTER FOUR

Gathering Stormclouds
1932–1939

Vice Admiral J A Edgell, CB

Edgell took over as Hydrographer from Douglas in October 1932, and was to serve until 1945, a longer period in office than any except Beaufort and Wharton. A surveying specialist since 1902, and with command of surveying ships intermittently since 1912, he had also served twice as Superintendent of Charts and twice as Assistant Hydrographer. He was a delegate to four of the five International Hydrographic Conferences during his active service, those in 1919, 1929, 1932 and 1937, at the last being elected President of the Conference. He thus brought to the post of Hydrographer varied and valuable experience both afloat and ashore. He had a prodigious capacity for detail, and a talent for leadership which was to be tested to the utmost during the difficult conditions of the war, where the affectionate esteem in which he was held by both naval and civilian staff was rewarded by loyalty and hard work from all.

When Edgell assumed office there were eight surveying ships in commission, the four *Aberdares* at home, *Challenger, Endeavour, Herald,* and *Ormonde* abroad, with the South Coast of England Survey Unit under Cowan carrying out inshore surveys in the Naval ports and their appproaches from a boat during the summer months and drawing up their charts in Portsmouth during the winter.

Challenger, under Wyatt, and later Jones and E H B Baker, worked off Labrador in the summer and in the West Indies in the winter as well as making oceanographic observations in the North Atlantic. While returning south through her surveying area at the end of her work in Labrador at the end of her 1932 season she struck a pinnacle rock and was only got off with difficulty, her divers working in water barely above freezing to stop her leaks. It is reported that Wyatt's first reaction on feeling the ship strike was to hurry to the bridge and make sure that the officer of the watch had fixed the position of the ship and the rock! She had to be escorted to Halifax where she was docked and repaired.

For the winter of 1933-34 a party was landed at Nain under E H B Baker. During this winter the Hudson's Bay Company trading station manager at Hebron, 150 miles north of Nain over a range of 1000-foot mountains, reported trouble with Eskimos which he was unable to deal with. Baker was at first reluctant to become involved, but was persuaded, and on 31 January set off with three dog sledges. After a hard journey across the mountains he and his team made a spectacular entry into Hebron, speeding across the frozen bay with White Ensigns flying from staves on each sledge. He found that the Eskimos had been breaking and entering the store and stealing from it. Interviewing the Eskimos individually through an interpreter they all named one Renatus Tuglavina as the ringleader. Renatus was initially truculent, but Baker soon gained the ascendancy.

'Do you know God?', he asked.

Renatus said that he did.

'Do you know about King George?'

Again Renatus agreed that he did.

'Well,' Baker continued, 'I come next'.

An impressed Renatus came to heel. Baker told him that he would take him to Nain to be judged by the magistrate when he came in the spring. The ringleader clearly quelled, the other Eskimos came to ask for guidance about their future conduct. Baker told them to lead the normal life of the North, to go hunting and trade with their kills, and not to hang about the trading station waiting for handouts and getting into trouble.

Renatus and his family returned to Nain with Baker on their own sledge. At Nain he was allowed to hunt, and when not away hunting worked with the survey party making himself useful and giving no trouble at all. When in the spring the magistrate arrived Baker acted as the Eskimo's defence counsel at the trial, and though Renatus was sentenced to two months imprisonment, he and Baker parted firm friends.

In October 1935 *Challenger*'s company also gave assistance to the civil power during anti-government rioting at St Vincent. In 1936, when her surveys in the Gulf of Paria, between Trinidad and Venezuela, indicated the possibility of substantial oilfields, a security embargo was placed on that aspect because of the territorial waters implications. In 1938 *Challenger*, now with E H B Baker in command, was transferred to the Middle East to carry out surveys off the coast of Oman and in the Persian Gulf. She replaced *Ormonde* on this work until she returned home in May 1939 for a refit.

Endeavour continued to divide her time between the west coast of Africa and the Mediterranean, where her main survey area was on the coast of Palestine. In 1934 she went east to the Malay peninsula, working on the north-west coast and also making oceanographical observations in the eastern Indian Ocean. She returned home in June 1936 for a major refit. When in Aden on the way home she came under the orders of the Commander in Chief during a period of rioting ashore. This, together with *Challenger*'s experiences, led to the question being raised of whether surveying ships should carry more than small arms. It was agreed after some argument that in peace time the advantages of their being unarmed outweighed any gain which might be achieved by arming them.

In January 1937 *Endeavour* recommissioned at Sheerness under Wyatt to go east to start a major programme, planned to last ten years, for the resurvey of New Zealand waters. New Zealand and the Pacific Islands had been neglected through the '20s and '30s after the formation of the Australian hydrographic service removed the Royal Navy's surveyors from the southern continent and the south west Pacific except as assistants attached to the Australian service. Unfortunately the advent of the Second World War in 1939 cut the programme short before it had fairly got under way.

Herald completed the Malacca Strait survey in 1932, then divided her time between the east coast of Malaya, Borneo and the shoals in the South China Sea, with occasional visits to Hong Kong and work in the colony and its approaches. In 1938 and 1939 she worked in Singapore and the Johore Strait, amplifying the work done by *Merlin* under Edgell in the early '20s

Ormonde spent her winters in the Persian Gulf, mainly between the Qatar peninsula and the coast of Trucial Oman. In the summers she retired to the Mediterranean, progressively surveying the coasts and ports of Cyprus.

The war cast its shadow ahead when the Abyssinian crisis arose in 1935. A surveying unit under N A C Hardy was sent to join the Fleet at Alexandria, and a cartographer, Pascoe, joined the Survey of Egypt in Cairo, where special charts and diagrams were to be printed. The manpower shortage which the combination of rearmament and the Abyssinian affair caused required the paying off of *Ormonde* at Malta, her officers and men being used to man minesweepers. Day, who had been in command of *Ormonde*, went to Alexandria to relieve Hardy as Fleet Hydrographic Officer. Not only did the supply of charts to the Fleet have to be augmented. The state of surveys of the Red Sea was reviewed, not all work done during the Kaiser War having been included in charts in an area which had commanded little priority in the immediate post-war years.

In 1936 the consequences of the manpower shortage, together with the start of the new ship programme about which more later, spread to the home ships. Neither *Beaufort* nor *Fitzroy* were brought forward from their winter lie-up in the spring of 1936. To minimise the effect on the output of surveys a party under Farquharson was sent to the west coast of Scotland to work in the sea lochs and sounds, most of which had only been surveyed sketchily in the last century or earlier, if at all. *Beaufort* never recommissioned, being sold in 1938 for scrap. *Fitzroy* returned to active service in 1937, was refitted to her original minesweeper configuration in 1939 and sunk by mine in 1942 off Great Yarmouth.

International co-operation in oceanography was furthered when Farquharson was lent to an expedition mounted by the John Murray Foundation in the Royal Egyptian Research Vessel *Mabahiss* for research in parts of the north west Indian Ocean not visited by the *Challenger* in the 1870s. The ship sailed from Alexandria in September 1933 and returned in May 1934, having gathered much useful data including details of the seabed topography which foreshadowed later developments in the theory of plate tectonics.

With the advent of the automatic echo-sounder recorder and the magneto-striction oscillator the requirement to differentiate soundings obtained by echo from those by lead-line or wire was dropped in 1932. All soundings were now ordered to be recorded in fathoms and feet up to ten fathoms (i.e. 'Under Eleven in Fathoms and Feet', as the subscription in the title of fair sheets used to read). The echo-sounder was to be checked regularly against wire, and in shallow water the transmission lag adjusted so that the machine recorded the depth below the surface and not that below the keel. Tables of correction for the speed of sound in sea water had been prepared by Dr D J Matthews and published for general scientific information in 1926. All deep water echo soundings were now ordered to be corrected by these to give true depths. All wrecks believed to carry less water than 45 feet over them were to be closely examined and reported on.

Soon after his arrival in office Edgell turned his attention to the replacement of the coal-burning surveying fleet with a more modern one built for oil firing and for echo sounding. It was also necessary to consider the employment of the fleet in the war which was even now being seen as an increasingly ominous cloud on the horizon. During 1933 it was agreed that the fleet should remain at the established size of four smaller ships for home waters and four larger ones abroad, but that only four, two at home and two abroad, would be retained on surveying tasks in wartime. It was proposed to replace the four *Aberdares* by two vessels designed for surveying and two primarily designed as minesweepers. *Ormonde* and *Herald* would be replaced by vessels primarily designed as convoy escorts, while *Iroquois* would not be replaced. Edgell agreed with this, but entered a caveat that *Endeavour* and *Challenger* would also need replacing in due course with ships of similar size designed for surveying.

A programme was drawn up as follows:

BUILDING PROGRAMME	VESSEL TYPE	TO COMPLETE	REPLACES
1934	Survey Convoy Sloop	1936	*Ormonde*
1935	Small Survey Ship	1937	*Fitzroy*
1935	Survey M/s Sloop	1937	*Beaufort*
1936	Small Survey Ship	1938	*Kellett*
1936	Survey M/s Sloop	1938	*Flinders*

Iroquois was to be refitted to replace *Herald*, and herself to be replaced in 1940 by another convoy sloop to be inserted in the 1938 building programme, while *Endeavour* was to run on until 1943. On examination, however, *Iroquois* was found to have a weakening hull. This had been feared for the class from the outset because of the additional weights built into them when the original conversions were put in hand in 1920. The plan was therefore amended to cancel her refit and to replace

Herald with another Convoy Sloop in the 1937 programme, and also to advance *Endeavour*'s replacement by another sloop to the 1938 programme.

Designs for the Convoy Sloop and the necessary modifications for her surveying role were agreed, and invitations to tender issued in December 1934. The first new ship, to be named *Stork*, would be one of the *Bittern* class, of 1,100 tons displacement, and would be built without armament, fire control gear, depth charges or asdics but fitted so that all these items could be installed with the minimum of work on the outbreak of hostilities. In place of the weapon fit she would carry a full outfit of surveying boats, a derrick forward for handling beacons, be fitted with echo-sounders, and have an enlarged bridge and modified accommodation. Built by Dennys at Dumbarton, she was launched on 21 April 1936 by Mrs Edgell and accepted for service in September 1936. She went directly out to the Far East and began her first survey on the Malay-Siamese border north of Penang at the end of the year.

Both the small surveying ships and the survey minesweeping sloops were built to the same hull design as the *Halcyon* class minesweepers, of roughly 850 tons, which were entering service from 1934 onward. The small surveying ships, named *Franklin* and *Scott* after explorers in continuation of the line started by *Beaufort* and the other *Aberdare*s, had larger bridges than the minesweepers, a chartroom on the upper deck aft, a full outfit of boats and a foremast stepped on the forecastle in place of 'A' gun from which the beaconing derrick was rigged. No provision was made in their fitting out for their conversion to minesweepers.

The two survey minesweeping sloops, given the traditional small ship names *Jason* and *Gleaner*, had a similar fit except that their foremast was stepped abaft the bridge like their pure minesweeping sisters, with a stump mast for the derrick on the forecastle which could be readily removed to allow the forrard four inch gun to be fitted rapidly. In fact all wiring and strengthening was built into these two to allow for their speedy conversion to full minesweeping configuration on the outbreak of war.

All four *Halcyon*s were completed in 1938. The first three began surveying that year, to be joined by the last, *Scott*, early in 1939. In 1939 *Franklin* was sent across the Atlantic to carry on *Challenger*'s work on the Labrador coast, the only one of the original four to serve overseas.

No sooner had *Stork* been completed than doubts were expressed about the wisdom of completing three of the most modern escorts without armament at a time when it was no longer a question of whether war would break out or not, but merely of precisely when. Two of the *Egret* class, improved versions of the *Bittern*s, had been earmarked for surveying, and the *Heron* had been renamed *Auckland* in anticipation of her going out to New Zealand to relieve *Endeavour* in her surveys of that Dominion. It was decided to complete both *Auckland* and her sister *Pelican* with full armament, and to disarm and convert two older sloops for surveying. At a meeting on 27 April 1938 chaired by Edgell, *Scarborough* and *Folkestone* were selected for conversion. At the same time, *Stork* would be brought home and re-armed.

The two ships selected were of the *Hastings* class, completed in 1930, slightly smaller and slower than the *Bittern*s and *Egret*s, but not enough to be significantly worse as surveying ships. The conversions would be along the same lines as the design of the *Stork*, though the mainmast would be removed to compensate for the topweight being fitted to a smaller hull. Rapid rearmament was not a consideration, the Controller pointing out that though they were nominally at six months notice for rearmament the supply situation for spare guns and mountings meant that in practice they would be at twelve months notice or more until 'about 1940'.

Scarborough returned from the West Indies in July 1938 and was taken in hand at Chatham, emerging in her survey guise to leave Sheerness at the beginning of March 1939 to start surveying in the Indian Ocean, working off Ceylon and on the Somali coast. *Folkestone*'s conversion was started in Hong Kong on 1 March 1939, and was still incomplete on the outbreak of war.

As well as the conventional surveying ships approval was given to build a vessel specially for research into magnetics. The ship was to be of entirely non-magnetic construction, brigantine-rigged with an auxiliary diesel engine with a displacement of 770 tons. The design was developed in consultation with the Carnegie Institute of Washington, who had operated a ship, the *Carnegie*, for magnetic research intermittently from 1909 to 1929. The *Research*, named both for her task and for the last of the paddle survey ships, was laid down at Philips of Dartmouth in September 1937. She was due for completion in September 1939. Though almost finished, work was immediately stopped when war broke out, and was never re-started. She languished at buoys in the River Dart until 1952, when she was towed away and broken up.

Ashore, with the Chart Branch in Cornwall House and the Department's own chart production unit at Cricklewood, the organisation had settled by the time Edgell took office into the form it was to keep until the expansions and changes of war.

At the Admiralty were Hydrographer himself, with a captain (H) as Assistant Hydrographer, in charge of Sailing Directions, Notices to Mariners, Light Lists, Instrument Officer and Territorial Waters Officer, as well as Chart Branch (Admiralty), which dealt with incoming printed information, as opposed to charts or surveys. It also maintained a stock of charts for use by the Naval Staff. All the Admiralty branches of the Department were staffed mainly by serving or retired naval officers, backed up by draughtsmen and clerical staff. Also housed alongside Hydrographer in Whitehall was the Chief Civil Assistant, the senior administrative civil servant of the Department, with a registry and clerks.

At Cornwall House was the Chart Branch, staffed by a commander (H) as Superintendent of Charts, with the Superintending Cartographer, 26 cartographers, 38 draughtsmen and 3 paperkeepers under him. They were organised into four geographical sections, dividing the world between them. Each section compiled new charts and kept up to date the existing charts covering its own area. A fifth section compiled and kept up to date the Admiralty List of Wireless

Organisation before the Second World War – 1938
(At Admiralty or as shown)

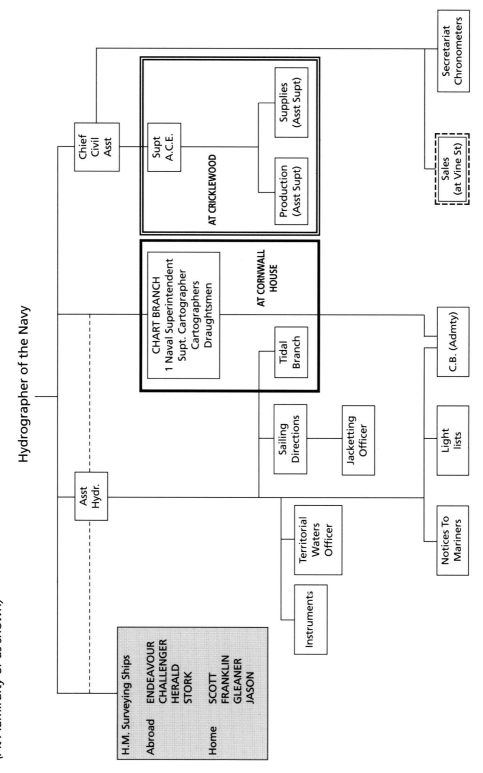

Hydrographer of the Navy

Signals and the Telegraph Charts. With them was the Tidal branch, staffed by a naval Superintendent and four naval assistants. In 1937 a sixth section was formed to produce air charts. The Curator, a senior draughtsman, looked after the Original Documents, manuscript charts dating back to the mid eighteenth century, foreign government charts, and copies of cancelled Admiralty charts, amounting in all to some half a million sheets.

At Cricklewood the Superintendent, Admiralty Chart Establishment had under him some 114 non-industrial staff and 222 industrials (the exact number varied, these are the figures for 1938). From 1936 he had as his Assistant Superintendent (Production) a senior cartographer. He also had an Assistant Superintendent (Supplies) dealing with the chart depot side of his business, the issue of charts and other publications to the Fleet.

Sales were dealt with through a main agent, J D Potter, at Vine Street, in the City. In February 1939 Potters became an agent rather than as hitherto the sole agent for Admiralty charts and publications, and a small sales staff from the Department operated from the Vine Street premises until evacuation to Bath in September.

With the printing of charts since 1929 under the direct control of the Department it became possible for the first time to obtain accurate costings for the printing process. In 1931 the Treasury began to ask questions about the comparison between costs and the sale price. Edgell took the line that by far the greater part of the costs of running the Admiralty Chart Establishment, and indeed practically the whole expenditure on the Hydrographic Service, would be necessary even if not a single chart was sold, since the services provided were required for the Fleet. Prices remained as set by the Department, varying between charts depending on their size, their complexity, and their popularity.

Since soon after Dalrymple first started publishing Admiralty charts they had borne at the head of the title block a badge known as the 'Seal of the Hydrographic Office'. Over the years it had been modified, until by the first quarter of this century it had become stylised by individual engravers out of all recognition from the original simple design. In 1934 the seal was redesigned, retaining the elements of the early designs but cleaning up and clarifying the whole. The new design was engraved on all chart plates by photographic etching, and more recently onto zinc enamels by direct photography. Creeping corruption of the design has thus been eliminated, and the 1934 design remained standard until the setting up of the Hydrographic Office as a Defence Support Agency in 1990, and even now is only slightly modified.

All stages of the chart production process, from the examination of incoming material to the issue of the finished product to the Fleet or its sale to the mariner at large, were now under Hydrographer's immediate control. However, the places in which the various interdependent functions were carried out were spread over a number of buildings in widely separated parts of the capital. This made for inefficiency and delay, and Edgell wished to concentrate operations on one site. To find such a site in London was practically impossible, and if one had been found with the requisite space it would have been prohibitively expensive to acquire. In any case, with the warclouds gathering the government was looking to disperse non-essential elements away from the capital and the risk of bombing.

Approval was given in principle in 1938 for concentration in purpose-built premises on a green-field site. A number of possible places were looked at, and a position on the outskirts of Taunton was selected. Departmental legend has it that Llewellyn, the Chief Civil Assistant, paid down his own money to secure the land. The unkind also said at the time that he chose the site because he wanted to retire to Somerset. In fact it was chosen because it was well away from likely bombing targets, and had good road and rail links with the two main naval bases in the south of England, Plymouth and Portsmouth. The war began before building started, and only the chart reproduction, printing and issues sections moved to the new establishment in 1941. However, enough land was bought in the original acquisition to allow for expansion, an act of vision for which successive Hydrographers have been grateful as the Taunton establishment has grown over the years.

As part of the war planning process, a Chart Reserves Committee was set up in September 1938. Made up of representatives of the Operations, Plans, Navigation and Stores Divisions of the Naval Staff as well as Hydrographer, it reviewed the stocks of charts maintained at the depots and the likely need in emergency or war. It determined that the chart reserves held should be increased from 200% of the normal demands to 300%. In the event, with the bringing forward of the Reserve Fleet at the time of the Munich crisis and after, this was soon found to be inadequate to fill all demands and still to have some stocks in reserve.

Up to 1938 all chart printing had been by direct impressions of copper plates or lithographic stones on flat-bed printing machines. This was a very precise but slow method. The use of the rotary offset process, printing from a zinc plate itself copied from the original copper, both allowed copies to be printed much more quickly and also preserved the copper original from wear and deterioration. Trials of the printing zinc rotary offset process early in 1938 were very successful, and an immediate programme put in hand to convert the whole printing of charts to this method. By January 1939 1,600 charts had been transferred to zinc, and by the outbreak of war all the just under 4,000 charts in the Admiralty series were on zinc. Without the faster production that the rotary offset process permitted there is no way the Department could have met the demands placed on it in the war.

When the Treasury queried the expenditure on new machinery and extra staff the Naval Staff insisted that no postponement of the chart reserves augmentation programme was acceptable, and the outlay was approved. To make room at Cricklewood the Supplies Division was moved to Park Royal under its own Superintendent.

The pay of the cartographer class continued to occupy their minds. There had been no change since the parsimonious revision of the scales in 1923. In 1929 a committee under Professor Sir Harold Carpenter, FRS had been set up to examine the organisation and conditions of service of Research and Experimental

Establishments under the Admiralty, War Office, Air Ministry and the Department of Scientific Information and Research. Though the Hydrographic Department was not within the remit of the Carpenter Committee, the cartographers hoped that from it would come general recommendations which could be applied to them. It did come up with a scheme for the organisation of all scientific and technical personnel, dividing the staff into 'officers' and 'assistants', and further subdividing the 'officers' into Scientific and Technical grades. However, the Treasury and the departments dragged their heels over implementation, the slump of 1930 with its train of financial stringency intervened, and implementation of the Carpenter recommendations was not agreed until October 1934.

Staff inspections of the Department failed to agree how the cartographers could be divided along Carpenter lines, and no action was taken to amend their rates of pay. Eventually it was agreed that all the cartographer class had supervisory duties, and should be equated with the scientific grades, though their actual rates of pay would continue to be set separately.

In 1929 and 1938 draughtsmen had received rises in maximum pay, eroding the differential between them and the cartographers who were in charge of them. At the time of the 1938 award to draughtsmen the Association of Cartographers printed a booklet submitting in detail their grounds for claiming a substantial rise in pay. This was presented to the Admiralty with the backing of the Institution of Professional Civil Servants. However, the war intervened here as in so many projects at the end of the 1930s, and it was not until December 1940 that new pay scales were awarded. With cartographers starting at £225 and rising to a maximum of £585, and the Superintending Cartographer's range from £850 to £1000, they were a considerable improvement on the old 1880 scale obtaining hitherto. The IPCS, though, was not fully satisfied, claiming that it was only a partial recompense for what had been scandalously inadequate scales, and reserved their right to press for more later.

The 1932 International Hydrographic Conference was held in the conference room of the new building erected by the government of Monaco, and since then there has been no suggestion of any movement away from the Principality. With the world slump biting there was a close examination of the costs of the organisation. It was pointed out that only three similar bodies had a higher budget than the IHB, and the new Directing Committee promised to exercise stringent economy. This committee included a British representative again. Nares, now a rear admiral on the retired list, was elected President, with de Vanssay again and a new American, Rear Admiral A T Long, USN. Long's candidature caused some argument, as some delegates considered that he had not sufficient hydrographic experience to be eligible, and accused the United States of putting undue prerrsure on member states to ensure his acceptance.

Only 15 of the 22 member states were represented at the conference, and shortly after it no less than five resigned. All pleaded financial stringency, but as two were Germany and Italy one need not be unduly cynical to detect political motives in at least their cases. The 1937 Conference was also thinly attended, with 12 member states represented, though the membership had begun to revive after the exodus of 1932, with three new members (or strictly two, since the third was Chile, rejoining after suspension). Nares and de Vanssay were re-elected, Nares, by now a vice admiral, again as President, with another American, Rear Admiral W S Crossley, as the third Director.

In 1939 plans were drawn up to evacuate the Bureau from Monaco to Vichy, and in August a United States destroyer conveyed the Bureau to Seté, from where they travelled by rail to Vichy. When violent conflict did not immediately break out the Bureau returned to Monaco on 7 September. Crossley had resigned in 1938 on health grounds, and had died in 1939, being replaced by Rear Admiral L R Leahy, USN. Leahy left for the States in August 1939, but Nares remained in post until June 1940, returning to England when France fell. De Vanssay stayed in Monaco throughout the war, keeping the Bureau in being, albeit inactive.

Principal Surveys of 1932

HOME

Beaufort	Turner	England, West Coast	Approaches to Padstow.
		Scotland, West Coast	Approaches to the Clyde; Loch Long.
Fitzroy	Wyatt, Day	England, East Coast	Hartlepool Bay; Berwick to Holy Island.
Flinders	Simpson	England, South Coast	Exmouth Harbour.
		England, West Coast	Bristol Channel.
		Scotland, East Coast	Edrachilles Bay.
Kellett	Southern, Bamford	England, East Coast	Thames Estuary; The Downs; River Medway.
	Cowan	England, South Coast	Sandown Bay; Portsmouth; Plymouth.

ABROAD

Challenger	Jackson	North America, East Coast	Coast of Labrador.
		North Atlantic Ocean	Oceanography.
Endeavour	Rice	Africa, West Coast	Approaches to Sierra Leone.
		Mediterranean	Coast of Palestine.
Herald	Hardy	Malay Peninsula	Malacca Strait.
		South China Sea	Scarborough Reef; Royal Captain and Half Moon Shoals
Ormonde	Fryer	Persian Gulf	Qatar to Oman; Bahrain harbour.

Principal Surveys of 1933

HOME

Beaufort	Tennent	Scotland, West Coast	Edrachilles Bay; Iona Sound; Loch Linnhe.
		Ireland, East Coast	Belfast Lough.
Fitzroy	Day,	England, East Coast	Yarmouth and Lowestoft Roads.
	Fryer	Scotland, East Coast	Dornoch Firth; Fraserburgh.
		Shetland Island	Sumburgh Head to Helliness; Levenwick; Quendale Bay.
Flinders	Simpson	Bristol Channel	Barry Island to Blackmore.
		England, South Coast	Sandown Bay; Nab Tower; Bognor Regis.
Kellett	Bamford	England, East Coast	Thames Estuary; Orfordness to Outer Gabbard.
	Cowan	England, South Coast	Portsmouth; Spithead; Plymouth.

ABROAD

Challenger	Wyatt	N. America, East Coast	Labrador, Approaches to Nain; Port Manvers.
		West Indies	Grenadines, Hillsborough Bay.
		North Atlantic Ocean	Oceanography.
Endeavour	Southern	Africa, West Coast	Sierra Leone Coast.
		Mediterranean	Palestine, Jaffa to El Arish.
Herald	Hardy,	China, South Coast	South West River entrance.
	Law	Malay Peninsula	Perhentian Islands.
		South China Sea	Jackson Atoll; Mischief Reef; Palawan Passage.
Ormonde	Fryer	Persian Gulf	Bahrain; Sir Beni Yas;Ajman to Dubai.
		Mediterranean	Cyprus, Approaches to Famagusta.

Principal Surveys of 1934

HOME

Beaufort	Tennent, Farquharson	Scotland, West Coast Ireland, West Coast, England, South Coast	Loch Linnhe; Loch Sunart. Pollack Shoal; Killary Bay. Newlyn.
Fitzroy	Hughes	England, East Coast Shetland Islands	Covehitheness to Winterton; Yarmouth Roads. Helliness; Fitful Head; Fair Island Channel.
Flinders	Jones	England, South Coast	Bognor Regis to Worthing; Poole harbour; White Nose to St Albans Head.
Kellett	Bamford, Baker Fryer	England, South Coast England, East Coast England, South Coast	Folkestone to Kingsdown; Dover. Shipwash; Galloper; Cork Sand. Portsmouth; Plymouth; Devonport.

ABROAD

Challenger	Wyatt	West Indies N. America, East Coast North Atlantic Ocean	Grenadines, Carriacou. Labrador, Cartwright and approaches. Oceanography.
Endeavour	Southern	Malay Peninsula Indian Ocean	Langkawi Island and approaches. Oceanography.
Herald	Law	Malay Peninsula Borneo, East Coast	Trengganu. Approaches to Sarawak; N. of Palawan Passage.
Ormonde	Day	Persian Gulf Mediterranean Read Sea	Tunb to Farur I; Sir Beni Yas; Bahrain, Sitra I. Cyprus, Larnaka; Kyrenia; Karavostasi. Port Berenice; Hassa lagoon.

Principal Surveys of 1935

HOME

Beaufort	Farquharson	England, South Coast	Plymouth; Mounts Bay.
		Scotland, West Coast	Firth of Clyde; Loch Sunart;
Fitzroy	Hughes	England, East Coast	Pakefield to Winterton; River Medway.
		Shetland Islands	S.Nesting Bay to Yell Sound; Fair Island Channel.
Flinders	Wyatt, Jenks	England, South Coast	Bognor Regis to Brighton; Portland.
Kellett	Baker	England, East Coast	Thames Estuary; Goodwin Sands; River Medway.
	Fryer, Turner	England, South Coast	Portsmouth; Devonport.

ABROAD

Challenger	Jones	West Indies	Grenadines, St George's Harbour; Trinidad, Carriacou; Tobago Cays.
Endeavour	Southern	Malay Peninsula	Port Swettenham; Langkawi approach; Bass harbour.
		Siam, West Coast	Butang Is; Terutan; Pulo Lankar.
Herald	Law	Malay Peninsula	Port Swettenham.
		Borneo, West Coast	Sarawak, Rajang River; N. of Palawan Passage.
Ormonde	Day	Mediterranean	Cyprus, Limassol; Paphos; Kyrenia.
	Hutchison	Falkland Islands	Stanley harbour and approaches.
	Hardy	Mediterranean	Alexandria harbour.

During the Abyssinian crisis *Ormonde* was paid off at Malta, her officers and men manning minesweepers.

Principal Surveys of 1936

HOME

Flinders	Jenks	England, South Coast	Bognor Regis to Beachy Head; Portland.
Kellett	Baker	England, South Coast	Folkestone to Kingsdown.
		England, East Coast	Thames Estuary; The Downs; Approaches to Lowestoft.
	Turner	England, South Coast	The Solent; Portsmouth.
	Farquharson, Sabine	Scotland, West Coast	Loch Crinan; Seil and Easdale Sounds.

ABROAD

Challenger	Jones	West Indies	Trinidad, Gulf of Paria.
Endeavour	Southern	Gulf of Aden	Aden and approaches; Berbera.
Herald	Hardy	Borneo, North Coast	Sarawak, Cape Sirik toTanjong Datu; Rajang River; Brunei.
		Malay Peninsula	Trengganu; Endau; Gt. Redang Harbour.
Stork	Farquharson	Siam, West Coast	Hin Dang to Butang I.
	Hutchison	Falkland Islands	Stanley harbour and approaches.

Endeavour returned to England in June for a major refit. Owing to shortage of manpower *Beaufort* and *Fitzroy* were not commissioned this year. *Stork* commissioned on 10 September for Far Eastern surveys

Principal Surveys of 1937

HOME

Fitzroy	Jones	England, East Coast	Harwich; Lowestoft; Yarmouth; Approaches to Sunderland.
		Shetland Islands	Fair Island Channel; S. Nesting to Yell Sound.
Flinders	Jenks	England, South Coast	Brighton to Beachy Head; Dolphin Sand to St Catherines.
		England, West Coast	Workington Bank to Silloth Channel.
Kellett	Foulerton	England, East Coast	Thames Estuary; North Falls to Margate Road
	Turner	England, South Coast	Portsmouth; The Solent; Plymouth.
	Farquharson	Scotland, West Coast	Loch Killisport to Loch Crinan.
		England, Lake District	Lake Windermere.

ABROAD

Challenger	Baker	West Indies	Trinidad, Icacos to Siparia; Cedros to Soldado; Bermuda channels.
Endeavour	Wyatt	New Zealand	Hauraki Gulf.
Herald	Hardy	Borneo, North Coast	Cape Sirik to Tanjong Datu.
		South China Sea	Minerva and Kiev Banks.
		Malay Peninsula	Trengganu; Endau approaches; Kemaman.
Stork	Farquharson,	Siam, West Coast	Hin Dang to Butang Islands.
	Jackson	Ceylon, East Coast	Approaches to Jaffna; East Channel.

Endeavour recommissioned at Sheerness on completion of her long refit on 15 January for service on the New Zealand station. She arrived in Auckland on 15 June to start what was to have been a 10-year programme, but which was interrupted by the war in 1939.

Principal Surveys of 1938

HOME

Fitzroy	Jones, Boxall	England, East Coast	Thames Estuary; Approaches to Sunderland.
		Orkney Islands	Gutter Sound.
		Shetland Islands	Fetlar to Muckle Flugga.
Flinders	Torlesse	England, South Coast	Portsmouth Harbour entrances.
Franklin	Sabine	England, East Coast	Dover Strait; The Downs; Yarmouth and Lowestoft Roads.
Gleaner	Southern	England, South Coast	English Channel.
		Irish Sea	Isle of Man.
Jason	Hardy	England, South Coast	Christchurch and Swanage Bays.
		Bristol Channel	Newport to New Passage; Swansea Bay.
Kellett	Foulerton	England, East Coast	River Medway.
	Turner, Torlesse	England, South Coast	Portsmouth; Plymouth.

ABROAD

Challenger	Baker	West Indies	Trinidad, Gulf of Paria; Barbados.
		Arabian Sea	Ras al Hadd.
Endeavour	Wyatt	New Zealand	Great Barrier I to Mercury Bay; Hauraki Gulf.
Herald	Jenks	China Sea	Mischief Reef.
		Borneo	Tanjong Datu to Po Point; Saracen Bay to Bunbury Shoal.
		Malay Peninsula	Singapore, Keppel Harbour; JohoreStrait.
Stork	Jackson	Thailand, West Coast	Chance I to Sayer I.
		Ceylon	Trincomalee West Channel.

Jason and *Franklin* replaced *Flinders* and *Kellett* in June and August respectively.

Principal Surveys of 1939

HOME

Franklin	Sabine	England, East Coast	Thames Estuary.
		Labrador	St Lewis Sound; Battle Harbour.
Gleaner	Price	England, South Coast	Approaches to Dartmouth.
		Scotland, West Coast	Tiree to Skerryvore.
Jason	Jones	England, South Coast	Christchurch to Swanage.
		Bristol Channel	Scarweather to Helwick; Barry Roads.
Scott	Day, Jenks	Scotland, East Coast	Bass and Bell Rocks; River Tay.
		Orkney Islands	Entrances to Scapa Flow.
		England, East Coast	Harwich; Ramsgate; River Medway.
	Torlesse	England, South Coast	Portsmouth; Plymouth.

ABROAD

Challenger	Baker	Arabia	Ras Tannura; Ras al Hadd; Masira Channel.
Endeavour	Wyatt	New Zealand	Cape Brett to Great Barrier I; Bay of Islands.
Herald	Southern	China, South Coast	Hong Kong harbour.
		Malay Peninsula	Johore Strait.
Stork	Jones	Thailand, West Coast	Chance I to Sayer I.
Scarborough	Law	Ceylon	Mullaittivu to Point Pedro.
		Africa, East Coast	British Somaliland.

War Operations : *Franklin* and *Scott* Dover Strait minelaying. *Challenger* laid East Coast war channel buoys.

Biographies

1932–1939

Vice Admiral Sir John A Edgell, KBE, CB, FRS
Hydrographer 1932–1945

John Augustine Edgell was born in 1880, the younger son of James Edgell of Teddington. He entered the Royal Navy through the *Britannia* in 1893. He joined his first surveying ship, the *Triton*, Purey-Cust, as a sublieutenant in 1902, and did a season on the east coast of England. In 1903-4, by which time he had been promoted to lieutenant, he was in the *Egeria*, Parry, in British Columbia for a year, and then spent two years in the *Rambler*, Monro, on the China coast and in Borneo waters. After a course in magnetic observations he went, in September 1906, to the *Merlin*, Parry and later Walter, for two and a half years in the Red Sea and on the coasts of Malaya and Borneo. This was followed by a commission in the *Sealark*, Davy, in the Indian Ocean and the south west Pacific until the end of 1911.

In 1912 Edgell obtained his first command, the *Mutine*, for two years on the west coast of Africa. The ship fractured a propellor shaft so that in 1912 she was towed to Gibraltar where the Board of Admiralty were present and inspected the ship. It was of this ship that Edgell used to say that he was the last naval commanding officer to sail out of harbour with the yards manned.

In May 1914 Edgell moved to the *Hearty*, surveying on the east coast of Scotland and in the Shetland Islands, and in the next year on the east coast of England. He was promoted to commander in mid 1915, and that September took the *Endeavour*, specially fitted with chart production equipment, out to the eastern Mediterranean and made surveys in support of the Dardanelles operations. In 1917 he was on the Admiralty War Staff for six months, and was Superintendent of Charts from September 1917 until the end of 1920.

In 1921 he took command of the *Merlin* in the Far East, where he made surveys for the projected naval base in Singapore. He received Their Lordships' appreciation for the work and for his assistance to the Admiralty Committee studying the question. In 1923 he again became Superintendent of Charts, being promoted to captain in that year. In April 1925 he was sent to command the Australian surveying ship *Moresby*, returning home in 1928. He was then Assistant Hydrographer for two years before going to his last sea command, the *Endeavour*, in the Red Sea and on the Palestine coast. He came ashore in May 1931 for another spell as Assistant Hydrographer.

Edgell succeeded Douglas as Hydrographer in October 1932, a post he filled for thirteen years, a span only exceeded by Beaufort and Wharton. Both in the run-up to the Second World War and during the war he ensured that the Hydrographic Service fulfilled all the demands made upon it. He was promoted to rear admiral in 1935, and to vice admiral on the retired list in 1938, made a CB in 1936 and a KBE in 1942. He was succeeded as Hydrographer by Wyatt on 1 May 1945.

He was the Admiralty's representative on the Port of London Authority from 1941 to 1961, and Acting Conservator of the River Mersey from 1945 to 1951. As a member of the Royal Society's committees on geodesy and geophysics he was a prime mover in the establishment of the National Institute of Oceanography in 1951, serving on its executive committee and on the National Oceanographic Council. He died in his 82nd year in November 1962

Captain E H B Baker, DSO

Edmund Henry Buckingham Baker, known to his contemporaries as 'Buck', began surveying as a newly promoted lieutenant in 1922, joining the *Kellett*, Haselfoot, on Thames Estuary and south coast surveys. In 1924 he went to the *Endeavour*, Geary-Hill, on the west coast of Africa and in the Red Sea, and in 1926 he was back in the *Kellett*, Maxwell, Silk and Cary successively, working in the Thames Estuary again.

In 1928 Baker went to the China station in the *Iroquois*, Nares and later Law, surveying on the coasts of Malaya and Borneo and in the South China Sea. He returned home for another spell in the *Kellett*, Southern, in 1930, working on the east coast of England. In 1931 he stood by the new ship *Challenger*, and on the arrival home of the *Iroquois* he commissioned *Challenger* under first Jackson and later Wyatt for surveys off the east coast of Scotland and then in Labrador, where he had charge of a shore party through the winter of 1933- 34, when he made his epic sledge trip to Nain.

By 1934 Baker was again in the *Kellett*, now in command, for surveys on the east and south coasts of England. On promotion to commander in 1937 he took the *Challenger* first for work in the West Indies and then to the Red Sea and Persian Gulf. In 1939 she returned home for refit, and on the outbreak of war was engaged in laying east coast war channel buoys in co-operation with Trinity House. Baker then exchanged commands with Jenks, and in the *Scott*, temporarily an anti-submarine vessel, was senior officer of a striking force on the west coast of Scotland. In 1940 he went to Norway for surveys under the Commander in Chief, and on the evacuation in May joined the staff of the Headquarters, Combined Operations. In 1941 he became deputy convoy officer in Western Approaches.

Early in 1942 Baker went to Aden to take command of the *Endeavour*, which had escaped from Singapore with a scratch crew largely made up of survivors from the

Repulse and *Prince of Wales*. In her he made surveys in the Red Sea and the Gulfs of Suez and Aqaba, and was also Fleet Hydrographic Officer. In September 1943, when operations in the Aegean were planned, he became SBNO Aegean with the acting rank of captain. When these strategically unsound plans went awry Baker was captured at Leros and spent the rest of the war a prisoner. He was awarded the DSO in 1944 for his actions.

On his return from imprisonment in 1945 Baker came to the Department as Territorial Waters Officer, and on his promotion to captain in 1946 took over as Superintendent of Charts. In 1949 he went back to sea in the *Dalrymple* in the Persian Gulf and the Red Sea, and next year he was back again in the Department as AH(1) and Superintendent of Charts. In 1952 he took his last seagoing command of the *Cook* for surveys on the west coast of Scotland and in the Bristol Channel, ending his sea service at the Coronation Review in 1953.

Baker retired in July 1953. He then did two years, 1954 to 1956, as Senior Hydrographic Officer with British Petroleum in Papua before retiring to Somerset.

Commander K F Boxall, DSO

Kenneth Frank Boxall took up surveying as a lieutenant of one year's seniority in 1924, joining the *Flinders*, Henderson, for a season on the south and west coasts of England. From 1925 to 1928 he was in the *Herald*, Harvey, Silk and Haselfoot in succession, on the north and east coasts of Australia and then in Borneo waters. In 1928 he did a season in the *Beaufort*, Wyatt, on the west coast of England and Scotland, and then in 1929 moved to the *Fitzroy*, Fryer, on the east coast of England. In 1930 he went out to the *Iroquois*, Law and later Jackson, on the China station, working mainly on the coast of Malaya.

In 1932 Boxall came home to the *Beaufort*, Turner and later Tennent, on the west coasts of England and Scotland again, and then there followed one more commission abroad in the *Ormonde*, Day, working in the Persian Gulf and in the eastern Mediterranean until the ship paid off in September 1935 during the Abyssinian crisis. Boxall then commanded the minesweeper *Aberdare* for nearly a year. On his return to surveying late in 1936 he went to the *Fitzroy*, Jones, on the east coast of England and in the Northern Isles. He succeeded to the command of the ship for the latter part of 1938, and thereafter came to the Department as a naval assistant until the outbreak of the war in September 1939.

Throughout the war Boxall gave distinguished service as an acting commander in charge of minesweeping operations first in the Dover Strait and later in South East Asia Command based on Mandapam. In 1946 he became a commander on the retired list, and joined the Department in charge of Light Lists, a post he held until his death in 1958.

Commander W I Farquharson, OBE

William Ian Farquharson joined the *Fantome*, Maxwell, as an acting lieutenant in 1921, surveying in the Torres Strait and on the Great Barrier Reef. He returned home in 1924, going to the *Kellett*, Haselfoot, mainly working in the Thames Estuary. In 1925 he went to the *Iroquois*, Jackson, on the China station working in the approaches to Hong Kong and in Singapore. During the troubles in China he volunteered for service at Hankow, where one of his companions from the *Iroquois*, Lieutenant Higgins, lost his life.

After another season in the *Kellett*, Silk, in 1928, Farquharson was again abroad from 1929 to 1931 in the *Ormonde*, Wyatt, for surveys in the Persian Gulf and on the Cyprus coast. In 1931 he joined the *Beaufort*, Turner and later Tennent, for west coast of England and Scotland surveys, and then in 1933 and 1934 was lent to the John Murray Expedition to the Indian Ocean in the Egyptian research vessel *Mabahiss*, where he was responsible for drafting the report on bathymetry.

Late in 1934 Farquharson was given command of the *Beaufort*, employed on west coast of Scotland surveys, which he continued in 1936-37 with a shore-based party when *Beaufort* was immobilised during the Abyssinian crisis. He left this work when Jackson went sick to take his place and to steam the new *Stork* out to the the Far East.

He came ashore in 1938 to become Superintendent of the Tidal Branch in the Department, a post he filled for the next 18 years. He retired with the rank of commander in 1945, but continued in the Tidal Branch. He was awarded the OBE in 1954.

On leaving the Department in 1956 Farquharson joined the Canadian Hydrographic Service. In 1963 he transferred to the newly opened Bedford Institute of Oceanography at Halifax, Nova Scotia. He retired from this work in 1966, and then took part in a National Institute of Oceanography expedition to the Indian Ocean early in 1967.

Commander A B B Foulerton

Alexander Barclay Blood Foulerton joined surveying as a lieutenant in 1923, being appointed to the *Flinders*, Jackson and later Henderson, working on the south coast, in the Bristol Channel and on the west coast of Scotland. He was then attached to the RAF for three years, became a pilot of naval Flycatchers, and went afloat in the aircraft carrier *Glorious*. However, the system of parallel promotions in RAF and RN ranks was unattractive to him, and he returned to surveying in 1927.

After a few months in the *Fitzroy*, Harvey, on the east coast of England Foulerton went out in 1928 to the *Iroquois*, Nares, working in the Malacca Strait and on the reefs in the South China Sea. He next served in the *Beaufort*, Turner, on the coast of Cornwall and on the west coast of Scotland. In 1932 he went out to the *Herald*, Hardy and later Law, working again in the Malacca Strait and the South China Sea.

During this time he was employed on a secret survey from the air of Scarborough Reef, between Manila and Hong Kong. He came home for the 1935 season, which he spent in the *Fitzroy*, Hughes, and in 1936 went to the West Indies in the *Challenger*, Jones.

He was given command of the *Kellett*, working in the Thames Estuary, in 1937. He remained with her until August 1938, when he came into the Department, working on Air Pilots and in 1940 forming the Air Information Section. After the section moved to Bath it became a Branch, with Foulerton as Superintendent in the acting rank of commander.

After the war, disliking office work, Foulerton obtained his release in December 1946 as a commander on the retired list, and became an estate bailiff.

Captain C A G Hutchinson, DSO*, OBE

Colin Alexander Gordon Hutchinson, as a sublieutenant and lieutenant, did a commission in the *Sealark*, Davy and later Glennie, in 1910-11, surveying on the north-west Malayan coast, the Solomon Islands and the Great Barrier Reef. He then returned to general service but was disappointed at not being selected for the long (N) course. During the First World War he commanded destroyers, and in 1924, after promotion to commander, he did three years in the Plans Division of the Naval Staff and then two years as captain of the *Bee*, the flagship of the Yangtse Flotilla.

In 1935 he retired with the rank of captain, and from September 1935 to July 1936, at Edgell's suggestion, was in charge of a party surveying in the Falkland Islands. He worked up the results in the Department, subsequently becoming the Hydrographer's assistant dealing with territorial waters matters and the construction of the *Research*. When the Second World War broke out he also took responsibility for mine charts. Before leaving the department he was one of several officers who took part in a hasty reconnaissance of the north coast of France before the enemy overran it.

He returned to sea in July 1940 where he gave distinguished service first on Malta convoys, where he was awarded the DSO and bar, then in command of a squadron for the Normandy landings, and lastly in the Pacific where he was awarded the OBE. After the war he spent five years with the Allied Control Commission in Germany. He retired in 1952 to Southsea, where he founded a flourishing Portsmouth-Duisberg Association.

Commander A M Hughes, OBE

Alfred Marcus Hughes was a newly-promoted lieutenant when he joined the *Flinders*, Jackson and then Henderson, in 1921 for three years surveying on the west coast of Scotland, the south coast of England and the Bristol Channel. For the next three years, 1924 to 1927, he was in the *Ormonde*, Douglas, Knowles and Wyatt successively, in the Caribbean. He came home in 1927 to the *Fitzroy*, Harvey and later Fryer, working on the east coast of England. Abroad again in 1929, Hughes spent two years in the *Herald*, Maxwell, in Borneo, Hong Kong and Singapore waters, and then from 1931 to 1933 was in the *Endeavour*, Rice, the ship's time being divided between Sierra Leone and the coast of Palestine. On Rice's death at sea Hughes took temporary command until the arrival of Southern.

His next ship was the *Fitzroy*, working on the east coast of England and in the Shetland Isles. He served under Fryer from August 1933 to February 1934, and then took command himself until April 1936. He then came ashore to a post as naval assistant in the Department, dealing with instruments and with territorial waters matters. At the end of 1936, as a lieutenant commander on the retired list, he took up the position of Assistant Port Surveyor to the Rangoon Port Commissioners.

On the outbreak of war in 1939 Hughes joined the Naval Control Service at Rangoon until mid 1940, when he came home to command the minesweeper *Corfield* engaged in magnetic mine sweeping in the Thames Estuary. From 1941 to 1945 he served as a commander, still on the retired list, attached to the Interservices Topographical Division, first at Oxford and then from 1944 in South East Asia Command at Delhi and Kandy. One of his tasks at Oxford was to work out the tides off Huelva in south west Spain for the dumping of the body of 'the man who never was' as part of the invasion deception plan.

During 1945 he returned to Rangoon, first with a naval party and then as Port Surveyor to the Commissioners until 1947. He was awarded the OBE in 1946.

From March 1948 to January 1950 Hughes was at the National Maritime Museum in charge of the instrument room. His last appointment was on the Port Emergency Planning Staff at the Ministry of Transport, from which he retired in September 1965.

Hughes had a bent for natural history, and made several collections for the Zoo, the Natural History Museum and the Hospital for Tropical Diseases. He coupled this with considerable artistic ability, illustrating several books on birds as well as painting a series of naval cartoons, many reproduced and sold by Gieves Ltd.

Commander W C Jenks, OBE

William Corfield Jenks joined the *Kellett*, Haselfoot, as a lieutenant of one year's seniority in 1923, working on the south and east coasts of England. By the end of the year he had been appointed to the *Herald*, Harvey and later Silk, and spent the next three years surveying on the north and east coasts of Australia. He came home in 1927, and spent that year under Henderson on the River Severn survey. The following year he went to the *Flinders*, Cary, on the south and west coasts of England.

In 1929 he was in the *Endeavour*, Law and later Edgell, on Red Sea and Palestine surveys, and in 1931 came home to the Fitzroy, Wyatt, on the east coasts of England and Scotland. He spent the next two years in the *Challenger*, Wyatt, working in Labrador and the West Indies.

He joined the *Flinders*, Jones, in 1934, working on the south coast of England, and succeeded to the command in September 1935, remaining until the end of 1937. From January 1938 to March 1939 Jenks had the *Herald* on the China station, and then went to the *Scott*, on the east coast, until on the outbreak of war he transferred to the *Challenger*. In that ship Jenks made a survey of Hvalfjordur in Iceland to enable it to be used as a fleet base, and also rendered assistance to the aircraft carrier *Argus* when she grounded off Reykjavik, for which he received Their Lordships' appreciation, as he also did later for his surveys on the west coast of Africa.

He came ashore in 1942 to become Superintendent of Charts, broken by a brief spell with the Allied Naval Commander in Chief Expeditionary Forces, and followed by six months at the Interservices Topographical Division at Oxford. In June 1944 he went to Alexandria as Fleet Hydrographic Officer, Mediterranean. He died there tragically in March 1945.

Commander A Jones

Alun Jones became a surveyor fortuitously and unintentionally after an elementary course in land surveying at Cambridge in 1922. Then, as a lieutenant of two years' seniority, he joined the *Endeavour*, Geary-Hill and later Nares, for two years mainly in west African surveys. In 1923, on the Hydrographer's advice, he declined the Navigation School's invitation to become a (N) specialist, and in stead was attached to the Admiralty Research Laboratory for work on the development of the echo-sounder. In 1924 he went to the *Kellett*, Haselfoot and later Maxwell, on Thames Estuary and English Channel surveys, and to carry out sea trials on the new device. He next returned to the *Endeavour*, Geary-Hill and Law, for two years on Red Sea surveys, and then came back to the *Kellett*, Silk and Hardy, from 1928 to 1930 mainly working in the Thames Estuary.

In January 1931 Jones joined the *Herald* under N A C Hardy, who he succeeded in command in 1933, on the China station. From November 1933 to February 1935 he had the *Flinders* on English Channel surveys, and then took command of the *Challenger* in the West Indies until February 1937. He was promoted commander in June 1935. He continued in command; in 1937-38 of the *Fitzroy*, working on the east coast of England and in the Shetlands, in 1938-39 of the *Stork* surveying in Ceylon and on the west coast of Siam, and in 1939 of the *Jason* in the Bristol Channel and the Channel Islands.

Soon after the Second World War broke out Jones became Superintendent of Charts at Bath for two years. From May 1942 to June 1944 he was in the Mediterranean as Fleet Hydrographic Officer, first at Alexandria and then at Algiers. In July 1944 he returned to the Department as Superintendent of Sailing Directions, in which post he remained until March 1956, though placed on the retired list in 1949. After leaving the Department he became a reviser of Sailing Directions, continuing in this occupation until his death in 1969.

Commander H P Price, DSO, OBE

Hugh Perceval Price was a lieutenant of two years seniority when he began surveying in 1925, joining the *Beaufort*, Rice, working at Falmouth, in Loch Torridon and in the Shetlands. The following year he went to the Severn Barrage survey under Henderson, based at Chepstow. He went abroad in 1927 to the *Ormonde*, Rice, surveying in the Malacca Strait, the Maldives, and the approaches to Aden. During this last survey he and a small party spent the night on Socotra, the first Europeans to do so since the lighthouse keepers were withdrawn many years previously.

Returning home in 1929 Price joined the *Kellett*, Hardy and later Southern, for two years' work in the Thames Estuary, and then in 1931 went to the *Beaufort*, Turner, surveying on the west coast of Scotland and in the Bristol Channel. From 1931 to 1933 he was again in the *Ormonde*, Fryer, engaged in Persian Gulf and Cyprus surveys. He came home in 1933 first to the *Flinders*, Simpson and later Jones, working on the south coast of England, and then in the *Fitzroy*, Hughes, in the Fair Island Passage and off Lowestoft. There followed two years on the China station from 1935 to 1937 in the *Herald*, Law and later Hardy, working on the Borneo coast and in the South China Sea, and taking temporary command in Hong Kong between captains.

In 1937 Price stood by the building of the new surveying ship *Gleaner*, commissioned by Southern in 1938 for surveys on the south and west coasts. He took over the command from Southern in 1939, and soon after was engaged in the operations to salvage the sunken submarine *Thetis* in Liverpool Bay.

For the first two years of the war Price remained in command of the *Gleaner*, now rearmed for anti- submarine duties. During this time he destroyed a minelaying U-boat, for which he was awarded the DSO. In 1941 he went to the *Franklin* on the east coast, where a head-on meeting of two convoys involved him in two collisions, and where only his skilful handling of the ship avoided her loss. After a short spell in the Department he went to the Mediterranean for survey work under the direction of the Fleet Hydrographic Officer, successively Collins, Jones and Southern, working mainly in Algeria and Tunisia in the wake of the Allied advances.

In 1944 he returned to the Department, assisting with Notices to Mariners, then in 1946 took charge of the South Coast of England Survey until 1950. He retired with the rank of commander in 1946, and was released from Naval service in 1948, serving with the Unit for his last two years as a civilian. After leaving the Unit he became a reviser of Sailing Directions until 1965.

Commander H P L Tennent

Hugh Patrick Lorraine Tennent began surveying as a newly promoted lieutenant in 1921 when he joined the *Ormonde*, Douglas, working in British Honduras and Bermuda. In 1924 he went to the *Fitzroy*, Woodhouse and later Silk, for two and a half years on the east coast of England, and from 1927 for another two and a half years he was in the *Ormonde*, Rice, surveying in the Malacca Strait and the Maldive Islands.

In 1929 Tennent did another season in the *Fitzroy*, this time under Fryer, on the east coast. In 1930 he was in the *Endeavour*, Edgell, in the Red Sea, and in 1931 he went to the *Iroquois*, Jackson, on the China station. In 1932 he came home to go yet again to the *Fitzroy*, now under first Wyatt and later Day, still working on the east coast.

He was appointed in command of the *Beaufort* in 1933, surveying on the west coast of Scotland. This was his last sea service, and he came ashore in 1934 to the Department, where he served for eighteen years in the Notices to Mariners Branch, for the last nine in charge of it. He was placed on the retired list with the rank of commander in 1944. After he left the Department in 1955 he became a reviser of Sailing Directions until 1960.

Lieutenant Commander J Y G Torlesse

John Ynyr George Torlesse began surveying as a lieutenant in 1925 by joining the *Endeavour*, Geary-Hill, for two years on the West African coast and in the Red Sea. In 1928 he came home to the *Beaufort*, Wyatt and later Rice, working on the south and west coasts of England and the west coast of Scotland.

He spent 1930 and 1931 in the *Ormonde*, Wyatt, in the Persian Gulf and the Mediterranean. He was at home again in 1932 and 1933 in the *Kellett*, Southern and later Bamford, on the east coast and in the Thames Estuary. During the lie-ups he did both the standard gyro course and the long meteorological course. In April 1934 Torlesse joined the *Challenger*, Wyatt and later Jones, in the West Indies and the Labrador coast for two years. He had the 1936 season in home waters in the *Flinders*,

Jenks, and in 1937 went to the *Endeavour*, Wyatt, in New Zealand. Here, in August, he was taken ill and invalided home.

In June 1938 he took charge of the South Coast of England Survey, but fell sick again in the next year and had to relinquish the appointment. He died in September 1961.

Commander C W Sabine, OBE

Charles Wheatstone Sabine entered the surveying service in 1923 just before his promotion to Lieutenant, going for two years to the *Fitzroy*, Woodhouse followed by Silk, working on the east coast of England. In 1925 he went out to the *Iroquois*, Jackson, for three years surveying in the South China Sea and off Malaya. In 1928 he came home to the *Beaufort*, Wyatt, and in the following year went to the *Flinders*, Cary, working mainly on the west coast of Scotland. In 1930 Sabine joined the *Endeavour*, Edgell, for surveys in the Red Sea and on the Palestine coast, and two years later returned to the *Flinders*, now under Simpson, for two seasons on the south and west coasts of England. In 1934 he went to the *Challenger*, Wyatt and then Jones, and worked in Labrador and the West Indies for two years.

In 1936, when some of the surveying ships were laid up owing to manpower shortages, he joined the West Coast of Scotland Survey under Farquharson, taking charge of it himself later in the year.

Sabine next stood by the new surveying ship *Franklin*, taking command on commissioning for surveys in Labrador. On the outbreak of war in 1939 he brought the ship home for minelaying operations in the Dover Strait, followed by work in the Faeroe Islands and on the east coast of England. He was promoted commander in 1939 and awarded the OBE in 1940. From 1941 to 1943 he was Staff Officer (H) to Vice Admiral Dover (Ramsay followed by Pridham-Whippell), and then took command of the converted yacht *White Bear*, fully equipped with chart production facilities, sailing her to Colombo. On arrival, when Day took over from Wyatt as Fleet Hydrographic Officer, Sabine transferred to the *Challenger*, in which ship he surveyed Exmouth Gulf and started the survey of Torres Strait which Tripp completed with the assistance of Royal Australian Naval vessels. In 1945 the *Challenger* returned to the South East Asia Command, surveying in Ceylon and in the re- entered ports of Singapore, Saigon and Hong Kong.

At the close of 1945 Sabine returned home to work in the Department, first as Territorial Waters Officer and then as Superintendent of the Air Information Branch until he retired in 1951. In retirement he continued to work for the department as a reviser of Sailing Directions until 1975.

CHAPTER FIVE

The War Years
1939–1945

Vice Admiral Sir John Edgell, KBE, CB

Edgell continued as Hydrographer for the whole of the war, only turning over to Wyatt in May 1945. He thus operated the machine he had tuned in peacetime in the stress of war, and the machine fulfilled all the demands made upon it by the Navy and the nation.

As we have already seen, the newest of the foreign- going surveying ships, *Stork*, had already been recalled for re-armament in the spring of 1939, to be replaced in the Indian Ocean by the older, though newly converted, *Scarborough*. In September 1939 *Scarborough*, *Herald* and *Endeavour* were ordered to Singapore to pay off. A small surveying team under Beech Thomas remained to work from the naval base there on operational surveys. The remainder of the three ships' officers and men were dispersed throughout the Fleet. The conversion of *Folkestone* at Hong Kong was halted not far short of completion. Both she and *Scarborough*, despite the Controller's pre-war minute, were armed as escorts by the end of the year, though as late as July 1942 inspections were complaining about excessive topweight remaining from both ships' surveying conversions.

At home *Jason* and *Gleaner* were immediately taken in hand for conversion, not for minesweeping but as anti-submarine escorts. They served in this capacity throughout the war, and were sold out of service shortly after the war's end. *Franklin* was recalled from Labrador. She, together with *Scott*, was immediately put to work providing the positioning for the laying of the Dover Strait mine barrage, while *Challenger*, fresh from her refit, joined Trinity House tenders in laying the complex of war channel buoys up the east coast of England. *Franklin* and *Scott* were armed with a three-inch anti-aircraft gun on the forecastle and a scattering of close-range artillery. *Challenger* received only close- range anti-aircraft guns.

Franklin soon relieved *Challenger* on the east coast, and was constantly employed there, locating wrecks of ships sunk, sounding diversionary channels, and assisting minesweepers. She also made surveys in Scapa Flow to help blocking operations, at Dundee for the submarine base there, and at Skaalefjord in the Faeroes for its use as a fleet anchorage. She was also involved in the very large scale surveys for positioning the Maunsell pre-fabricated forts in the Thames Estuary for the anti-aircraft defence of London.

Between her surveying tasks, or when moving from one to the next, she was often called upon to act as a convoy escort. In July 1941 this was nearly her end when leading a convoy north along a buoyed route in thick fog. Her convoy met a southbound one head on, and she herself was first overrun by her own convoy commodore's ship which scraped up her port side, and immediately afterwards had her starboard side savaged by one of the opposing convoy. She was the only ship in either convoy damaged in this encounter, and only Price's unperturbed handling of her avoided her loss.

Scott remained for much of the next two years employed on mining, providing precise positioning for the minelayers and, where necessary, carrying out surveys of the intended minefields before they were laid to determine the depth of water, and hence the length of mooring needed, as well as measuring the tidal streams and currents which the minelayers could expect to encounter. She was principally engaged on the northern barrage, between Scotland, Iceland and Greenland. Only the week before the *Bismarck*'s break-out in May 1941 *Scott* was in the waters the German squadron passed through, surveying for the next tranche of the barrage. Those who were in her at the time tell with feeling of the lonely nature of her work, and of the discomfort of bobbing about in a sounding boat moored to a deep-laid beacon in the middle of the Denmark Strait observing currents.

As well as making the surveys to provide data before laying, *Scott* also herself accompanied the minelaying sorties for the northern barrage, and surveying officers were carried in each of the minelayers, mainly large converted merchantmen.

In December 1941 *Scott* was a key participant in the second raid on the Lofoten Islands. This was planned as a pair of operations, ANKLET* and ARCHERY. ANKLET was a landing in force on the south-western tip of the Lofoten Islands to establish a base from which German communications south from northern Norway could be harrassed. ARCHERY was a diversionary raid on Vaagso, 350 miles south of Vestfjord, to divert enemy forces and attention from the northern operations. In ANKLET Commando forces were to land at Nappsund, Reine and Sorvag and neutralise German forces on Moskenes and Flakstad islands, the outer two sizeable Lofotens. Minesweepers were to sweep a path for the squadron, the cruiser *Arethusa*, seven destroyers and two corvettes, to enter Skelfjord once *Scott* had found and buoyed a dangerous pinnacle in the entrance. *Scott* was then to survey the larger and more sheltered Kirkefjord for longer-term use by the squadron. All went according to plan, the islands were seized without significant opposition on 26 December, *Scott* buoyed the rock in the entrance to Skelfjord, the squadron entered and fuelled

---

*Originally there were three operations, ANKLET, BRACELET and ARCHERY. A reconnaisance phase, ANKLET, was distinct from the follow-up phase, BRACELET, in which shore anti-aircraft batteries and larger occupying forces were to be landed. C-in-C Home Fleet successfully argued against a substantial land base being established, and BRACELET was dropped.

from its accompanying tankers. In what remained of 26 December and the following day *Scott* completed her survey of Kirkefjord while the destroyers made a sweep through the waters of Vestfjord, and in the evening of 27 December the squadron anchored in Kirkefjord. But during the day *Arethusa* had been bombed and near-missed by a single Heinkel 115 seaplane. And intelligence began to come in that German divebombers and other aircraft were moving north in some force. It had been hoped that the ships would be able to hide under the shore in Kirkefjord, but this was not possible, and the surrounding hills made it likely that any air attack could take the force by surprise. The force was therefore withdrawn over the night of 28 to 29 December.

During the withdrawal *Scott* collided with *Arethusa*, both ships sustaining slight damage. Apart from pricking the hide of the German occupation, the only harvest from this operation was one German patrol trawler sunk. The diversionary raid on Vaagso, with much more limited objectives, was a success. At this distance the idea that a British force without air protection could maintain itself in the Lofotens for any length of time against German air attack seems unrealistic, and bears all the marks of a Churchillian pipe-dream. The Prime Minister was certainly acid about the withdrawal so soon after the force's arrival.

By the end of 1939, when the intensity of the German mining offensive, including magnetic mines, on the east coast was appreciated by the Admiralty, surveying officers were established at Sheerness, Great Yarmouth and the Humber on the staffs of the local Naval Officers in Charge or Commanders M/S. They worked on the fixing of wrecks and maintaining the channels using minesweepers or other small craft. At Yarmouth the drifter *Valesca* was allocated to this task, to be succeeded by the *Astral* at the beginning of 1944. Surveying officers were also attached to the staffs of the various area Commandars in Chief and Flag Officers, performing a variety of tasks from advising the operational staff on charting to fixing wrecks and helping to position local controlled minefields.

A minor task undertaken in 1940 in the field by surveying officers, largely from Headquarters staff, was to have important consequences later. When it became apparent that France would fall, surveyors were sent at an hour's notice to make rapid reconnaisance surveys of ports, coastline and beaches along the Channel coast against the day when we would want to re-enter Europe. These surveys, made in the midst of a flood of refugees and with the Germans close behind, were to provide invaluable in the planning for OVERLORD.

Challenger and the survey launch *Gulnare,* a 54 foot long craft bought in 1938 for the South Coast of England Survey, spent the first year of the war making rapid surveys of possible bases and anchorages, mainly in the north-west. *Challenger* subsequently went to Iceland to chart the fleet anchorages which were to play such a part in the Battle of the Atlantic and the Russian convoys.

In 1941 *Challenger* was sent out to West Africa, where she made surveys of the Gambia River and the approaches and harbour at Freetown, Sierra Leone. While on passage she rescued 823 personnel from the torpedoed troop-ship *Anselm.* After the entry of Japan into the war she was given a printing unit and was sent out to Mombasa, where by the end of 1942 she was producing charts for the Eastern Fleet as well as surveying possible fleet anchorages and harbours.

With the increasing pressure for surveys in all parts of the world, it was planned at the end of 1941 to re-commission *Endeavour* at Singapore for work in the Indian Ocean. The Japanese attack brought this forward, and she was manned with survivors from the *Repulse* and *Prince of Wales* and steamed to Aden. Here E H B Baker took command of her for surveys in the Red Sea of possible ports for use if Egypt had to be evacuated. By September 1943 the urgency had gone from this task, and the old ship was worn out well beyond any economical repair. She was paid off at Suez to be used as an accommodation ship, and her surveyors divided up into parties to follow the advancing Allied armies first along the North African coasts and then through Sicily and Italy. The surveyors were among the first into each newly occupied port. Often still under enemy fire they found and charted obstructions alongside wharves and jetties and in the approaches so that the ports could be brought back into use as soon as possible. Baker himself went as Senior Naval Officer to Leros in the ill-starred Aegean operation of 1943, and was taken prisoner when the island fell back into German hands.

The main difficulty facing the survey parties was the lack of their own boats. However anxious the Naval Officer in Charge of a newly-captured port may have been to have his port surveyed and an up-to-date chart produced, he could ill spare any boat which may have survived in a seaworthy condition. Boats had to be begged, borrowed, or in a few cases, stolen. DUKWs were obtained fairly late on in the Italian campaign, and proved very effective when fitted with portable echo-sounding gear.

Transport was also a problem, and often had to be improvised on the spot. Perhaps the most outstanding example in the campaign was the journey of Ritchie and his team, ordered from Bizerta in Tunisia to Syracuse immediately after the Sicily landings. They hitched a lift across the water to the western Sicilian port of Licata in a US landing ship, with all their gear in one large crate but with no wheeled transport of their own. In Licata they loaded their precious crate onto a flat- car rail truck and were taken to Ragusa, high in the hills which separated the American and British sectors of the Sicilian operation. At Ragusa they commandeered a train of their own to convey them down to Syracuse in style. The only hitch was that Ritchie was not allowed to leave Ragusa until he had carried out the correct administrative procedure. This he did by writing on a page of his field book 'Received one locomotive, No 4724, one carriage and one box-car', signed it and gave it to the Italian stationmaster. On arrival in the British sector the Royal Engineers in charge of the railway were not best pleased at this intrusion on the part of a team of amateurs onto their permanent way.

Surveys of Syracuse, Augusta and Catania were made while the invasion fleet for southern Italy was gathering, and two Mobile Survey Parties, under Irving and Ritchie, were set up. Irving's was to follow the armies up the west coast of Italy,

Ritchie's the east. One of the east coast party's first tasks was to survey the port of Taranto, during which Hunt's commandeering of a boat which turned out to be the Port Admiral's barge caused dissent between the party and what were by now our allies. On both sides of the peninsula the survey parties entered each small port with the support infantry close behind the spearhead of the attacking forces. Minefields, both land and sea, were a constant hazard. The results of the initial surveys were drawn up on the spot and printed by the Army Corps HQ Map Sections. When the front stabilised, as it did from time to time, the survey parties would return to consolidate their work in ports behind the lines.

Hunt, initially working under Ritchie in the east coast party, was later given an HDML and made surveys of Corfu, and of Zara and other Yugoslav ports after their capture by the Partizans.

Herald had also been at Singapore, laid up and inactive, when Malaya was overrun. An attempt was made to scuttle her before the fall of the fortress, but she was raised, repaired, and taken into service by the Japanese as the patrol vessel *Heiyo*. She was mined in the Java Sea in November 1944.

By the end of 1943 in the Indian Ocean Wyatt as Fleet Hydrographic Officer and also as commanding officer of *Challenger* had been joined by a commander (H) as his assistant, based ashore in Colombo, with a chart production unit (about which more later) at Kandy. Surveys of the Palk Strait were carried out with the idea of using its waters as an exercise and assembly area for Combined Operations craft. Detached parties made surveys of Cox's Bazaar and the Naaf River entrance on the India-Burma border, the latter an interesting exercise as the east bank was in Japanese hands. A covert survey was also made by a special party of the Cocos Islands to allow them to be opened up and used as an advanced air base. It was vital that Japanese air reconnaisance did not detect our interest in the islands before the base was established and able to protect itself.

In June 1944 there was a lull in operations with the onset of the south-west monsoon. It was approved that *Challenger* should proceed to Australia, leaving the Assistant Fleet Hydrographic Officer in charge at Colombo with the yacht *Nguva*, requisitioned earlier in East Africa, to continue the survey of the fleet base at Trincomalee and with a Harbour Defence Motor Launch allocated for any extra commitment which might arise.

In Australia surveys, with a careful sweep of possible obstructions, of the Torres Strait, certain parts of the North East Channel, and Exmouth Gulf were required in case it was necessary to pass aircraft carriers and other large ships round the north of the Australian continent through to the Pacific.

In 1943 the auxiliary patrol vessel *White Bear*, formerly the yacht *Iolanda*, of some 3,000 tons displacement and launched in 1908, was taken over as a second surveying vessel for the Far East, and equipped with a full printing and reproduction outfit complete with compilation and reproduction staff from Taunton who were enlisted as RNVR officers or as Royal Marines. Her completion was delayed because the fitting out of landing craft prior to the Normandy landings was given higher priority, and she did not sail from England, with Sabine in command, until August 1944. She was to have gone directly to Australia via the Panama Canal, to join *Challenger* on her Australian surveys. In the event, with South East Asia Command planning an advance in Burma on the change of monsoon, she was diverted through the Mediterranean to the East Indies. She arrived in Colombo in November 1944, where Day, who had relieved Wyatt in *Challenger* and as FHO, took over from Sabine in command of *White Bear*, and Sabine flew on to Australia to take over *Challenger*.

Almost immediately *White Bear* and her people were involved in the increased level of activity at the onset of the north-east monsoon. The army advanced along the coast from the Naaf River to Ramree and Taungup with continuous naval support. HDML 1248 surveyed for the Army Inland Water Transport on the coastal supply lines, and was among the first craft into Akyab. She later led the assault across the uncharted Hunter's Bay to the Myebon Peninsula. *Nguva* also came forward from Colombo and took soundings in the tortuous narrow chaungs, channels through the coastal mangrove swamps, to allow bombarding sloops to enter them. Surveying personnel were also lent to the minesweepers which led the assaults. Once Akyab had been captured *White Bear* based herself there and acted as the co-ordinating centre for the surveying teams and small craft, printing the results of their surveys and distributing them to the attacking forces.

In March 1945 *White Bear* and all the surveying personnel were withdrawn to Calcutta and Colombo. For the assault on Rangoon surveyors were embarked in minesweepers, in the yacht *Virginia* and in R-craft. The FHO was Force Commander for minesweeping and surveying. After the minesweepers had led the assault convoy into the river the survey parties charted the channels so that larger ships could enter and berth without delay. Though the assault was in the event unopposed, the danger from mines was very real, and one LCT was sunk by a mine.

In the final assault on Malaya *Challenger* was to go with the minesweepers, three HDMLs with the port occupation parties, and *White Bear* in the follow-up. The surrender of Japan brought these operations to a premature close, and the emphasis was switched to rehabilitation surveys.

Throughout the war a very close liaison was maintained between Hydrographer and his staff on the one hand and the Naval Staff on the other. Board members and directors of staff divisions were frequently, and often urgently, in consultation with Hydrographer on operational matters and the supply of charts for special operations. The Assistant Hydrographer and a senior cartographer from Chart Branch continuously discussed details with officers from Operations, Plans, Minesweeping, Trade and Signals divisions, with Combined Operations headquarters, and with the Navigation Division, at that time still under Hydrographer. Requirements could be quickly agreed, and passed to Bath or Taunton for production.

Hydrographer and his Chief Civil Assistant were also able to gain early approval for major projects like the expansion and housing of Chart Branch, the Supplies Establishment and the Royal Observatory.

The problems of amphibious operations always loomed large. Particularly intractable was the need for accurate and up-to-date intelligence on the beaches on which it was planned to land. To plan a successful amphibious operation it is essential to know the gradient and bearing capacity of the beach from a depth of about three fathoms offshore to the hinterland behind the beach, and to obtain the information without a hint of our interest in the particular beach being disclosed. Air photography at low tide could give the information down to the low water mark, but unless there had been recent surveys the gradient to seaward had to be filled by observation, often by a covert operation. Surveyors were attached to the Special Operations Executive for these surveys, of which those before D-Day were only the most famous of many.

The plans for the Department on the outbreak of war were to remove it, lock, stock and barrel, to Bath. Shortly before war actually broke out this was modified to recognise the need for the very close liaison already described, and so provision was made for a Headquarters Staff to remain in Whitehall. However, the whole Cornwall House staff of Chart Branch and Tides, with Sales Branch from Vine Street as well as Sailing Dirctions and part of Chart Branch (A) from the Admiralty itself, left London.

Two neighbouring buildings in the centre of Bath were allocated to the Department, the Royal School and the Laggan, with a third, the Kingswood School, being used as a canteen shared with other rusticated departments. Chart Branch was to be accommodated in the Royal School, with the administrative sections in the Laggan. The Chief Civil Assistant, Llewellyn, and a Higher Clerical Officer were despatched a few days after the declaration of war to fill in the outlines already planned and to arrange billetting for the some 125 people involved. A Chief Cartographer and one draughtsman followed on 14 September, to arrange the space at the Royal School to the best advantage. The main body of Chart Branch, with 9 crates each 6 feet in length and as many smaller ones with the papers and equipment needed immediately on arrival, travelled on 21 September. Most of the people in the main body did not know, when they boarded the train at Paddington, where their destination was to be! A retard party remained at Cornwall House to deal with urgent operational work, and to pack and send on the rest of the papers and equipment, including the irreplaceable original documents, many dating back to Cook's days. The whole move was completed by the end of October, and little important work had been delayed or disrupted during the process of moving.

Compared to the well-established conditions at Cornwall House the arrangements at the Royal School were primitive. Sections were deliberately mixed up, so that damage from enemy action would not result in the loss of the whole of any single vital operation. Those who worked there found that this led to an excellent working relationship between branches and people who might have little to do with each other back in London. This, together with the wartime atmosphere, made for an excellent esprit de corps which Edgell and first Jones and then Nares as AH(1) deliberately fostered. Living in commandeered billets in the city, the staff could walk to work. In the icy winter of 1940 the hilly streets of Bath were only passable with thick socks pulled over one's shoes to give a grip on the slippery slopes, but most people made it in to work each day. The senior staff insisted on pre-war standards of accuracy and checking which some of the newcomers found irksome. The temporary recruits also, not knowing the background, found what they considered an inordinate sensitivity on the question of cartographers' pay. As we have seen, this was to some extent ameliorated by the pay award of December 1940.

By 1941 the Royal School was becoming overcrowded, and in November the whole Department moved again, this time only a couple of miles to the newly-constructed hutments at Ensleigh on the high ground at the top of Lansdown Hill. While the more spacious conditions were appreciated, the long climb in wheezy wartime busses was not as pleasant a way to get to work as the walk through the centre of Bath to the School.

In formulating the role of Chart Branch in war the following outlines were drawn early in 1939:

(a) All work already in hand should be completed.

(b) New charts and other work should be held in abeyance until instructed to proceed, to free effort for operational tasks.

(c) Heavy demands from the Fleet should be expected.

(d) Much increased reference to original documents would be required by officers both within and from outside the Department.

(e) Personnel would have to be re-organised to cover the war areas.

(f) Additional staff would have to be transferred to Production Division to speed output.

(g) Temporary staff would have to be entered to boost numbers.

This proved a remarkably accurate prediction. The two major difficulties were due to the already large arrears of chart maintenance work, and the difficulty of acquiring the necessary number and quality of extra personnel.

As has been mentioned in Chapter 3, the arrears of work brought about by the diversion of staff from navigational chart maintenance in the First World War were never completely recovered because of the reductions in staff imposed on Hydrographer after the Armistice in 1918. In the Second World War the need to concentrate on work of immediate operational importance meant that other areas slipped further and further out of date. Little could be done about this, but it had the effect that when a new theatre of war came into prominence much effort had to be devoted to bringing forward information which should have been incorporated on the charts as it was received.

The recruiting of additional cartographers had been begun in 1938 with a trawl of University geographical departments for suitable candidates. This continued during 1939 and 1940, but the supply never managed to meet the demand, either of degree-qualified cartographers or of draughtsmen. The problem was aggravated by two factors. One was that the Army and the Royal Air Force took cartographers and draughtsmen for mapping and air photographic interpretation, but put them into uniform, which was more attractive to young men in wartime. The second factor was the continuing disgracefully low rates of pay for cartographers, which was only remedied in 1946.

As the Naval Staff expanded there was a heavy demand for special charts. For example, a series of small-scale charts on the gnomonic projection was required for plotting bearings obtained by radio direction finding of raiders and U-boats.

Until 1938 it had been anticipated that Britain would become involved in the war in the Far East already raging between Japan and China before hostilities broke out in Europe, and charting activity had concentrated on the Pacific. When the war came in Europe a requirement arose to produce rapidly a set of some 180 large-scale navigational charts of the Mediterranean. In addition, because of the inadequacy of our own charts resort had to be made to photo-reproducing large-scale foreign charts, with all the disadvantages of language and different symbology that entailed for the users. Some 2,000 of these foreign charts were reproduced during the war, with special abbreviation sheets which served to reduce the inconvenience to some extent.

Another early commitment was to produce gridded charts for the various theatres of war. By 1943 these had developed into Chart Maps, which showed very full land detail as well as the usual hydrographic features. They were printed in as many as six colours, each of which had to be drawn separately. To speed production Chart Maps were drawn directly by Chart Branch draughtsmen and not re-drawn by Production draughtsmen before being reproduced for printing.

An Air Chart series had been started in July 1937, just as the Navy was regaining full control of the Fleet Air Arm from the RAF. By the outbreak of war 36 of these charts, 17 inches square on a scale of 1:1,000,000, had been produced. This total was to rise to some 508 by the end of the war, with a further 87 on the smaller scale of 1:2,000,000.

Various other series were also produced, including latticed charts for use with the electronic position fixing systems which began to enter service in the later years of the war. A 'Summary of Special Charts and Publications Produced by the Hydrographic Department 1939-1945' was produced as CB 3200 in 1946.

The whole Department at Bath was under the charge of a captain (H) as Assistant Hydrographer (1)*, with a naval Superintendent of Chart Branch, a Superintending

---

*To confuse matters the titles of the two Assistant Hydrographers, (1) at Bath and (2) in Whitehall, were reversed in February 1942. After that date AH(1) was in Whitehall and AH(2) at Bath.

Organisation at Wartime Peak, 1944/45
(At Admiralty or as shown)

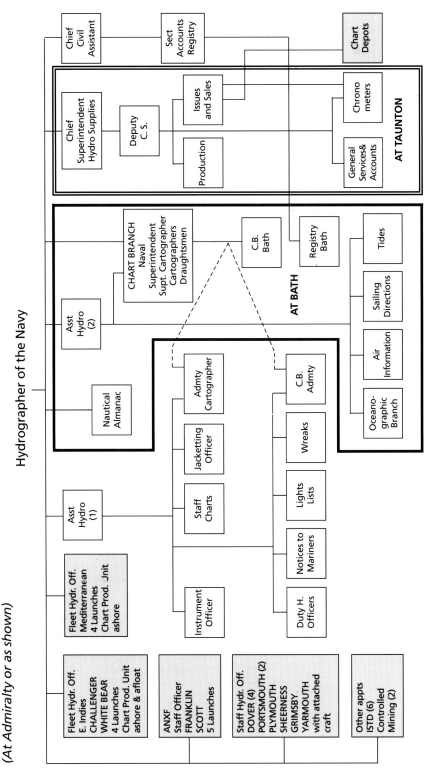

Cartographer and an ever-increasing number of cartographers, draughtsmen, naval assistants and clerical staff under him.

Remaining in Whitehall, as well as the staff engaged in direct liaison with the operational divisions, were the branches concerned with the more immediate types of navigational information; that which required promulgation by signal or in Notices to Mariners. They were, in no particular order, Chart Branch (Admiralty), Wrecks, Light Lists, Notices to Mariners, Territorial Waters Officer, Jacketting Officer and the Instrument Officer, with the Officer in Charge of Staff Charts and the Duty Officer who both maintained a twenty-four hour service. There was also a small secretariat and registry to keep the paperwork tidy.

Before going into the work of these various branches it is necessary to spell out the principle which governed all promulgation of hydrographic information during the war. This was to keep out of the public domain any information which could be of value to the enemy, while ensuring that British and Allied warships and merchantmen received everything which they needed to assure their safe navigation.

It was difficult to satisfy both sides in this conflict of interests, and the basic method adopted built on the experience of the First World War.

All new information likely to be of use to the enemy was promulgated in Fleet Notices to Mariners, initially classified 'For Official Use Only' but later upgraded to Confidential. These notices quoted normal sales charts, and Naval recipients corrected their copies of unclassified navigational charts accordingly. These Fleet Notices were printed in red ink*, and were known as 'Red' Notices to distinguish them from the unclassified Notices printed in normal black ink and known as 'Black' Notices. These latter were still issued, though in smaller numbers than before the war.

The Hydrographic Supplies Establishment corrected the chart plates, and thereafter charts for sale or for issue to the Fleet, from both Black and Red Notices, so that the closely-supervised sales to ships and others allowed to buy charts in wartime carried all the amendments. The possibility of sales charts getting into the wrong hands existed, but it was argued that no unauthorised recipient would easily recognise what was new and significant, and that in any case the delay before the amended chart reached any such recipient would greatly reduce if not entirely remove any security risk.

To cover British and Allied merchant ships, Naval Control of Shipping Officers and routeing authorities transcribed the relevant details from Fleet Notices into Route Instructions. This was not entirely satisfactory, and it was recognised that after a time merchant ships could be carrying charts which lacked important corrections.

---

*Changed to magenta in 1944 to be readable under red lighting in darken ship conditions. At the same time other red printing on charts and publications was changed to magenta, and the colour of light flashes on charts was changed from orange to violet.

As well as the printed Notices, there were a number of series of radio navigational warnings. The local broadcasts issued by the Admiralty in conjunction with the Board of Trade pre-war were discontinued, while the plain-language 'W' messages issued by the Navy on each station were kept in being though greatly reduced, corresponding to the Black Notices to Mariners which were still issued in small numbers to the world at large. To the 'Q' Message system, developed as a classified system to promulgate routing and mine danger information, was added a 'Q-H' series for classified hydrographic information, which worked for urgent information exactly as the Red Notices operated for less urgent data. From 1943 a joint Anglo-American system of Naveams, Hydrolants and Hydropacs was developed which grew into the post-war radio warning system with world-wide coverage. Once the information, if of a permanent nature, was incorporated on the chart; or if ephemeral the danger had passed, the radio warning was cancelled.

On some stations, where there was a Fleet Hydrographic Office, a local series of warnings was issued. These could be sent to the Admiralty with a 'Request for Notice to Mariners', and again would be cancelled once the information had been incorporated onto the printed charts.

Chart Branch (Admiralty) began the war, after the move of the main Chart Branch to Bath, with two retired naval officers (former surveyors) and four draughtsmen. This soon had to be increased to three officers and eight draughtsmen. As well as the drawing for all Notices to Mariners work, the Branch produced special charts such as the top secret charts of our minefields, and a series of wreck charts. Complete sets of charts, corrected up to date, were kept for Admiralty staff to take and use in operational planning. These had been increased from the peacetime level of six copies to a maximum of twenty in the areas where action was expected. Demands on them were heavy, and keeping them corrected when large numbers were returned after activity shifted was a constant problem. Eventually only eight sets were kept up to date, and the remainder stamped 'Not to be Used for Navigation'.

One series of special charts produced for the first time in 1942 were the Ships' Boat Charts, a set of very small scale charts covering the world's oceans packed in waterproof covers and issued through the Ministry of Transport to all merchant ships for placing in ships' lifeboats. They were the brainchild of one of the temporary cartographers, Mr A A L Caesar, who was gratified later in the war to receive letters from mariners who owed their lives to these charts.

While the separation of CB(A) from the main Branch at Bath was sometimes acutely felt, the close liaison with the Naval Staff divisions was essential to the planning and fighting of the war at sea, and the services of CB(A) were invaluable.

In the organisation for war there had been no more than a thought that there would be a need for a comprehensive list of wrecks promulgated periodically, probably as a Fleet Notice to Mariners. Sinkings soon beame heavy, and one officer was employed solely on keeping full records and promulgating details. Moreover, with home waters coming fully under Admiralty control it was the local naval authority's responsibility to mark or to remove wrecks. Admiralty approval was required before buoys were laid, and when wrecks lay near swept channels it was often possible to use the channel buoys in a double role, thus conserving the stock of buoys.

Wrecks dangerous to navigation were promulgated by Red Notice, starting with a Preliminary Notice when, as was normal, details were initially lacking. A Black Notice was issued after one month, the Naval Staff having agreed to this so that all merchant ships should have this vital information. If the wreck had neither been sunk by enemy action nor lay in or near a swept channel the original Notice could be Black. The names of ships sunk were treated as Confidential in the case of merchant ships and Secret for warships, and did not normally appear in Notices. Wreck buoys were usually put onto charts by Red Notice, and only rarely by Black Notice.

Non-dangerous wrecks were not shown on navigational charts, though their details, where known, were fully recorded. It was not long, though, before there were requests from sea, which were backed by the Naval Staff, for this information. Anti-submarine ships hunting submarines with Asdic wanted to know where to expect echoes from objects on the sea bed. A series of 20 charts covering British waters was therefore produced showing all wreck and 'non-sub' echoes in over three fathoms of water. A Wreck List corrected by monthly supplements was also produced, which gave the names of merchant ship wrecks, though for warships only 'HM Ship' was given. Charts and lists were initially issued in February 1940, and their maintenance occupied one cartographer full time.

As soon as war broke out many navigational lights were extinguished, or were only exhibited at reduced power or for a limited time. It had been envisaged that the requirement to promulgate these limitations would be covered by a monthly supplement to the normal Lists of Lights. In the event a special publication, HD 335 'Navigational Aids in War', was produced, and kept corrected by its own section in the Notices to Mariners. HD 335 only covered home waters, naval stations abroad being responsible for promulgating information about their own lighting restrictions by station message, Notices or memoranda. A manuscript master set of Light Lists was kept in the Department to record all these matters, for Office use in compiling and correcting charts.

The post of Officer in Charge of Staff Charts was instituted very early in the war, with a room in the Citadel and a staff of one commander (H), three Reserve officers and two draughtsmen. His job was to keep a fully corrected set of world-wide charts, sailing directions and other publications available for personal reference by departments and divisions of the Naval Staff. The charts, besides being corrected for navigational changes, showed secret information concerning searched channels, coastal routes, mined areas, booms, underwater defences and all other artifacts of war. Not only Allied material was shown. All such data as was available about enemy or neutral war material was also portrayed on these charts, and records were kept from which the state of affairs in any locality on any date after November 1939 could be reconstructed.

At first Divisions were instructed not to circulate relevant papers to OCSC, but to extract the information which he needed and to send it to him. This was soon abandoned, and all staff papers with any navigational content were sent to him. The Staff Chart Room was open day and night, and soon became, as was intended, the navigational reference point for the whole War Staff. The questions put to OSCS were limitless in both number and variety. 'When was Q message number XXX cancelled and by what?' 'What is the authority by which xx buoy was established?' 'Is fishing permitted in position X?' 'What time is moonrise at xxxx?' 'Does Commander in Chief Xxx issue local reprints of xxx?'

To avoid total disruption if the Citadel was damaged or destroyed a second set of publications was kept up to date by a staff of two Reserve officers in the shadow Admiralty at Cricklewood.

Before the war the Territorial Waters Officer was mainly concerned with problems of territorial water limits and the allied subject of monitoring national and international prohibitions to navigation in waters outside those limits. His interests also included questions of fisheries limits, discovery and sovereignty, and liaison with the International Hydrographic Bureau. Though all these subjects remained within his purview in wartime, the volume of work naturally greatly reduced in all cases. TWO assumed responsibility for the various charts produced to show surface and deep minefields, both Allied and Axis, and the swept channels in home waters. Stemming naturally from his pre-war responsibilities, he was also charged with recording and promulgating declared dangerous areas to navigation in accordance with international maritime law.

Like TWO, the Instrument Officer's prewar duty of arranging the supply of the necessary instruments to surveying ships to allow them to conduct the surveys ordered by Hydrographer continued in war. It was, though, vastly complicated by the need to equip the various special parties, units and officers detached to support operations and local area commanders. The surveying instruments were kept at Cricklewood before the war, but were moved to Exeter in May 1940 for safety. They were returned to Cricklewood in May 1942.

The Duty Officer was instituted at the outbreak of war, using those officers available. The manning of this post was, once the war organisation was run in, provided by the Instrument Officer (in addition to his other duties) and two retired (H) officers. They kept watch throughout the 24 hours, and were responsible for answering all queries or referring them to the relevant branch of the Department; for issuing radio navigational warnings of all types, frequently having to re-draft them into the standard format; and to ensure that all telegrams and signals addressed to Hydrographer were distributed to the appropriate branch including the Hydrographic Supplies Establishment. They were to the Department what OCSC was to the Naval Staff, and there was much overlapping between the two.

Having seen how the requirements for navigational information were formulated and the resulting charts and publications drafted, it is now necessary to look at the way in which those publications were printed and distributed during the war, and the effects of enemy action on the steady supply to the Fleet and the forces minimised.

At the outbreak of war Reproduction, Printing and Issues were concentrated in the Admiralty Chart Establishment at Cricklewood. A plan had been floated (see chapter 4) to concentrate the Department at Taunton, but this was a long-term project for which the first foundations had not yet been laid. Accommodation outside London was required both to meet the increasing requirements and also to provide cover against damage to the Cricklewood establishment.

A scan of likely contractors soon showed that there was simply not the capacity within the printing trade with enough machines of sufficient size to be able to handle bulk printing of Admiralty charts. Moreover, the need for proofing to allow last-minute corrections to the printing zincs required a special organisation. Contracting out the extra printing and providing for dispersion by this means was therefore ruled out.

Additional printing machines had already been installed at Cricklewood to cope with the work of increasing the reserve stocks of charts. On the outbreak of war approval was given to buy additional machinery, and to requisition five buildings in Exeter. This location was chosen as the nearest litho printing centre to Taunton, and as less likely to be subject to severe bombing than the next nearest, Bristol. This proximity was important, as approval was given to proceed with the Taunton establishment in December 1939, design was quickly completed and construction began in March 1940, and it was always the aim to concentrate at least the printing and distribution at Taunton as soon as practicable.

By November 1939 the Exeter plan was sufficiently advanced for staff to begin to move there. During 1940 all engravers and copper plate printers, as well as a proportion of the litho draughtsmen, printers and photographic staff, were moved from Cricklewood. As at Bath the scene was one of improvisation far from the well-established routine of Cricklewood. Problems like the need to cope with frozen printing ink in an unheated building, or the liberal watering of fresh litho plates by a family of cats which had made their home among the stock, tested both the ingenuity and the sense of humour of the staff.

In the meantime the ravages of war, and the increasing risk of invasion, stimulated further dispersal. By November 1940 a useful group of disused printing machinery of a suitable size for printing charts had been found at Nottingham, and despite the fear of bomb damage in a large city it was requisitioned and put into working order for use in an emergency. In the event it was Exeter which suffered from enemy bombing, though fortunately not until the move into permanent quarters at Taunton was well under way. Two of the five buildings originally occupied, one of them still with some equipment and work being done in it, were destroyed in the raid of the night of 3 to 4 May 1942. By then additional emergency premises had also been set up at Ironbridge (Shropshire) and Armadale (West Lothian). Ironbridge was also used as a second major chart depot, where stocks were kept and some of the load of hand correcting taken from Taunton. Armadale was equipped with the surviving machinery from Exeter after the bombing there, for use in emergency.

Even when Taunton was brought into full operation at the end of June 1941, the establishments at Nottingham, Ironbridge and Armadale were kept open. While Ironbridge concentrated on its work as a chart depot, a wide variety of printing was done by both Nottingham and Armadale, relieving the pressure on Taunton when demands exceeded the capacity of that establishment. Cricklewood, too, had never been entirely evacuated, and bore a charmed life, going through the whole war without serious bomb damage despite its position close to the railway marshalling yards which were a prime target.

Throughout the war a major preoccupation was the safety of the original plates of the navigational and Fleet charts. Almost all of them were copper engravings, some dating back over one hundred years and all subject to hand correction. While reconstruction from paper proofs or the zinc printing plates would have been possible, precision would have been lost and much valuable time consumed. At the beginning of the war they were transferred from their quite unprotected home at Cricklewood to the underground vaults of a neighbouring building. In January 1940 they were taken by lorry to a special stowage prepared for them at Exeter. With the total weight of metal in excess of 70 tons, and every plate needing careful handling to avoid scratches or other damage, this was a major undertaking. At Taunton, where they found their final resting place in 1942, the expense of an underground stowage was not allowed, and their safety remained a matter for concern until the end of the war in Europe.

Measures were taken to ensure that any damage to the plate collection would not cause delay in chart production. It has already been told how, in the last years before the war, the method of printing was changed from flat-bed printing directly from the coppers or litho stones to offset printing from zinc plates. This not only made the printing process much faster; it also allowed the copper originals and the printing zincs to be kept in different parts of the building when they were both housed in the same establishment. With the move of the coppers to Exeter at the beginning of 1940, a start was made on producing a duplicate set of printing zincs. Despite difficulties, mainly in devising a system for keeping both sets fully corrected up to date, by April 1941 a third set of zincs, to be kept at Armadale, was started.

During the changes in printing techniques in the late 1930s one introduction, seemingly of little importance at the time, was the use of baryta-coated paper to obtain proofs from the coppers which were particularly clear and sharp. Baryta proofs of the whole world-wide series were made and kept, first at Plymouth and Bath, and later at Nottingham and in Canada. The scheme was also later extended to provide sets of baryta proofs covering their own areas to the various Fleet

Hydrographic Offices, Dominion Hydrographic Offices and the United States Hydrographic Office. Not only did this ensure against invasion of the United Kingdom homeland, but it also enabled stocks of fairly satisfactory charts to be printed locally if supplies from the Department at home were lost or delayed in transit.

Printing the charts was only part of the service provided by the Department. A stock of charts is useless if it cannot be got to the ships and the staffs which need them. It has always been Hydrographer's policy that charts should be fully corrected up to the date of sale or issue, and that is even more important in time of war, when busy staffs or ships' hard-pressed navigators have not time to insert large quantities of corrections on receipt of a new batch of charts.

The increase of stocks at the time of re-armament has already been mentioned, with the removal of the supply organisation to Park Royal and its erection into a Division of its own. Even before the outbreak of war unexpected demands were being received, such as the requisition for 60,000 charts ordered for cross-channel transports to be supplied in August 1939, for which one month's notice was given.

In the dispersal in September 1939, the Central Chart Depot was moved to requisitioned premises in Taunton, followed by a further move to Exeter in June 1940. The last move came in June 1941, when Production, Supplies and Sales Divisions were once again co-located at the new Creechbarrow House at Taunton. At that time Supplies Division took over responsibility for the issues of chronometers and watches, and was renamed Issues Division. Later, in July 1942, the post of Superintendent of Sales was abolished, and the Superintendent of Issues became responsible for sales as well as for issues to the Fleet.

Initial outfits of charts, and the supply of new editions and new charts to keep a ship's outfit up to date, remained direct from the Central Chart Depot. Nevertheless, the number of emergency requirements from ships and staffs was limitless, and the number of chart depots at the ports was increased accordingly. To the five home and six overseas* depots in existence at the start of 1939, Cardiff, Liverpool, Newcastle, Portland, Grimsby and Colombo were added early in 1939, followed at the end of the year by Kingston, Jamaica. In February 1940 a depot was opened at Freetown, Sierra Leone, and in the autumn at Alexandria and Saltcoats. Portland was closed, and Kingston transferred to Bermuda. In 1941 Ironbridge and Exeter were opened. In December of that year Hong Kong and Singapore were lost, and Kilindini (Mombasa) set up to replace them. As late as February 1944 a new depot was opened at Bombay to cater for the needs of the expeditions mounted by South East Asia Command. Last of all was the floating depot set up in the Fleet Supply Ship *Aorangi* with the British Pacific Fleet Train. For this duty two chart depot assistants were given temporary RNVR commissions.

---

*Cricklewood, Portsmouth, Plymouth, Rosyth and Sheerness at home, Gibraltar, Malta, Port Said, Simonstown, Singapore and Hong Kong overseas.

As with the cartographers, the poor rates of pay proved a hindrance to recruitment and retention of staff for the Chart Depot Service. Young men Assistants were not exempt from military service, and many experienced men were lost at a time when they could ill be spared. Fortunately this had to some extent been foreseen, and the practice of employing women started early in 1939.

Liaison with the Naval Staff was essential here as in so many other hydrographic areas, to allow intelligent anticipation of heavy demands, and the Superintendent of Supplies made frequent visits to the Admiralty, both for direct talks with the Operations and Plans Divisions and to keep in close touch with the Department's headquarters staff.

Dunkirk brought the first heavy and urgent demand, if one of very brief duration. Single charts rather than folios were needed by the host of small craft taking part in the evacuation. Transport was as big a problem as any, and road transport was generally used. One telephone demand for charts for Harwich was met from Park Royal within three hours, one hour of which was spent finding a suitable vehicle.

By 1943 the normal commercial arrangements for supplying charts to merchant ships were breaking down. At the request of the Ministry of Transport chart outfits were supplied on loan to all ocean-going British ships not already requisitioned. A special series of chart folios was established for this purpose, and arrangements made for the outfits to be landed as necessary for correction up to date by the chart depots free of charge.

Learning from the experience of the First World War, the supply and issue of chronometers was closely controlled from the outset of the war. Only one firm, Mercers of St Albans, remained in Britain in the business of manufacturing marine chronometers, and supplies throughout the war had to be obtained from Switzerland to augment their output. This had its problems. Watches came from their Swiss makers through neutral Spain, and on one occasion the expected box arrived, to be found when it was opened to contain only sand.

The system was strained by a demand for a thousand chronometers from the United States when they entered the war, as chronometers of suitable quality were not made in America. Though procurement sufficed for British requirements there seemed little chance of meeting the American requirement in full. Stringent restrictions were imposed. With the exception of foreign-going surveying ships no vessel, naval or mercantile, was allowed to carry more than one chronometer, and many second-hand chronometers were purchased or given by their owners following a broadcast appeal. Several consignments were despatched to the States, and it was with great relief that it was learnt, before the British stocks had been completely drained, that an American firm had started production.

In 1944 Hydrographer became responsible for supplying wrist and stop watches to Naval Aircrew. This involved obtaining and issuing thousands of watches to pilots and observers, and later to Telegraphist Air Gunners. Initially separate wrist and stop watches were issued, but in 1945 the chronograph wrist watch with a 'stop' mechanism was introduced to replace both earlier types. All these watches came from Switzerland.

Considerable difficulty was experienced in keeping track of all the chronometers and watches. Though the standing instructions required reports annually and on certain other specified occasions, in the heat of war this was honoured as much in the breach as in the observance, and such reports as did come to hand often lacked precision and accuracy. At the end of the war strenuous attempts were made to account for all the timepieces issued, but it was necessary in the end to write off more than 2,000, mainly the smaller watches. This represented some 10% of the timepieces on the books.

The activities of the surveying ships overseas have already been dealt with. It is now time to look at the shore organisations set up abroad to provide hydrographic services to the fleets on their respective stations. Essentially their aims were all the same, though the method of execution varied to suit local conditions.

The task of the Fleet Hydrographic Officer and his unit was to provide his Commander in Chief with special charts produced locally, carry out operational and other surveys with such craft as were available, sift and promulgate incoming navigational information, and advise on all matters connected with hydrography.

In the Mediterranean a commander (H), Southern, was appointed as FHO in February 1940. Italy was not yet in the war, and the fleet was as yet small though already based, since the Abyssinian crisis, at Alexandria. As before, the help of the Survey of Egypt was sought, and freely given throughout the war. From 1941 a cartographer from the Hydrographic Department was attached to the Survey at Giza. Since Egypt was an independent country which was not, technically, at war, the relationship was a delicate one, but with tact and understanding no trouble was ever experienced.

Initially the major task was to produce large numbers of gridded charts of operational areas for the use of ships on coastal operations, and for the reporting and recording of intelligence. Foreign charts of larger scale than the Admirlaty charts also had to be reproduced. Soon, when Italy entered the war in June 1940 and convoys were diverted round the Cape, the Fleet Hydrographic Office was to be more or less isolated from the home Department. For over two months no mail or supplies were received from the United Kingdom. Stocks of navigational charts dwindled, and since baryta proofs were not yet available normal printed charts had to be copied by photo-lithography.

A second surveying officer joined in June 1941 as assistant to the FHO. Activity in the eastern Mediterranean was intense, with the Greek and Syrian campaigns as well as the ongoing fighting along the North African coast. Demands for surveys were correspondingly heavy, and the *Arpha*, a 600 ton former pleasure steamer built in 1901, was allocated to FHO. With some improvisation she carried out useful work with AFHO and a surveying recorder embarked. Even after *Endeavour* appeared on the scene in 1942 there was much work for both FHO and his assistant away from the office.

19 H.S.E. *Taunton from the air*

Two views of the Hydrographic Supplies Establishment, Taunton as built. Though only the printing works was built in 1940, the extent of the land bought, which allowed for later expansion, can be seen in the upper photgraph.

20 H.S.E. *Taunton from the ground*

21 Surveying during the war, *Scott* was armed with a 3″ AA gun and smaller weapons and was camouflaged. Here she is at Harwich in 1941. (Imperial War Museum)

22 The old coal-burning *Kellett,* paid off in 1938, was armed and re-commissioned as a minesweeper when war broke out. She is shown in Plymouth Sound in 1942. (Imperial War Museum)

23 Ship sounding from the bridge of *Scott*, taken from the crow's nest on her foremast in the immediate post-war years.

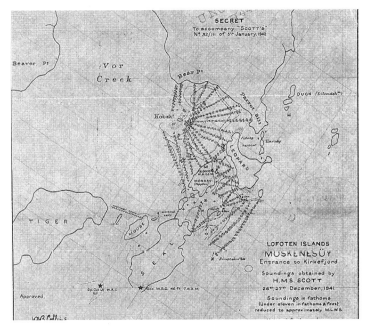

24 Survey of the entrance to Kirkefjord on the island of Moskenes in the Lofotens, made by *Scott* on 26 and 27 December 1941, during Operation ANKLET.

25 HDML 1248, one of the motor launches used for surveying in the Bay of Bengal to support the Army's advance down the coast of Burma in 1945.

26 The converted yacht *White Bear*, fitted with chart printing equipment and sent out to the South East Asia command in 1944.

27   Lieutenant N. C. Glen and his crew in an LCP(S) off the Arromanches Mulberry on 9 June 1944. The QH receiver is visible on the pole carrying the survey flag. (IMPERIAL WAR MUSEUM)

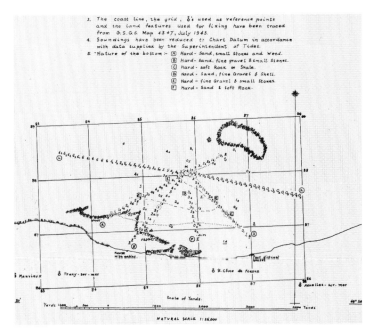

28 Tracing rendered to Hydrographer of the soundings taken by Berncastle and Glen on the night of 27 November 1943 at the planned position of Mulberry B, off Arromanches.

29   Chart published on 28 July 1944 of the Arromanches Mulberry (B), showing blockships and jetties. As piers and jetties changed and weather shifted the blockships, frequent new editions were produced.

30   The pilot vessel *Astral* was first a balloon escort and then allocated to the survey officer at Great Yarmouth. She was with the assault forces on D Day. (IMPERIAL WAR MUSEUM)

31   This view of the Penfeld at Brest, taken by Leading Seaman L Gawan of *Scott* in August 1944, shows the conditions the survey parties faced on arrival in a devastated port. (L. GAWAN)

32 The SMLs did sterling service at the end of the war, marking wrecks and surveying the shifting sandbanks off the east coast. SML 325 in 1951. (WORLD SHIP SCOCIETY)

33 *Franklin* in March 1946, the only ship to have the heavy rubbing strake aft, to cushion the SMLs attached to her for the east coast surveys.
(IMPERIAL WAR MUSEUM)

When, at the time of Rommel's furthest advance in the summer of 1942, it appeared that the Delta might be overrun, the Fleet Hydrographic Office withdrew from Alexandria to Suez from June to October.

With the landings in Algeria a new Fleet Hydrographic Officer, Mediterranean, Southern again, returning now as a captain, was appointed to the staff of the Commander in Chief in Algiers, Jones remaining at Alexandria as FHO Levant, a title later amended to Staff HO, Levant. The main bulk of local chart production was still done at Giza, but some printing work was done at Algiers by Military Survey printers.

FHO was in overall charge of the survey parties working at the front as the Allied armies advanced through Sicily and Italy whose activities have already been noticed in the section on surveying operations. FHO went himself with the landings in the south of France in August 1944 to survey the ports of Toulon and Marseilles to re-open them for shipping, since his people were already fully occupied elsewhere.

In the Far East only a small surveying unit was left after the surveying ships had been paid off and their personnel dispersed at the outbreak of the war in Europe. It consisted of two officers, one surveying recorder and a 28-foot boat with its crew. They made surveys for the naval base and its defence. The officer in charge, Beech Thomas, was drowned when trying to save the crew of another craft which had run onto one of our own mines, and Menzies sent out from England to replace him.

In the *sauve-qui-peut* as Singapore fell the survey party commandeered the Straits Steamship Line steamer *Darvel*, loading their boat on board and, by way of paying their passage, replacing the native crew most of whom had deserted on the approach of the Japanese. After touching at Batavia they finally arrived safely at Colombo, where they remained as the Colombo Survey Unit until the arrival of *Challenger* in May 1943.

While *Challenger* had been at Mombasa she had not only produced charts from her own surveys of Port Kilindini and its approaches. She had also arranged for the production by the East African Survey at Nairobi of gridded charts and maps required by the Eastern Fleet. Her commanding officer, Wyatt, held the appointment of FHO, Eastern Fleet.

With the revival of British fortunes in the Indian Ocean *Challenger* moved from Mombasa to Colombo. FHO sent the commander from the Colombo Survey Unit, Menzies, to Delhi to represent him at South East Asia headquarters, and started planning for a chart production unit. This started in a modest way in November 1943 when Hoborough, who had been the first of the hydrographic cartographers with the Survey of Egypt in Cairo, went to Dehra Dun with two draughtsmen. Though the Survey of India officers were very co-operative two factors militated against the long-term use of Dehra Dun as the seat of the chart production unit. One was the difficulty of ensuring security in a civilian establishment. This could have been overcome. What was insuperable was the distance of Dehra Dun from the theatre of operations and the Supreme Commander's staff. So in August 1944 the chart production unit moved to Ceylon, to premises close to SEAC headquarters at Kandy, where it remained until the end of the war.

The final organisation comprised the Fleet Hydrographic Office at Colombo manned by AFHO, a junior reserve officer, a secretary, a typist and one survey recorder. The chart production unit had a cartographer in charge, holding an RNVR special commission, a WRNS officer curator, two WRNS secretarial ratings, one CSM and 12 other ranks Royal Engineers on loan from the Director of Surveys, India; 7 cartographic draughtsmen from the Hydrographic Department enlisted as Royal marines tradesmen, and 12 naval ratings. In addition there was the production unit in the *White Bear,* with three cartographers with RNVR commissions and six production staff from Taunton as RM tradesmen. At SEAC headquarters at Kandy there was also Menzies, in close touch with all three and able to give warning of future operations so that the necessary publications could be prepared in good time.

A good example of the requirements met by the units is the programme of work for Operation ZIPPER, the assault on the coast of Malaya on 9 September 1945. There were to be eight chart maps, a fighter direction chart, a series of tidal diagrams and a set of radar PPI predictions with chartlets. Drawing began in May. Proofs were issued in the third week in July, and printing began on 23rd. 2,250 copies of six chart maps, each in six colours, with an operational overprint on three of them, were printed by 9 August. Then the magnitude of the distribution problem and the need to produce more navigational charts made it necessary to cancel the last two chart maps. Land maps to the tune of 170,000 sheets weighing over 5 tons also had to be demanded and distributed.

There were no less than 23 different scales of distribution, with a total of over 900 separate packages to be made up and despatched. Two deliveries were made to Colombo on 20 and 24 August for ships at Colombo, Bombay, Madras, Vizagapatam, Mandapam and Calcutta, and two deliveries to Trincomalee on 23 and 28 August.

This was a considerable operation for a small unit far from home. It pales into insignificance, though, beside the effort required at home for the invasion of Europe, which deserves a chapter of its own.

CHAPTER SIX

Overlord and after

Vice Admiral Sir John Edgell, KBE, CB

The work of the Hydrographic Service, both afloat and ashore, in support of the invasion of Europe in the summer of 1944 was of an entirely different order of magnitude from that called forth by any other single operation or series of operations. It, and the follow-up work of the surveying ships as the Allied armies advanced eastward along the coasts of France and the Low Countries, need a separate chapter if the one on the war is not to be unduly large or the tale cut unjustifiably short.

When planning started for the return to the continent of Europe in 1942, a commander (H), Collins, was appointed to the naval staff formed for the purpose in Norfolk House. Part of this staff, including the Staff Officer (H), was soon diverted to the planning of the landings first in North Africa (TORCH), followed by those in Sicily (HUSKY), but the long-term main purpose of the staff remained the cross-channel operation, NEPTUNE (the codename for the first, maritime phase of OVERLORD, the whole operation of invading and maintaining Allied forces in Europe).

The experience gained in earlier amphibious operations, from Dunkirk onwards, was invaluable in planning NEPTUNE, but the landing by the Allies on the north coast of France was a much vaster undertaking, in terms of scale, risks and importance, than anything contemplated hitherto. The scope of the operation can be seen from the opening words of the Operation NEPTUNE Naval Orders :

> 'The object of Operation NEPTUNE is to carry out an operation from the United Kingdom to secure a lodgement on the Continent from which further operations can be developed. This lodgement area must contain sufficient port facilities to maintain a force of 26 to 30 divisions and enable this force to be augmented by follow-up formations at the rate of three to five divisions a month.'

The full story of the invasion, from planning to execution, has been told so often and so fully that there is no need to repeat it here. However, little has been said in any account that I have seen of the hydrographic aspects of NEPTUNE, though they were vital to its success. This is perhaps understandable as no Hydrographic Appendix was provided either in the Operation Neptune Naval Orders or in the Allied Naval Commander in Chief Expeditionary Force's Report on the operation. This is because it was felt that all hydrographic matters were in the hands of Hydrographer, who would, as in the case of TORCH and HUSKY, take steps to ensure that requirements would be met for, and lessons drawn from, the operation.

A 'NEPTUNE Hydrographic Report' was made by SOH to Edgell, though the Hydrographic Department seems no longer to have copies of it. I have had to reconstruct the events and considerations of the day from the section on NEPTUNE in the general unpublished account of the activity of the Department in the war, personal recollections of those serving at the time, and such miscellaneous papers as have survived. Successive Hydrographers, from Douglas through to Day, have shown extreme reluctance to publicise their work at the time it was being done. This has over the years, and not least in the war and immediate post-war periods, encouraged the general service attitude which accepts that the Hydrographic Department is equal to any task imposed upon it, and that complete reliance can be placed in any product emanating from it. It also means that it was very difficult, even at the time, to discover whether any innovations provide what the user really wants. For example, the chart-maps developed first for HUSKY were said by users in conversation to be just what was needed, but no report was ever sent to Hydrographer stating this. The presence of SOH on the ANCXF's staff from the earliest stages was vital to the timely provision of the material needed by the invasion fleet. A full statement of requirements was never made by the planners. Collins had to keep himself acquainted with all the plans and projects. He had to deduce the needs of first the planners and then the forces to be involved for charts and other publications, and for any new types of information. Then he had to make arrangements with the Department for getting them produced and distributed.

Security was always a worry. Too many copies of charts of the Bay of the Seine being drawn from the shelf stocks of charts in CB(A) by staff officers working on the plans would have drawn unwelcome attention to the area. It was therefore arranged that all chart demands had to be made through SOH, who could balance the real demands with phantom ones covering a wide area, and giving emphasis, though not too much, to the Pas de Calais area which was the cover plan. It was also necessary to insist that all charts were locked away when offices were not in use, since they would even more obviously than secret papers reveal to a casual visitor not 'in the know' the locality of interest even though the chart itself, if not marked up with invasion plans, might not be classified.

As planning developed a catalogue was maintained of charts for the operation, both those already available and those being produced. SOH's office kept a set of sample copies, so that other officers could readily see what was available. This helped to keep demands for special 'one-off' charts to a minimum.

The basic information needed by the planners before deciding on D-day and H-hour came under two headings: beach intelligence and tidal data.

Data had to be provided for the planners to select a day and time such that :

(a) There would be sufficient time after daylight for the bombing of the beach defences;

(b) The initial assault wave would have the minimum time in daylight under fire while running in to the beaches;

(c) The tide should be as high as possible to shorten the distance for the troops from landing to the shelter above the high water line;

(d) The tide should be low enough to allow obstacles to be seen and removed;

(e) The tide had to be high enough to carry the landing craft over certain outlying rocks and shoals;

(f) High tide had to be as early as possible to allow two daylight tides on the first day for beaching and floating off the 'build-up' craft.

To the basic information on times and heights of tide needed to allow this selection to be made, information had to be added on the tidal streams to be expected, since this would affect the slow-moving landing craft, and would be the most likely cause of drift away from the ordered beaching points.

Many members of various arms of all three services took a keen personal interest in the information, and early on it had to be decreed that no data not approved and promulgated by Hydrographer would be accepted for planning purposes.

The detailed tidal data available was scanty, but in the event the predictions provided by Tidal Branch proved accurate within the variation expected from the effects of the weather.

To augment the information on the beaches and their approaches obtained from French charts, the data gathered in the hasty surveys before the fall of France, and air photographs, a clandestine unit was set up in October 1943 based at Cowes with two surveyors, Berncastle and Glen. They were given six 32-foot, 9 knot Landing Craft Personnel (Large). The craft were chosen because they had a low profile which would not be detected by German radar. They were modified as LCP(Survey) with a light-tight superstructure inside which the surveyor could plot fixes and track, a 9-mile Taut Wire Measuring Machine, an echo-sounder and a QH receiver. The QH system was the precursor of the later navigational Decca, and sweeps off the French coast by motor gunboats had proved that it was effective in the survey areas.

A total of six survey sorties were made between October and the end of December. Most operations used three LCPs, and never employed less than two for mutual support in case their single engines broke down, though in the event they experienced no breakdowns. Because of the limited fuel the craft carried they were towed half way across the Channel by motor gunboats, and were met and towed home on completion of their work. Nights were chosen with high tide in the small hours and no moon. The craft arrived in the survey area for the night about 2345, and had strict instructions to break off work and leave the coast at 0400 whether they had finished or not. One craft would anchor as a reference point, from which the other two, each with a survey officer in charge, would sound in a star. On completion they would run away from the coast up a prearranged red QH line to rendezvous with the towing craft to take them home. The sites of both planned Mulberries were covered, as were the approaches to the main assault beaches. The last operation landed an Army team to take samples of sand from the beaches.

One navigational point which was only resolved after the landings was a discrepancy between the surveys and the air photographs about the depths over certain rocks in the approaches, where the air photographs showed some two feet less than charted. It was agreed to accept the shoaler figure for safety, and the assault planned accordingly. Examination of the rocks in daylight after the landings showed two feet of seaweed over them, which would not have been a serious obstacle.

The hydrographic work required for the assault and immediate follow-up was detailed by Collins in a letter to Hydrographer in November 1943. It included laying of buoyage to mark assembly points and swept channels before the assault wave went in; rapid surveying of beaches immediately after the landing to mark any uncharted dangers and for beachmasters to determine the best places for the subsequent landing of back-up support troops, equipment and stores; making detailed surveys of the sites for the two Mulberries, and marking the positions for the piers and breakwaters to be laid. As our forces moved out of the beach-head it would also be necessary to survey the wreckage in and then to chart minor, and later major, ports as they fell into Allied hands to allow them to be used for bringing in supplies.

Before D-day Edgell issued his instructions to the surveying forces to be engaged. They were in very general terms, detailing the ships and craft to specific forces and tasks, and then telling them to be ready to act in accordance with the wishes and needs of the various force commanders to which they were attached. They were as follows :

Scott, under Hennessey, and the pilot cutter *Astral*, under Wood, based at Portsmouth, were to lay the pre-assault buoys, assisted by the Trinity House vessels *Warden, Discovery II, Alert, G.de Joli* and *A. Blondel*, and then to stand by to assist the survey party for the western, US Mulberry off St Laurent. Thereafter *Scott* was to survey minor ports as they were captured and to be ready to work for the opening of Cherbourg and ports west of the Cotentin. *Astral* would maintain the swept channel buoyage and survey and mark any wrecks.

Franklin, under Irving, was held in reserve at the Nore during the assault, and would then support the detailed survey of the site for the Arromanches Mulberry and follow up with port surveys to the east, hopefully culminating in opening Le Havre.

Two HDMLs, 1001 and 1053, were allocated to hydrographic duties and fitted with echo-sounders. 1001 was given a full surveying crew under Lansdown, and was allocated to the party to survey and mark the Arromanches Mulberry, with one 28-

foot survey motor boat and a motor dinghy. 1053 was held in reserve with a general service crew, in case 1001 should break down or be damaged.

Gulnare, under Passmore, also with a survey motor boat and dinghy, would survey and mark the St Laurent Mulberry, while Marshall, with a survey motor boat and dinghy, was to stand by to enter Cherbourg and work with the US Officer in Charge of the port as soon as it was taken.

Berncastle, with his formerly clandestine party and their LCP(Svy)s, would go in with the assault wave and carry out the immediate survey of the beaches, two being allocated to each force.

As D-Day approached the volume of publications prepared and delivered stretched the whole organisation of the Department at Bath and Taunton to its limits. The special products included chart-maps and accompanying map sets, beach chartlets, route and passage chartlets, berthing charts, 'Overcover' charts for the covering and hunting screens, radar charts, fighter control gridded charts, plotting charts for the Mulberries, a special English Channel Handbook, coastal views, shoreline sketches, and tide and astronomical tables. All had a high security classification - so much so that in Taunton until very recently the establishment was known to older residents as 'that secret Admiralty place'.

All Allied naval forces carried the Admiralty publications, and over 6,000 ships, craft and authorities were supplied, the whole running to 30,720 packets. Most of them were despatched in the last few days before D-Day.

On D-Day itself everything went, hydrographically, according to plan. Thereafter the AGA buoys used initially to mark the channels (similar to dan buoys and thus light enough to be carried and laid by the smaller survey ships and craft) proved both too inconspicuous and too easily carried away when struck by passing vessels. They were replaced by a smaller number of navigational buoys, laid by the Trinity House tenders, and by two lightships at key points. Until this could be done *Scott* and *Astral* were kept busy replacing AGAs.

Scott also acted as mother ship to the smaller survey units until she moved west to work in the approaches to Cherbourg, being relieved off Arromanches by *Franklin*. Cherbourg fell on 26 July, and as soon as Marshall's party had surveyed a route into Cherbourg *Franklin* entered, releasing the motor boat team to return to England to prepare for their next task in the Channel Islands, though in the event this was delayed. *Scott* then leap-frogged west, to St Malo and Morlaix.

Franklin, after completing a detailed survey of Cherbourg, moved east to Dieppe. While there Le Havre fell, and a 16-foot motor skiff was sent by road to start the reconnaisance. This soon met a short hostile reception from a pocket of German resistance on the South breakwater. *Franklin* herself, with ML 1001, entered the port early in September despite some reservations on the part of the minesweeping authorities. A detailed survey occupied four weeks, during which mining was a constant worry. The ship also acted as British Senior Officer Afloat, and provided provisions, fuel and water to many British auxiliary craft as well as helping put right their mechanical defects.

ML 1001 continued the survey of the River Seine up to Tancarville while *Franklin* returned to Portsmouth to embark Edgell for a visit to Le Havre, Rouen and Paris, where he called on the French Office des Phares et Balisage, the lights and buoyage authority, just re- establishing itself after the liberation. *Scott* came east to open Calais and Boulogne, where the entrance was blocked by no less than 26 sunken ships. It was at Boulogne that one of the few fatalities of the campaign for the survey ships occurred when a boat and her crew of five were lost in heavy weather going to the assistance of another boat in difficulties.

Franklin had meanwhile moved further east, to Ostende. It was of the utmost importance that the port of Antwerp be opened to Allied shipping at the earliest possible time to cut down the lines of communication along which supplies of all kinds had to be brought to the armies striking north into Holland and east into Germany. Passage up the Schelde was blocked by enemy forces still holding the east bank. Irving arranged for a motor boat and her crew to be taken by tank transporter to Ghent, and to make their way by canal thence to Terneuzen to start the survey of the upper Schelde and the port before ships or craft could reach the higher reaches from the sea. The full survey was completed by 14 December, but before that, on 28 November, *Franklin* had the satisfaction of seeing the first laden Liberty ship convoy proceed upriver to unload. General Montgomery himself subsequently visited the ship to thank her and her company for their work. Irving persuaded him to order the mainbrace to be spliced, which caused some fluttering in the Admiralty dovecots when the rum consumed was brought to account.

Throughout the invasion and follow-up surveys the results of the work of the ships and units were sent back to Bath by the most rapid means, often by special messenger, to be incorporated in Port Handbooks, amended or new charts, and Sailing Directions. Surveys are of no use at all if their results are not published and made available to the mariner, and throughout 1944 and 1945 Bath and Taunton worked at high pressure to ensure that the surveys made by the ships and parties in northern Europe, the Mediterranean and the Far East were published quickly and accurately.

Just before his tragic death in an air crash in January 1945 Admiral Ramsay, ANCXF, wrote personally to Edgell to thank the Hydrographic Service for its part in NEPTUNE and OVERLORD. It is not too much to say that without the work of the surveyors and the cartographers the invasion could not have taken place, much less been the overwhelming success that it was.

Principal Surveys of 1940

HOME

Challenger	Jenks	Scotland, West Coast	Clyde; Kyle Akin.
		England, South Coast	Solent; Plymouth.
		Wales, West Coast	Milford Haven.
		Orkney & Shetland Is	Underwater defences.
		Iceland	Hvalfjordhur
Franklin	Sabine	England, East Coast	Dover Strait and harbour; The Downs.
		England, South Coast	Spithead underwater defences.
		Scotland, East Coast	Cromarty Firth; River Tay entrance.
		Orkney Islands	Shapinsay.
		Faeroe Islands	Skaalefjord.
Gulnare	Sharpey-Schafer	Scotland	Oban; Sound of Sleat; Millport; Kyles of Bute; Rothesay; Kames Bay; Holy Loch; Rosyth; Burntisland; Ardnadam Bay; Ruchnell Bay.
Scott	Collins	Scotland, West Coast	Loch Ewe; Kilbrannan Sound.
		North Atlantic	Minefields between N.W.Scotland, Faeroes, Iceland & Greenland.

ABROAD

	Beech Thomas	Singapore	Underwater Defences; D/F charts.
		Ceylon	Trincomalee.

Principal Surveys of 1941

HOME

Challenger	Jenks	Scotland, West Coast	Bute, Kames Bay; Loch Ryan.
		Northern Ireland	Lough Foyle; Lough Larne.
Franklin	Price	England, East Coast	Thames Estuary; Humber approaches; East Coast War Channels.
		Scotland, East Coast	River Tay; Inverness.
		Scotland, West Coast	Firth of Clyde.
		Orkney Islands	Scapa Flow; Firth Flow
Gulnare	Sharpey-Schafer, Irving	Scotland, West Coast	Loch Linnhe; Loch Etive; Loch Fyne; Rothesay; Greenock; Helensburgh.
		Bristol Channel	Burry Inlet.
Scott	Collins	Scotland, West Coast	Loch Ewe; North Minch.
		North Atlantic	Minelaying & deep sounding between Scotland & Greenland.

ABROAD

Challenger	Jenks	Africa, West Coast	Gambia River, Bathurst & approaches.

Principal Surveys of 1942

HOME

Challenger	Jenks	England, West Coast	Morecambe Bay.
Franklin	Stokes	England, East Coast	Thames Estuary fort sites; Dudgeon Channel; River Swale; East Coast War Route wrecks.
Gulnare	Passmore	Scotland, West Coast	Firth of Clyde.
Scott	Collins,	Scotland, West Coast	North Minch.
	Sharpey-	North Atlantic	Faeroes Bank.
	Schafer	Iceland	South east coast.

ABROAD

Challenger	Jenks,	Africa, West Coast	Gambia River approaches.
	Wyatt	Africa, East Coast	Mombasa, Kilindini.
Endeavour	Baker	Red Sea	Suez Canal; Ports on the coast of Egypt and Sudan.

Principal Surveys of 1943

HOME

Franklin	Stokes	England, East Coast	River Colne; The Wash, Docking Channel.
		Scotland, East Coast	River Tay; Dornoch Firth; Invergordon.
Gulnare	Passmore	Scotland, West Coast	Firth of Clyde; Loch Ryan.
		Wales, West Coast	Milford Haven.
		Bristol Channel	Port surveys.
Scott	Sharpey-Schafer	Scotland, West Coast	Loch Alsh; The Minches.
		Iceland	Eyjafjordhur

ABROAD

Challenger	Wyatt	Africa, East Coast	Mombasa, Port Reitz.
		Ceylon	Palk Strait; Trincomalee.
		Seychelles Islands	Port Victoria.
Endeavour	Baker	Red Sea	African coast ports; Gulf of Suez.

Principal Surveys of 1944

HOME

Franklin	Irving	Orkney Islands	Scapa Flow radar triangulation.
		Scotland, East Coast	Firth of Forth.
		English Channel	Normandy landings; North European ports.
Gulnare	Passmore	Scotland, West Coast	Loch Ryan.
		English Channel	Normandy landings.
Scott	Sharpey-Schafer Hennessey	Scotland, East Coast English Channel	Firth of Forth. Normandy landings; North French ports.
White Bear	Sabine	Scotland, West Coast	Stranraer.
ML 1001	Lansdown	English Channel	Normandy landings.

ABROAD

Challenger	Wyatt, Bill, Sabine	Ceylon	Palk Bay; Approaches to Trincomalee.
		Bay of Bengal	Naaf River; Cox's Bazaar.
		Australia, North Coast	Exmouth Gulf; Torres Strait.
White Bear	Sabine, Day	Bay of Bengal	Karnaphuli River; Cox's Bazaar; Naaf River; Kutubdia Channel.

Principal Surveys of 1945

HOME

Franklin (with 3 MLs)	Irving	France, North Coast	Cherbourg; Le Havre; Dieppe.
		Germany	Wreck clearance surveys of ports & approaches.
		England, East Coast	Thames Estuary.
		England, South Coast	Portland Bay.
Gulnare	Marshall, Tripp	Channel Islands	St Helier; St Peter Port.
		England, South Coast	Weymouth; River Yealm; Lynher River; Portsmouth.
Scott	Hennessey	France, West Coast	Brest.
		England, East Coast	Sole Bank minefield; The Downs; Southwold to Winterton; Thames Estuary.

ABROAD

Challenger	Sabine	Australia, North Coast	Torres Strait.
		Ceylon	Northern approaches to Trincomalee.
		South East Asia	Singapore; Saigon; Hong Kong.
White Bear	Day	Bay of Bengal	Chittagong; Akyab.
		Malay Peninsula	Port Dickson; Port Swettenham.
		East Indies	Batavia; Ports in Sumatra; Lingga Archipelago.

Biographies

1939–1945

Lieutenant M Beech Thomas

Michael Beech Thomas did his first surveying season in 1928 as a sublieutenant in the *Fitzroy*, Harvey, on the east coast of England, and was then for three years in the *Endeavour*, Law and later Edgell, working in the Red Sea and on the Palestine coast. He was promoted to lieutenant in 1929. In 1932 and 1933 he was in the *Flinders*, Simpson, on the south and west coasts of England, doing the standard courses in meteorology and the gyro compass during winter lie-ups.

Beech Thomas was abroad again in 1934 and 1935 in the *Herald*, Law, on the China station, and then served for three years in the *Kellett*, Baker, Jenks and Foulerton in succession, working on the east and south coasts of England. At the end of 1938 he stood by the conversion of the *Scarborough* for surveying, sailing in her under Law in 1939 for surveys of Ceylon. When the ship paid off in Singapore on the outbreak of war Beech Thomas took charge of the Singapore Surveying Unit.

In April 1941 his promising carrer was ended when an RAF recovery vessel which his motor boat was leading through a line of our defensive mines inadvertently struck one of them. Taking his boat alongside the wreck, Beech Thomas, with his surveying Petty Officer Blunt, made several dives to release trapped men, and was himself trapped and drowned when the wreck rolled over.

Commander R Bill, DSO

Robert Bill began surveying as a sublieutenant in 1931 when he joined the *Ormonde*, Fryer, surveying in the Persian Gulf and in Cyprus waters. Two years later, by then a lieutenant, he went to the *Kellett*, Bamford and later Baker, working until 1935 on the east coast of England, in the Thames Estuary and in Dover Harbour. Between 1935 and 1937 he was on exchange service in Australia in the *Moresby*, surveying on the Australian coast and in Papua. He returned to England for the season of 1938, which he spent at first in the *Kellett*, Foulerton, and then in her successor the *Franklin*, Sabine, on the east coast and in the Dover Strait.

In 1939 Bill joined the *Scarborough*, Law, for service in the Far East, and surveyed in Ceylon until the outbreak of war, when the ship sailed for Singapore and Bill was flown home to join Captain M/S Dover in January 1940. He commanded a flotilla of minesweeping trawlers during the Dunkirk evacuation, and was awarded the DSO for towing the blazing wreck of the destroyer *Grenade* clear of Dunkirk harbour entrance. He continued at Dover during the anti-invasion period until 1941, when he joined the *Franklin*, Price, on the east coast of England.

In 1942 he went to the *Challenger*, Wyatt, and sailed to join the Eastern Fleet, working on the east coast of Africa, in the Seychelles and in Ceylon before going to Australia for a refit in 1944. From October to December he was in temporary command, surveying the North East Channel of the Torres Strait. He then spent a short period in the Department before being appointed in command of the *Scott* in August 1945, being promoted to commander in December. He surveyed on the east coast of England and Scotland with two attached Survey Motor Launches until the end of 1947, when he came back to the Department for two years as Equipment Officer.

In the autumn of 1949 Bill commissioned the *Challenger* for her oceanographic cruise, but was soon invalided home from Bermuda. On his recovery he returned to the Department until October 1952, when he took command of the *Dalrymple* for surveys in the Persian Gulf and on the east coast of Africa. In June 1954 he came ashore to take charge of Chart Branch (N).

Bill retired at his own request in 1955 to take up a post with Vickers as Managing Director of Tellurometer (U.K.) Ltd, after having been closely connected with the development of the equipment. In 1967 he set up in private practice as a surveying consultant. He died in 1989.

Captain S J Hennessey, OBE

Sydney John Hennessey entered the Navy as a boy 2nd class in March 1920, and began surveying shortly after being promoted from mate to lieutenant in 1928, when he went to the *Endeavour*, Law, for nearly two years work in the Red Sea. In 1930 and 1931 he was in the *Beaufort*, Rice and later Turner, on the west coasts of England and Scotland, and after that for two years in the *Ormonde*, Fryer and then Day, in the Persian Gulf and in the Mediterranean. From September 1933 Hennessey was again in the *Beaufort*, Tennent and then Farquharson, on the west coasts of Scotland and Ireland, doing gyro, meteorology and echo-sounding courses during the lie-up. At the end of 1935, after some months in the *Flinders*, he joined the *Herald*, Hardy, on the China station where he spent two years on surveys of the Borneo and Malayan coasts. He then went to the *Fitzroy*, Jones, for the first part of the 1938 season, working on the east coast of England until in August he stood by the new ship *Scott* building at Dundee, commissioning her under Day for the first half of 1939 surveying on the east coast of Scotland and in the Orkneys.

Hennessey's next appointment, to the *Endeavour*, was cancelled on the outbreak of war, and he was sent as Extended Defence Officer to Gibraltar. In the spring of 1940 he joined Vice Admiral Dover's staff for the Dunkirk evacuation, and received a mention in despatches for his part in the rapid reconnaissance surveys of north west European coasts which followed. For two years from August 1940 he served on the staff of Commander in Chief, Plymouth as Staff Officer (H), and then in 1942 went to take charge of the Sierra Leone surveying unit at Freetown, being promoted commander at the end of 1943. In February 1944 he was appointed in command of the *Scott*, and took part in the Normandy operations and the subsequent surveys of north west European ports, being awarded the OBE at the end of 1945.

In October 1945 he went as the British member of the Board of Directors of the Deutsche Hydrographische Institut at Hamburg, and in March 1946 came home to take charge of Staff Charts, Whitehall for two years. He was again at sea in 1948 in command of the *Seagull* on the east and west coasts of England, and in 1949 went to the *Dampier*, surveying in Borneo and Malaya. There followed two years as Assistant Hydrographer (2), and then three years first as Surveyor in Charge of the Marine Survey of India and then as Chief Hydrographer of the Indian Navy as an acting captain, though on the retired list from September 1953.

From 1956 to 1968 Hennessey served in the Department as Superintendent of Sailing Directions as an honorary captain. On relinquishing this appointment he became a reviser of Sailing Directions. In 1951 he was one of the first hydrographic surveyors to become FRICS, and contributed much to the development of relations between the Institution and the R.N.Hydrographic Service.

Commander C S E Lansdown, OBE, DSC

Charles Savage Ewbank Lansdown began surveying in 1926, shortly before promotion to lieutenant, when he joined the *Endeavour*, Geary-Hill and later Law, working in the Red Sea and off Malta. Two years later he went to the *Flinders*, Cary, for a season on the south and west coasts of England, and in 1929 was in the *Rosemary* when she discovered the Rosemary Bank north east of Rockall.

Lansdown did two more seasons at home, one in the *Fitzroy*, Fryer, on the east coast of England, and the other in the *Flinders*, Cary, on the west coast of Scotland. Then from 1931 to 1933 he was in the *Herald*, N.A.C.Hardy, working on the coasts of Malaya and Borneo, at Hong Kong, and on the reefs in the South China Sea 'dangerous area'. In 1934 he came home to the *Kellett*, Bamford and later Baker, on the south and east coasts of England, and in 1935 did a course in controlled minelaying. From 1936 to 1938 he was in the new ship *Stork*, Farquharson and then Jackson, on the west coast of Siam and in Ceylon. He came home in 1939 to the *Gleaner*, Price, working on the south coast of England and on the west coast of Scotland. During this time the ship was diverted to Liverpool Bay to help in the operations to raise the sunken submarine *Thetis*.

Lansdown's war service began with four years in the *Atreus*, a Blue Funnel liner converted for controlled minelaying. He was awarded the OBE in 1943 for his work in her. In 1944 he took part in the Normandy landings, surveying the site for the

Mulberry harbour at Arromanches in ML 1001. He then commanded the *Astral,* a former Belgian pilot vessel, surveying re-occupied northern European ports, for which he was awarded the DSC.

In 1945 he joined the Department, doing three years as Jacketting Officer and four as an assistant in the Sailing Directions branch. He was placed on the retired list as a commander in 1949. From 1952 to 1968 he held the post of Superintendent of Notices to Mariners.

Lieutenant Commander C P W Marshall, DSC

Charles Peter Warwick Marshall began surveying as a sublieutenant in 1932 when he did a season in the *Kellett,* Southern and then Bamford, on the east coast of England. In 1933 he was promoted lieutnant, and went to the *Ormonde,* Fryer and later Day, working in the Persian Gulf and in Cyprus until the ship was paid off in 1935 at the time of the Abyssinian crisis. He next did a season in the *Kellett,* Baker, on the east and south coasts of England, and in September 1936 joined the *Stork,* Farquharson and later Jackson, for passage to the Far East and then to survey on the west coast of Siam and in Ceylonese waters.

On the outbreak of the Second World War he went briefly to the monitor *Erebus,* and then served for three years in the minelayer *Teviot Bank,* being awarded the DSC in 1941. In July 1943 he was put in charge of the South Coast of England Survey, having in this post a brief period in command of the *Gulnare* in 1945 before, in September, he went to the Mediterranean in command of ML 1254, engaged on port surveys.

In 1947 Marshall came home to the Department, where he was an assistant in Tidal Branch until he retired at his own request in July 1955. He emigrated to Australia, where he worked with the Adelaide Harbour Board for a time. He died in February 1962.

Commander W M Passmore

William Maurice Passmore began surveying as a sublieutenant in the *Kellett,* Silk, in 1928, working on the east coast of England. After a few months he transferred to the *Endeavour,* Law and later Edgell, for three years in the Red Sea and on the Palestine coast. At the end of 1931 he came home to the *Beaufort,* Turner and then Tennent, working on the west coasts of England and Scotland and off Northern Ireland. In 1933 he went to the *Ormonde,* Day, surveying in the Persian Gulf, the Red Sea again, and off Cyprus. When, in 1935, the commission was interrupted by the Abyssinian crisis, Passmore went to the minesweeper *Harrow* at Malta, and then in the winter of 1936-37 took up the drawing of *Ormonde's* fair charts at Chatham.

During the 1937 season he went to the West Coast of Scotland Survey under

Farquharson, based at Crinan, and then in 1938 was appointed to the *Herald*, Hardy, Jenks and Southern successively, on surveys of the Borneo and Malayan coasts. On the outbreak of war he went in command of the minesweeper *Widnes* at Singapore until 1940, when he was sent to Sierra Leone as RN Surveying Officer at Freetown.

Early in 1942 Passmore took command of the *Gulnare*, working on the west coast of Scotland and in the Bristol Channel until, in 1944, he was attached to the US task force for the Omaha Beach landings, for which services he received the US Legion of Merit. In 1945 he went to Headquarters, Supreme Allied Command, South East Asia, as an assistant to the Fleet Hydrographic Officer, Day.

He came home in 1946 to the Air Information Branch of the Department, where he served until his retirement in 1950. From his home in Lyme Regis he then became a reviser of Sailing Directions until 1980.

Commander J M Sharpey-Schafer, OBE

John Michael Sharpey-Schafer joined the *Fitzroy*, Day and later Fryer, in 1933 shortly before being promoted lieutenant for a season's surveying on the east coasts of England and Scotland, doing the customary courses on gyro compasses and meteorology during the lie-up. From 1934 to 1936 he was in the *Challenger*, Wyatt and later Jones, in Labrador and the West Indies, following this with the 1936 home season in the *Flinders*, Jenks, on the south coast of England.

From January 1937 until the outbreak of war Sharpey-Schafer was in the *Endeavour*, Wyatt, on New Zealand surveys. Arriving home early in 1940 from Singapore, he spent a year in the *Gulnare*, in charge of surveys for harbour defences in Scotland. In 1941 he went to the *Challenger*, Jenks, working on the west coast of Africa, and in April 1942 he moved to the *Scott*, Collins, and succeeded to the command in August, working on surveys for the northern mine barrage, from Scotland to Iceland. He was mentioned in despatches in January 1944.

From 1944 to 1946 Sharpey-Schafer was lent to the Royal Australian Navy, commanding the *Shepparton* and being promoted commander in 1945. On his return home he worked in *Dryad* for six months on radar developments, and then for a year in the Department as Territorial Waters Officer for the International Hydrographic Conference of 1947. In 1948 he went in command of the *Challenger* in the Persian Gulf. From August 1949 he was lent for three years to the Royal New Zealand Navy to command the *Lachlan* and to set up a New Zealand hydrographic service. He was awarded the OBE in July 1952.

In October 1952 Sharpey-Schafer came home to join the Department, and was in charge first of Staff Charts and then of the Air Information Branch until his retirement from active service for age in October 1961. He then spent ten years in charge of geographical intelligence for the Fleet Air Arm, retiring finally in 1972.

Commander H J C Stokes

Henry John Cortlandt Stokes joined his first surveying ship, the *Kellett*, Silk, in 1928, spending a season working in the Thames Estuary. In the following year he went out to the *Herald*, Maxwell, for two years on the coast of Borneo and off Hong Kong. In 1931 he was at home for a season in the *Fitzroy*, Fryer and later Wyatt, and then in 1933 followed Fryer to the *Ormonde*, working in the Persian Gulf and off Cyprus.

When the *Ormonde* was paid off because of the Abyssinian crisis Stokes was put in command of the minesweeper *Aberdare*. He later steamed her to Singapore, where he was briefly Assistant King's Harbour Master. In January 1937 Stokes returned to surveying, joining the *Endeavour*, Wyatt, for surveys in New Zealand waters, remaining with her until she paid off at Singapore on the outbreak of war.

In 1940 he went to the *Franklin*, Sabine and later Price, in the Thames Estuary and on the east coast convoy routes. Next year he was sent to the *Challenger*, Jenks, in Scottish waters and then on the west coast of Africa, and was in the ship when she rescued 823 officers and men from the torpedoed troopship *Anselm*. In 1942 Stokes was appointed in command of the *Franklin*, surveying the sites for the Maunsell Forts in the Thames Estuary, sweeping wrecks in 'E-boat Alley' and northward to the Tyne, and sounding alternative channels for the convoys. In 1944 he was sent on detached service in charge of surveys of the Sherbro River in Sierra Leone, and later that year was in the Mediterranean in ML 1254 for the invasion of the south of France, and for surveys of recaptured ports on the west coast of Italy. In 1945 he became Staff Hydrographic Officer, Levant, being mentioned in despatches at the end of the year.

He concluded his service with four years from 1946 as an assistant in the Notices to Mariners branch. He retired at his own request in 1950 with the rank of commander, settling in Tasmania.

Commander R T Tripp

Roderick Trethewey Tripp began surveying in 1933 as a newly promoted lieutenant when he joined the *Flinders*, Simpson and later Jones, working on the south coast of England. In 1935 he went to the China station for two and a half years in the *Herald*, Law and later Hardy, surveying in Malayan and Borneo waters as well as in the 'dangerous area' in the South China Sea. For the season of 1937 he was in the *Kellett*, Foulerton, in the Medway, and in 1938 went to the *Challenger*, Baker, in the Red Sea and the Persian Gulf until shortly before the outbreak of the Second World War, when the ship was brought home to work on the buoyage of the East Coast War Channel.

At the beginning of the war Tripp reverted briefly to general service, before being appointed to Sheerness as Hydrographic Officer (Minesweeping). In 1940 he transferred to the converted merchantman *Queenworth* for magnetic minesweeping. In late 1940 he went to the *Scott*, Collins, working with the minelaying squadron on the Northern barrage. During Operation ANKLET in December 1941 he was involved in the rapid running survey of Kirkefjord to assess its suitability for a fleet base.

In 1942 Tripp went to the *Challenger*, Wyatt, with the Eastern Fleet, surveying in Mombasa, the Seychelles and Ceylon. In August 1944 she went to Australia and made a running survey of Exmouth Gulf, and on her departure Tripp was left with three Australian trawlers to carry out surveys in the Torres Strait. He returned to England in 1945, to the command of the *Gulnare* operating from south coast ports. From 1946 to 1948 he commanded the *Franklin*, mainly working in the Thames Estuary and on trials with the new Decca navigator.

In 1948 he was lent with the rank of commander to the South African Naval Service. Here he commissioned the *Protea*, a converted Flower class corvette, and before she became operational carried out running surveys of Marion Island in South African naval ships. When he retired from the Royal Navy in 1954 he transferred to the South African Naval Service as a commander, and set up the South African Hydrographic Office.

He resigned from this service in 1956 to take over the Lake Nyasa hydrographic survey from Day. Thereafter, until the Central African Federation broke up, he did various lake surveys, including one of the new Lake Kariba, for the Department of Federal Surveys. In 1964 he joined a commercial hydrographic firm in Sydney, Australia, and for a year was engaged on surveys in Papua-New Guinea. In 1965 he returned to South Africa to take up the newly-created post of Officer in Charge of the South African Oceanographic Data Centre.

He died in South Africa in 1990

CHAPTER SEVEN

Picking up the Pieces
1945– 60

Vice Admiral Sir Guy Wyatt, KBE, CB, 1945-1950

Vice Admiral Sir Archibald Day, KBE, CB, DSO, 1950-1955

Rear Admiral K.St.B. Collins, CB, OBE, DSC, 1955-1960

Wyatt was flown home from the Far East at the end of April 1945 to take over as Hydrographer from Edgell on 1 May. He travelled eastabout via the United States to make personal contact with the US Hydrographer and with the Director of the US Coast and Geodetic Survey. He had specialised in surveying in 1914, but had spent most of the First World War in general service, returning to hydrography in 1918. He obtained his first command, *Ormonde*, in 1926, and with one short break was at sea in command until 1939, when he first became Superintendent of Strategic Surveys at the Admiralty and then, when that short-lived post was disestablished, Assistant Hydrographer (2) in Whitehall. From 1942 he was Fleet Hydrographic Officer, Eastern Fleet and in command of *Challenger*. Not a natural administrator, he was impatient with what he saw as a lack of understanding of the need for hydrography among the Admiralty's naval staff and civil servants.

Shortly after Wyatt took office, Hydrographer's Whitehall staff were moved out to the shadow Admiralty building at Cricklewood, where he was joined by Chart Branch from Bath in the summer of 1946. The divorce of Hydrographer from the Naval Staff even before the pattern of the peace-time Navy was set was most unfortunate, and was not remedied by the return of Hydrographer himself and elements of his staff to the Archway Block of the Admiralty until 1951, shortly after Day had assumed office.

Day had begun surveying in 1920, and assumed his first command in 1932. In the Abyssinian crisis he served on the Commander in Chief, Mediterranean's staff as Fleet Hydrographic Officer. He was Superintendent of Charts from 1937 to 1938, and on the outbreak of war went to Dover, where he was Chief of Staff from February 1941 for two years. After a spell as Assistant Hydrographer in Whitehall in 1943-44 he went east to relieve Wyatt as Fleet Hydrographic Officer and in command of *White*

Bear. Unusually for a surveying specialist he was promoted rear admiral in 1949, over a year before he became Hydrographer. He spent the year as Flag Officer, British Naval Forces, Germany, with headquarters in Hamburg. He was promoted to Vice Admiral in 1953, and made KBE in 1954.

Collins took over from Day as Hydrographer in June 1955. He was appointed Commodore 2nd class in October, and was promoted to rear admiral in 1956. He took up surveying as a sublieutenant in 1926, the first Hydrographer not to have served in the First World War. His first command came in 1940, when he went for two arduous years to *Scott* surveying for the Northern Barrage. From 1942 he served on Admiral Ramsay's staff as SOH, planning for the North African, Sicilian and Normandy landings. Sea commands and periods in the Department ashore alternated until he took office as Hydrographer. A small, neat man known since his early surveying days in Borneo as 'kechil', the Malay for 'little', he was more concerned to communicate both with his own staff and with the outside world than his predecessors. After thirty years when it printed only arid statistics, Hydrographer's Annual Report under Collins once again became an interesting and informative document. He also introduced personal messages informing the staff of the Department and the ships of developments and achievements.

With the war in Europe ending in May 1945 and that in the Far East in September the first call on the Hydrographic Service was to survey and re-chart the devastated ports of Europe, the Mediterranean and the Far East, and to assist in clearing minefields and charting safe passages through those which could not be cleared immediately. Available already fitted and manned for surveying were *Franklin*, *Scott*, *Gulnare* and four Survey Motor Launches at home, with *Challenger*, *White Bear*, two MLs (1248 and 1368) and the *Nguva* in the Far East. In the Mediterranean were only six survey parties sharing two MLs (1254 and 1301) and a miscellaneous collection of boats and DUKWs. In northern Europe *Franklin*, still under Irving, carried out trials of QM, later to be developed into the Decca Navigator system, in April while waiting to enter German ports. She sailed from Sheerness for Cuxhaven on 19 May, and carried out wreck clearance surveys there, and at Hamburg, Heligoland, Kiel, Lubeck and Travemunde, as well as fixing navigational buoys in the Baltic. She had two HDMLs (SMLs 3 and 4) attached to her, with which she surveyed the Weser river from the sea to the port of Bremen in August and September. Another SML, 5, made a reconnaisance survey of the Rhine up to Cologne, while when the Weser survey was completed SML 3 went to Denmark to assist the Danes in opening up their ports.

Scott, meanwhile, under Hennessey, completed surveying Brest in comparative leisure since there was little strategic urgency, and then was given a rapid refit at Grimsby. Fully fit again, and now under Bill, she was put to work on the east coast of England between the Downs and the Humber assisting minesweepers in clearance work, and locating and sweeping some of the many wrecks in the channels between the east coast sandbanks. *Gulnare* took part in the relief of the Channel Islands and remained until mid June surveying ports and their approaches in the islands. Marshall was then relieved by Tripp, under whose command she spent the rest of 1945 working along the south coast until she was placed in dockyard hands for refit at the end of the year.

In the Mediterranean there were at first six units, working either from MLs or from local boats. They were run down at the end of 1945 to two, using Survey Motor Launches 1254 and 1301, under the overall command of Marshall. They worked from Pantellaria to the Adriatic and the Greek Islands, Cyprus and Beirut. In the Far East *White Bear* worked round the Eastern Archipelago, while *Challenger*, after a brief spell in Singapore, went north to Saigon and Hong Kong. Both ships returned to England in 1946, *White Bear* to pay off for disposal, *Challenger* to refit for further service.

Wyatt had no sooner taken office than he was agitating to bring the surveying fleet up to strength. As after the previous war, early replacements could not be new vessels when there was a vast surplus of shipping, including many nearly completed hulls, available. As an immediate measure two *Halcyon* class minesweepers, *Sharpshooter* and *Seagull*, were given similar conversions to those built into *Jason* and *Gleaner* pre-war, and replaced these latter in the post-war surveying fleet. With luffing davits and radar fitted, the mainmast which the other two had carried and which had in any case been removed to avoid fouling the AA arcs during the war was not replaced. Both were ready for service in the new role by early 1946. *Seagull*, the first all-welded ship built for the Royal Navy, was paid off for disposal at the end of 1950, with *Franklin* following at the end of 1952. *Scott* and *Sharpshooter*, the latter renamed *Shackleton* to pair with her remaining sister, continued in service throughout the 1950s.

In an early use of electronic aids for surveying Collins in *Seagull* in 1947 used constant radar ranges of a prominent object to control his lines of soundings, meanwhile fixing his position along them by sextant angles in the traditional way. In the strong tidal streams and difficult waters off Northern Ireland this expedited sounding quite considerably, and the method was promulgated in a Professional Paper to the fleet.

Sharpshooter, under Menzies, sailed in May 1946 for surveys in Malaya and Borneo, re-establishing the British presence in a constructive and peaceful way in some of the remoter areas, including the rivers of Brunei and Sarawak. She returned home at the end of 1947. Apart from this and *Franklin*'s pre-war sortie to North America, all the *Halcyon* class spent their entire working lives in northern European waters, often with one or two SMLs attached to them for shallow water work.

In 1947 approval was given to convert four uncompleted *Bay* class frigates for surveying. *Pegwell Bay*, *Luce Bay*, *Herne Bay* and *Thurso Bay* became *Cook*, *Dalrymple*, *Dampier* and *Owen* respectively. They lost all armament except for four three-pounder saluting guns, and gained a full outfit of boats, a chartroom below a more commodious captain's cabin and bridge, twin derricks on the forecastle for handling surveying beacons, and improvements in habitability over their general service sisters. *Dampier* and *Dalrymple* were completed with the short funnel of the *Bay*s, but soon found that smoke interfered with sextant fixing on the bridge and had six feet added at their first refits. *Owen* and *Cook* were completed with the taller funnels.

Dampier was the first to complete, and commissioned in May 1948 under Collins for service in the Far East, where she spent the whole of her working life. A pattern developed early on which was maintained for most of her life, surveys on the two coasts of the Malay peninsula and in Sarawak, Brunei and British North Borneo alternating according to the monsoon in the South China Sea, with a winter visit to Hong Kong to give her company a break from the equatorial climate. Apart from Singapore and Penang the opportunities for bright lights and entertainment ashore were few and far between, and though the surveying could be interesting *Dampier* was not a popular draft for her ship's company.

Dalrymple followed, commissioning in January 1949, briefly under Day and then under E H B Baker. After the summer in the Mediterranean, she departed for the Persian Gulf in September. For some years she followed a pattern of working through the winter in the Gulf and spending the summer in cooler climes, either in the Mediterranean or in East Africa. In 1952 she was at Aden when a merchant ship dragging her anchor broke no less than five telephone cables, disrupting communications between London and the Far East. With no cable ship near, *Dalrymple* was pressed into service and with the assistance of the chief officer and boatswain of the cable ship stationed at Mombasa who were flown up to Aden managed to recover and repair all five. From her first visit to Aden she acquired a supplement to her ship's company of Somali seamen. She also acquired a wooden hut on the after end of the boat deck in which they lived, and which was known for obvious reasons as the 'Somali Hut'. Also in 1952 she attended the Sixth International Hydrographic Conference at Monaco. As a result of the impression which she made on that occasion she was invited to be present at the wedding of HSH Prince Rainier III to Grace Kelly in 1956.

In the latter year *Dalrymple*, under Winstanley, had the distinction of taking part in the Suez Canal operation on both sides. Her boats, in best World War Two style, led the assault forces into Port Said on the first day of the Anglo-French invasion of the Canal Zone. Later, when American pressure had brought the operation to an abrupt conclusion and the Allied forces had withdrawn, *Dalrymple* hoisted the United Nations pale blue ensign and lent her surveying skills to the clearing up operations which opened the Canal again to commercial use.

Owen completed in August 1949, and after a brief work-up in the Hebrides sailed for the Persian Gulf under Menzies in October to start a similar cycle to *Dalrymple*'s. She too took a detachment of Somali seamen on board whenever she was working in the Gulf or the Indian Ocean, and built a Somali Hut in which they messed. When either ship returned to the Mediterranean or to England the Somalis were landed at Aden before the ship left the East Indies Station. In 1954, on her way out to the Gulf, she called at the island of Socotra to embark a cow of the island's miniature breed of cattle to take to Bahrain, to mate with a bull already held at the Experimental Agriculture Station there.

The last of the four, *Cook*, was not completed until the beginning of 1951. First under Collins and then E H B Baker she spent her first years in home waters, replacing *Seagull*, who paid off at the end of 1950. One of her first tasks was to search for the submarine *Affray*, lost while diving in the Channel with the whole of one year's intake of trainee submarine officers on board. At the Coronation Review in 1953 *Cook* flew Day's flag. In 1957, under Hatfield, *Cook* left Devonport for the Pacific, where she took part in the first British hydrogen bomb test at Christmas Island. She then remained in the South Pacific, surveying among the islands and repairing to New Zealand, Australia or Singapore for refit from time to time. Very much seen by the islanders as 'the Queen's ship' among them, participating in celebrations both British and island, her people led a life full of exotic interest as well as of interesting and important surveying in an area where all traffic must perforce go by sea.

Compared to the end of the First World War, in 1945 there was neither the conviction that an era of lasting peace had begun nor an immediate drive for economy of quite the ferocious cutting power of that in 1919. At the same time as approval was given to convert the four Bays, plans were put in hand to design and build two ships specially for surveying. Two names were selected, *Vidal* and *Wharton*, but in the event only *Vidal* was built. She was not designed purely for surveying, but was to be convertible to an escort in time of war, though as she emerged she was very much more survey ship than frigate. She had a number of new features. She was the first small ship to be designed to carry a helicopter, or to be designed for cafeteria messing. She was from the outset fitted to carry Two Range Decca. She was also the test-bed for the Admiralty Standard Range diesel engines. This last was to be her Achilles heel. Automatic watchkeepers for the engines had not been developed, and with eight of them to watch over her engine-room complement was over half her ship's company. Also the gearing which connected four engines to each propellor shaft gave endless trouble in her early years.

Vidal was designed and built at Chatham dockyard, laid down in 1949, launched on 31 July 1951, and commissioned by Collins in 1953, making her first surveys in Scottish waters early in 1954. She spent her first ten years working mainly in the West Indies. On 18 September 1955 her helicopter landed on Rockall to annex it formally for the United Kingdom, while in March 1957 she acted as the communication link with London for the meeting at Bermuda of the British Prime Minister, Macmillan, with the President of the United States.

Challenger had been surveying during the winters in the Persian Gulf until relieved by the two Bays, *Dalrymple* and *Owen*. She came home for a long refit at Chatham starting in July 1949, preparing her for her last major task, a world oceanographic cruise in emulation of her earlier namesake. She sailed from Plymouth under Bill early in May 1950. He was relieved by Ritchie at Bermuda in July. The ship then went on to cover 15,220 miles of deep ocean soundings including the deepest then recorded, 5940 fathoms, in what was named the Challenger Deep between Mindanao and the Caroline Islands in the western Pacific. She also obtained what were then the deepest samples of the sea bed from the bottom of the trench. She returned to Portsmouth at the end of her circumnavigation in October 1952. After short oceanographical voyages in the North Atlantic in the spring and summer of 1953 she paid off for disposal in October 1953.

By 1954 the Surveying Motor Launches, all converted HDMLs, had been organised into an East Coast of England Survey Unit, working between the Humber and Dover on the ceaseless task of charting the shifting channels and banks used by shipping up and down the east coast and in and out of the ports of London, Harwich, Lowestoft, Great Yarmouth and the Humber. They had by now all been renumbered in their own series, from 322 to 326, though they were later joined by 3516. These little craft, with one officer and a ship's company of only nine, led a highly informal but very productive life, lying overnight in the nearest small harbour to the survey ground and sallying out at first light to spend the day at work, sometimes bumping over sandbanks to delineate the shoalest contours.

At Portsmouth the *Gulnare* had been soldiering on as the surveying vehicle for the South Coast of England Survey, with a retired officer (Price) in charge of a Port Service crew. ML 1301 was shipped home from the Mediterranean at the end of 1948 to relieve her from the 1949 season, and named *Meda* in her new role. The Unit remained responsible for surveys in the Portsmouth approaches and the Solent, with occasional forays to Portland and the Channel Islands.

When ML 1301 was withdrawn from the Mediterranean C J de C. Scott was sent on a hydrographic mission to Turkey, where he spent 1949 surveying on the south coast of Asia Minor from an LCT. Much of his work was repeating Beaufort's surveys in the early years of the previous century, and despite the difference in equipment and methods he found very little that was not already charted by his illustrious predecessor.

By 1957 most of the SMLs were feeling their age, and were due for replacement. Approval was given to build three Inshore Survey Craft, using the hull design of the 'Ham' class Inshore Minesweepers, but with the bridge and internal arrangements redesigned for surveying. The *Echo* class was the result, *Echo* herself commissioning in the autumn of 1958 under Green. She was sent straight to the Goodwin Sands, where the New Zealand Shipping Company liner *Rangitiki* had grounded on the South Sand Head in a position where she should have had plenty of water. Fortunately she came off with the rising tide, but *Echo* found that the southern tip of the sands had moved over half a mile south from the 1947 position. The sands were normally surveyed at ten yearly intervals, but the 1926, 1936 and 1947 surveys had shown so little movement that a survey in 1957 had not been ordered.

Echo was joined in the East Coast of England Survey Unit by *Egeria* in July and *Enterprise* in August 1959. The remaining SMLs were paid off at the end of 1958, except for 3516, which was transferred to the West Country at the end of 1959 to work partly independently between Torbay and the Solway Firth, and partly as a tender to the Hydrographic School. She was renamed *Medusa* in 1960.

By 1957 it was ten years since the design for the Bay class conversions had been formulated. The first of the class, *Dampier*, had been in service for nine years, and the layout on board had not kept pace with the advances which had occured in equipment and techniques. Plans were drawn up for each ship to undergo a major refurbishment, including improving the bridge arrangements with an enclosed plotting room, and making better provision for accommodating a range of electronic fixing aids. *Dampier* was taken in hand in July 1957 in Hong Kong, leaving her boats and a party under Martin at Singapore to survey the Johore Strait. The remainder of the class went into refit one after the other, the last, *Cook*, emerging from Singapore Dockyard in March 1961.

The Australian hydrographic service was by now entirely self-sufficient, though a regular series of exchange appointments gave the Royal Australian Naval surveyors experience of another service and a wider circle of surveyors, while a succession of British surveyors had a chance to see and enjoy life in the great southern continent.

We have seen how the programme to resurvey New Zealand's coasts was cut short by the outbreak of war in 1939. After the war New Zealand shipping interests drew both the Admiralty's and the New Zealand government's attention to deficiencies in the charting of the Dominion's shores. In 1946 the New Zealand Chief of Naval Staff, on the instructions of his cabinet, wrote formally to the Admiralty proposing the resumption of the interrupted survey programme on the same terms as before: the Royal Navy to provide the ships and men, New Zealand to meet the running costs of the survey. The Admiralty reply was to the effect that while they recognised the need they regretted that the volume of urgent work nearer home made it impossible for them to contemplate sending a ship. They suggested that the Royal New Zealand Navy should build or convert a ship for surveying. The best that the Royal Navy could offer was to lend experienced surveying officers.

Observing that the task of charting New Zealand's coasts was likely to be an ongoing one, it was decided to set up a surveying service within the Royal New Zealand Navy, and discussions started on the ship for the job. The ideal was clearly a new, purpose-built vessel, but to provide this would take time. Early in 1949 the Royal Australian Navy, in response to an inquiry, offered the River class frigate *Lachlan*, already converted for surveying and at present laid up in Fremantle. She was accepted with alacrity, and Sharpey-Schafer loaned from Britain to command her. *Lachlan* was taken over on 5 October 1949, with Hall, also on loan from the Royal Navy, as First Lieutenant; two Royal New Zealand Naval lieutenants, W J L Smith, DSO and W J Doyle; and three Royal Australian Naval lieutenants completing her surveying officer complement. After passage to Auckland she was disarmed and re- equipped in the first weeks of November, and sailed for the first surveys of New Zealand waters by a RNZN ship on 14 November.

Initially it had been intended to send the surveys back to Taunton for compiling and printing. When it was stated that, due to pressure of work, such a process would take up to two years, Sharpey-Schafer decided to arrange printing locally. With draughting assistance from the Lands and Surveys Department, copy was prepared and printed by the Government Printer. Eventually a small Hydrographic Section was established, staffed at first in large part by former Admiralty personnel, with a strong admixture of local draughtsmen and a few WRNZN 'Wrens'. From 1950 *Lachlan* was joined by two Surveying Motor Launches, given the names *Takapu* and *Tarapunga* after the Maori names for two species of water birds.

The Marine Survey of India had been fully independent and efficient since the last century. On independence and partition it was split into Indian and Pakistani services, and incorporated into the respective new countries' navies. The Marine Survey of India remained in an office in New Delhi after partition, and for three years from 1953 Hennessey was lent to India to take charge of it. He arranged for the office to move from New Delhi to Dehra Dun, alongside the land surveyors, at first in temporary accommodation and then, from March 1957, in a purpose-built edifice. In 1954, shortly after the move to the hills, the service was renamed the Naval Hydrographic Office, and Hennessey's title became Chief Hydrographer, Indian Navy.

The River class frigate *Kukri* was converted for surveying along the lines of the British Bays, and given the old Marine Survey of India name of *Investigator*. She was later joined by the frigates *Jumna* (later spelt *Jamuna*) and *Sutlej*. Hennessey was succeded in November 1955 by Captain J Cursetji, IN, who later went on to become Chief of the Naval Staff, Indian Navy.

Similarly Grattan was lent to the Pakistan Navy from 1955 to 1957 to be their Director of Hydrography. Pakistan too provided a River class frigate for conversion to the surveying role, PNS *Zulfiqar*.

Royal Naval surveyors also spent time in the Antarctic, on loan to the Falkland Islands Dependencies Survey from 1950 onward.

It had always been the practice for young surveyors, both officers and ratings, to learn how to perform their tasks on board on first being appointed or drafted to a surveying ship. This had been sensible when the main skills had been the taking of angles by sextant and plotting them in a heaving small boat or on the ship's bridge, and the erecting of flags and other marks for those angles to be taken from, as had been the case before the Second World War. With the rise of technology, starting with the echo sounder in the '30s and increasing rapidly with the advent of electronic position fixing after the war, it was clear that the traditional 'on the job' apprentice system would have to be replaced.

In the middle of 1948 a Survey Training Unit was set up under Ritchie in the Royal Naval Barracks, Chatham. At first this only trained surveying recorders. In 1959 the Unit moved to the West Country, to hutments in the camp at St Budeaux, across Weston Mill Lake from the Royal Naval Barracks, Devonport. The Unit soon gained a reputation for sound practical training, and men from a number of Commonwealth Navies were sent first to Chatham and later to Devonport for hydrographic training. The lack of a career outlet for those Surveying Recorders who were too old when their potential was recognised to become 'upper yardmen' and go through for a general service commission had long been felt. For such men the only avenue for advancement was to abandon their surveying trade and become Commissioned Boatswains, or later Sublieutenants (Special Duties) (Boatswain). After much discussion a category of Special Duties Hydrographic specialists was created, and the first Sublieutenant (SD) (H), G.Boorman, was promoted in May 1958. Since then a steady trickle of these officers have been promoted.

It was in the late '50s that 'Work Study' became fashionable in the Navy, as it had in the country at large. The basic idea of looking at the way things were done and stripping away practices that had persisted long after they had any real purpose was a good one. The fervent proponents of Work Study, though, often seemed to take rigid prescription of methods and timings to a length as ridiculous as the traditions they were trying to replace. The Hydrographic Service, both afloat and ashore, was not immune from the virus, and Work Study teams were set up both for the fleet and for the Department. It had been thought that the printing works at Taunton would be a prime target for improvement, but this was prevented by the trades unions, two of which, the Society of Lithographic Artists, Designers and Engravers (SLADE) and the National Society of Operative Printers and Assistants (NATSOPA) had a national policy of non-cooperation with any form of time and motion study.

At Cricklewood the team found more scope for their work, and did much to advance the use of plastic drawing materials and to ensure that they saved time and staff effort. At sea they studied subjects as far apart as the erection of Two Range Decca stations and the cleaning routines of heads and passageways, besides giving the same encouragement to the use of transparent plastic in the place of tracing paper and linen-backed cartridge paper for the drawing up of surveys.

During the late '40s and the '50s rapid advances were made in electronic aids to surveying. The QH receivers used by the clandestine survey parties in 1943 operated by timing the difference between radio pulses from shore stations. This was soon developed into a more accurate system, QM, which measured phase differences rather than time differences. After the end of the war QM was rapidly developed further into the Decca Navigator system. Pulses transmitted from a master station were compared electronically with those triggered at a series (usually three) of slave stations, and the results shown as numbers on dials in a receiver. Plotting the numbers read off the dials on a specially latticed chart gave a three position line fix, whose accuracy depended both on various assumptions built into the receiver about the speed of radio waves in air and on the geometry of the network.

Theoretically a ship at sea could obtain a position anywhere within the cover of the chain of stations. This was soon found to be good enough for navigation, if used with prudence. But for surveying it was necessary to know the accuracy of the fix to a very much higher degree of precision. To find out this accuracy a surveying ship would place herself where she could both obtain a good Decca fix and also fix herself accurately by more conventional means, either by sextant angles taken on board or by being resected by theodolites from shore.

The first trials to determine its suitability for surveying under peace-time conditions of accuracy were undertaken, as we have already seen, by *Franklin* while waiting to enter German ports after the surrender. From then on, as Decca chains spread round the coast and as the system was further refined, Decca trials were a regular feature of home ships' programmes.

It was soon found that a pattern of Decca chains designed to give a cover and accuracy acceptable for commercial navigation all round the British Isles was not best suited to give the angle of cut and lane widths needed to achieve the higher degree of precision required for surveying a particular area of sea. The solution was soon found. The master station was mounted on board the surveying ship, and operated with two portable slave stations ashore placed to give optimum cut in the survey area. Two Range Decca was born. It was introduced to the surveying fleet in 1957, in which year *Dalrymple* carried out a series of trials to obtain an accurate figure for the speed of propagation of radio waves. With a slave station on the Mull of Galloway the ship, with the master on board, was intersected by theodolites at positions from off Lands End up through the Irish Sea.

By 1959 Two Range Decca had been fitted in all five larger ships, and would be fitted in *Scott* in 1960. The major drawback of the system was that careful watch had to be kept to observe if irregular power supply or other interference caused one or other of the received signals to slip lanes, thus giving a false position. Thunderstorms, or even the kind of interference commonly experienced near sunset, could cause the chain to 'lose lock' and the ship's position to be lost entirely. It was then necessary to return to a known point to line up the dials, losing valuable survey time. Decca's answer to this was to superimpose on the basic frequency a harmonic, giving a broader pattern and so allowing the correct lane count to be recovered electronically. This system went by the name of LAMBDA, an acronym for Low AMBiguity DeccA. It was first fitted in *Cook* in 1960, and successively replaced Two Range Decca in the other ships in the following years.

The successive Decca systems allowed surveying ships to fix their positions, and hence the positions of their soundings, out of sight of land with a precision not dreamed of before the days of electronics. The advent later of higher-frequency systems with very much narrower band width and hence higher accuracy, and also less affected by sky waves and other forms of interference, called into question the degree of precision of the early Decca and Two Range Decca surveys. In particular, it appeared that lane slips, and hence displacement of whole portions of the survey, may have taken place more often than was detected at the time. It must, though, be remembered that surveys in the North Western Approaches, the South Western Approaches and the North Sea could not have been undertaken anything like as expeditiously or as accurately without the Decca systems, and it was only with the experience gained with the early variants that the later advances could be made and used.

The lattice-generating electronic aids to surveying were augmented by the use of radar, both simple centimetric navigational radar applied to surveying, and special devices. The most common of these was the Decca 'Alpine' precision ranging equipment, by means of which the precise ranges of two prominent points could be measured continuously, the observer tracking the echoes rather in the manner of a gunnery radar. Where no suitable object existed, transponders could be placed ashore, their positions fixed and then the instruments used for ranging.

While returning from New Zealand, where he had been on loan service, Ritchie, now a captain, had seen in South Africa an electronic measuring device, the Tellurometer, which measured the distance between two instruments little larger than theodolites to a high accuracy using phase comparison of high frequency radio transmissions. Ranges of up to ninety miles, and an accuracy of centimetres, were claimed.

To be able to measure the ranges between desired points as well as the angles between them would greatly simplify putting in the control on which any survey must be based, and the Tellurometer allowed this. Two sets were obtained in 1958 and issued to *Vidal* for her West Indies surveys. She used them with great success to connect Trinidad, Tobago and Grenada, measuring very long oversea paths between peaks on the three islands. The Tellurometer quickly became as standard a part of the surveying ship's outfit as the theodolite.

Though the echo-sounder was a great advance over the lead-line for obtaining soundings, there was still no way that the surveyors could know, other than by inference, what lay between his lines of soundings. Experiments had been made in *Gleaner* in 1938 to see if Asdic could reliably detect wrecks or rock pinnacles which would otherwise be missed. They had not been pursued when war came, but in 1947 her report was taken down and dusted off, and a policy that survey areas where depths were critical should be swept with Asdic introduced. At the same time an Asdic set, Type 162, code named 'Cockchafer', which had been developed for detecting bottomed submarines, was fitted in the four *Halcyon*s. This had three strip transducers mounted near the bow of the ship, which emitted a fan-shaped beam. From the shadow which any obstruction proud of the sea bed threw against the returns from the remainder of the seabed the shape of the object could be seen on the recorder trace. 'Cockchafer' was, in effect, a hull-mounted side-scan sonar. Because it was hull mounted it was not effective in any but shallow water, and in the 60's its use was abandoned.

Between the Type 144 Asdic sets fitted in all the major ships and 'Cockchafer' in the home ships working in the North Sea there was at least some attempt to see between the lines of soundings run by the ships and their echo-sounders. However, the effectiveness of the 'blind man's stick' of the 144 depended on the aptitude and alertness of the operator and the water conditions, both widely variable. There was some way to go before any confidence could be placed in detecting any but the largest wrecks and pinnacles which had not shown some indication during sounding.

It had been hoped that, after the end of the war, the plans approved in outline in 1938 for the whole Department to be concentrated on the Taunton site would be implemented. Post-war shortages of building materials, the priority given to the rebuilding of war-devastated cities and the Admiralty's desire to maintain occupation of its shadow headquarters building at Cricklewood prevented the move of Chart Branch and the other sections at Bath to a new building at Taunton. In stead, the Bath sections moved into the Admiralty building in Oxgate Lane, Cricklewood. It was singularly ill-suited to the Department's needs, being a rabbit-warren of small rooms, both above and below ground, with none of the spacious, well-lit drawing offices easily supervised by a senior draughtsman which efficient working required. Perhaps the worst factor of all was the damp, poorly ventilated cellars in which the precious archives had to be kept.

Even the Hydrographer himself was cast out of Whitehall in 1945, and Wyatt had to maintain such liaison as he could with the Naval Staff from an office in the Cricklewood building. Only one (H) captain now acted as Assistant Hydrographer, also at Cricklewood, with the whole range of branches, including new Oceanographic and Air Information branches, under him. Chart Branch still had its naval Superintendent, in charge of the cartographers and cartographic draughtsmen with the Chief Cartographer as his Assistant Superintendent.

Only the Officer in Charge of Staff Charts, with a small staff known still as Chart Branch (Admiralty), remained in Whitehall to provide instant access to charts and hydrographic advice for the Naval Staff. It was not until 1951 that Hydrographer, with a small headquarters staff including a second captain (H) who dealt, among other things, with the appointing of surveying officers, returned to offices in the Admiralty Archway Block.

In August 1945 the Navigation Branch was formally separated from the Department, and became a separate technical division of the Naval Staff. Similarly, the Naval Meteorological Service became independent of Hydrographer in 1947, though as we shall see, this latter came back under Hydrographer's wing in 1966.

Tidal Branch saw the limelight in January 1953, when a combination of spring tides and a series of northerly gales caused water levels in East Anglia, the Thames Estuary and the Dutch coast to rise to record levels, flooding large areas of land with much damage to property and some loss of life. In the aftermath a Flood Warning Service was set up. This was initially based at Cricklewood, but soon moved to the Meteorological Office at Bracknell, though it continued to be manned by Hydrographer's people. After some years, and with the advent of very large vessels in the southern North Sea, it was realised that negative surges, reducing the expected sea level, could be as disastrous for these vessels as the flooding from positive surges was for those on land. The title of the service was changed to Storm Tide Warning Service in 1963, and predictions issued of negative as well as positive surges. The service continues to this day, though it is now manned and controlled by the Met Office.

At Taunton were the Production Branch and Issues and Sales, each under a civil

Organisation Post-World War II – 1950
(At Oxgate Lane, Cricklewood except where shown)

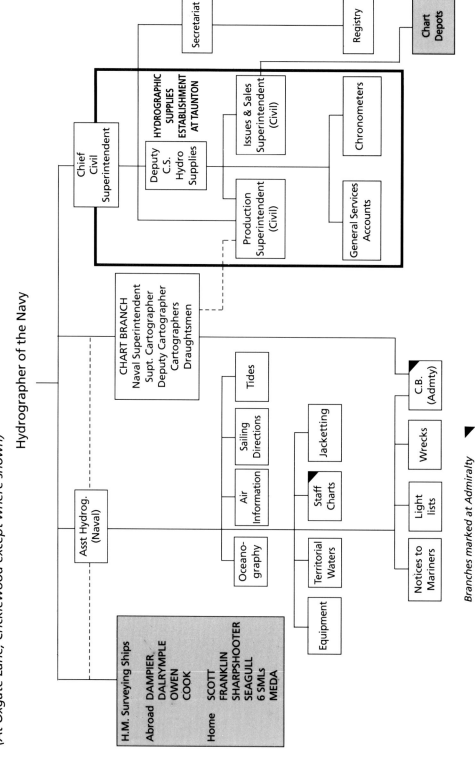

Hydrographer of the Navy

Secretariat

Registry

Chart Depots

Chief Civil Superintendent

HYDROGRAPHIC SUPPLIES ESTABLISHMENT AT TAUNTON

Deputy C.S. Hydro Supplies

Issues & Sales Superintendent (Civil)

Chronometers

Production Superintendent (Civil)

General Services Accounts

CHART BRANCH
Naval Superintendent
Supt. Cartographer
Deputy Cartographer
Cartographers
Draughtsmen

Asst Hydrog. (Naval)

Tides

Sailing Directions

Jacketting

Air Information

Staff Charts

C.B. (Admty)

Oceano-graphy

Territorial Waters

Light lists

Wrecks

Equipment

Notices to Mariners

H.M. Surveying Ships

Abroad DAMPIER, DALRYMPLE OWEN COOK

Home SCOTT FRANKLIN SHARPSHOOTER SEAGULL 6 SMLs MEDA

Branches marked at Admiralty ◢

Superintendent. The whole Hydrographic Supplies Establishment, as it was known, came under the supervision of the Chief Civil Superintendent, Hydrographer's senior administrative civil servant. Like Hydrographer, CCS had to maintain offices both at Cricklewood and at Taunton.

Transport of charting material between Taunton and Cricklewood was by 'basket'. Daily a courier left Cricklewood early in the morning with baskets of chart compilation drawings or corrected proofs. Driven by van to Paddington he went by train to Taunton, and returned later in the same day with new proofs to be seen and corrected, or with mint copies of new charts or new editions. Mistakes were always blamed on the 'other' end, and the system was a recipe for delay and inefficiency.

The vexed question of cartographers' pay was raised again as soon as the war ended. We have seen that the deliberations of the Carpenter Committee of 1929-1930 had helped to resolve some of the anomalies in the scientific and technical establishments, and that the cartographers received what they and the IPCS considered was only an interim award in 1940. Apart from the need to push any increase through the resistance of a parsimonious and short-sighted Treasury, the inclusion of the cartographers in the Carpenter scheme stumbled on the distinction made by Carpenter in the Scientific Class between Scientific Officers and Technical Officers, the latter supposedly having less supervisory responsibility and so attracting a lower rate of pay. It was argued that all cartographers had supervisory responsibilities over the draughtsmen in their sections, and should be assimilated at the Scientific Officer rates.

Finally, after a series of staff inspections at Bath and Cricklewood in 1943 and 1944, the position was conceded and it was agreed that cartographers equated to Scientific Officers. Their pay remained the subject of special negotiations, culminating in an award in December 1949 which gave a starting rate of £330 for all personnel, rising to £850 for men or £725 for women, with the Superintending Cartographer's maximum at £1400.

The new pay rates helped to encourage recruits for the large intake of young cartographers from 1947 to 1950. All graduates, some from pre-war study but more from the immediate post-war intake to universities, they were a stalwart and enthusiastic band who left a gap in the Department's capabilities when they retired in the late 1980s.

With virtual assimilation achieved, comparison with the staff of the Ordnance Survey and the newly formed Directorate of Overseas Surveys led to suggestions for a name for the class more in keeping with its work and status. Wyatt agreed with the cartographers' wish, but prolonged discussion failed to come up with a title all were happy with. Eventually 'Civil Hydrographic Officer' was taken as the basic title, rising through Senior CHO, Principal CHO, and Assistant Chief CHO to the dizzy heights of Chief Civil Hydrographic Officer. This change was introduced along with the new pay scale in December 1949.

Though assimilation of pay had been achieved, career prospects remained strictly limited to the Department, and promotion was very much a matter of 'dead mens' shoes'. This was particularly the case with promotion to the one CCHO post. Since these were always the best and brightest of their seniority, it followed that they were promoted at an early age, and with no outlet to rise further stayed in post for an inordinate time. Between 1938 and 1972 there were only three holders of the top professional post in the Department.

With the war at an end it had been hoped to tackle the back-log of charting work which had built up. Despite the general run-down the number of cartographers and draughtsmen actually increased from 45 cartographers and 102 draughtsmen in 1944 to 54 cartographers and 127 draughtsmen in 1950, but new commitments far exceeded the staff available, so the number of people directly engaged in chart work decreased. The production of latticed charts for the Decca chains now springing up was a major task, all lattices being computed and then drawn by hand. There was a great increase immediately after the war in the scope of the Admiralty Lists of Radio Signals, reflecting both the increase in facilities for ships and the number and size of ship carrying radio equipment, which placed a heavy and continuous load on the section concerned. The rise of interest in oceanography, both in the scientific community and for defence, called forth a demand for publications which also needed staff to produce.

Though most charts were still engraved on copper at the start of the period, all printing was now done from zinc-enamel positives by the rotary offset process. It was not long before the master bases began to be produced on enamelled zincs. The combination of photography and photosensitive coating on plates led to fair drawing to reproduction standard directly onto zincs, from which printing zincs were then copied photographically. At first the time and effort involved were little different from that taken by engraving. It was in the subsequent maintenance of the master base that the new process gained over the old. To produce photographically a new master with the area to be altered patched out, and then to redraw the altered work, was much easier than to hammer out a patch of copper and re-engrave it. An added factor was that it was extremely difficult to keep the amended area on a copper plate flat enough to photograph without errors.

In 1957 experiments were begun with plastic sheets in place of zinc or copper plates. After some initial difficulties in finding inks which were both permanent and kindly to the pen, plastic materials soon came to dominate the draughting processes.

Another factor encouraging the use of first zinc and then plastic rather than copper was the increasing use of colour on charts. In 1948 the washing of shallow water areas with a blue tint, to help make shoals and dangers stand out, was introduced. By 1954 some 530 charts had been printed with shallow water blue. It was extremely difficult to control the dimensions of overlays to copper plates to achieve the close register needed to print two or more colour areas which have to adjoin exactly, whereas it is comparatively easy when the different plates have all been produced from the same masters photographically.

The printing of Decca and Loran lattices on charts also required the use of up to three extra colours. Initially the latticed charts were not kept up to date, and navigators were expected to fix on the latticed chart and then transfer their position to an unlatticed, fully corrected navigational chart. This was clearly an unneccessary complication, and from the beginning of 1956 the latticed charts were kept corrected exactly as unlatticed ones.

In 1948 Wyatt resisted Treasury demands to raise chart prices by arguing not only that our prices needed to relate to other nations' chart prices, but also that after the war our charts were so much in need of correction and modernisation that they would not stand comparison with others. The situation did not greatly improve until the start of the modernisation and metrication programme in 1968, though it was not Departmental policy to publicise the shortcomings of the Admiralty chart series.

The mistake of trying to impose a overreaching system of chart distribution on the commercial market was not repeated after the Second World War. As early as July 1944 meetings were held with the British Nautical Instrument Trade Association to discuss the way in which Admiralty charts and publications would be marketed when peace returned. The system which had evolved after the withdrawal of direct supply from the Admiralty to ships in 1921, of a world-wide chain of agents selling charts and publications with a trade discount to them was reinstated. As before, major (Class A) agents were responsible for correcting charts up to the date of sale, and special daily sets of Notices to Mariners were supplied to them to enable them to do this.

The numerous chart depots set up during the war were soon closed down. The smaller home depots, as well as Alexandria, Freetown and Kilindini were all closed by the end of 1946, with Singapore and Hong Kong reopened by the same time.

The International Hydrographic Bureau had been kept in being by the French Director, Ingenieur General Hydrographique de Vanssay de Blavous, throughout the war, with considerable hardship to himself and his skeleton staff. Admiral Nares was released from Bath to go out to Monaco in November 1944, after the liberation of the south of France, to investigate the situation, and returned permanently in July 1945. The Bureau building had been badly damaged when a ship was torpedoed and sunk alongside the quay, but the Monegasque government arranged and paid for its repair.

Nares and de Vanssay summoned an International Hydrographic Conference for April 1947, ten years after the last. They were joined just before it started by the American Director, Rear Admiral L.R.Leahy. With only seventeen states now members the conference was a fairly low-key affair, though it was attended by a number* of other states who expressed their interest in joining at some future date. The statutes of the Convention were confirmed, and it was agreed that, despite the demise of the League of Nations, the member states did not want the Bureau to

---

*Chile, the Allied Supervisor of the German Hydrographic Office, Italy, Mexico, the Netherlands, Turkey and Yugoslavia.

come under the United Nations. With the membership both so small and likely to expand before long it was decided to elect only two Directors. Nares was re-elected as President, with Rear Admiral C.L.Nichols, US Coast and Geodetic Survey, as his co-director.

By the next conference, in 1952, the expected expansion had begun. The number of member states had risen to 30, with Belgium and Iceland attending as observers. The full three Directors were elected, Nichols as President, Nares yet again, and Captain A. Viglieri of Italy. Nares died in office just before the 1957 conference.

International co-operation burgeoned after the war, though no formal network was put in place before the next decade. It was, though, very much in the interests of the hydrographic offices maintaining a world chart series to obtain as much standardisation across the whole hydrographic community as practicable. It was also in the interests of the smaller nations, since if their methods were compatible with the larger services, they could benefit from training and exchange programmes. It was also always pointed out that marine accidents damage the coast off which they occur far more than the flag state of the vessel involved, and it is in the interest of any state that ships approaching its shores carry accurate and up to date charts. It has always been the Admiralty view that the surveys the Navy does outside the areas of direct United Kingdom responsibility are the subscription that they pay to gain access to the pool of information obtainable through the IHB.

The Principal Surveys of 1946

HOME

Franklin (+ 2 SMLs)	Tripp	England, East Coast	Thames Estuary;
Scott (+ 2 SMLs)	Bill	England, East Coast	Humber approaches; Yarmouth to Winterton.
		Scotland, East Coast	Approaches to Rosyth.
Seagull	Collins	England, West Coast	Liverpool Bay.
		Wales, West Coast	Milford Haven.
		Scotland, West Coast	Islay to Inishtrahull.
SMLs 585, 586	Dickson	England, East Coast	Thames Estuary wrecks.
South Coast of England Survey Unit	Price	England, South Coast	Portsmouth; Plymouth; Portland; Weymouth.

ABROAD

Challenger	Southern	Oman	Daimanyat Islands.
		Persian Gulf	Bahrain eastward.
White Bear	Day	Malay Peninsula	Approaches to Penang; Approaches to Port Swettenham.
		Mediterranean	Straits of Gibraltar, The Ridges.
Sharpshooter	Menzies	Malay Peninsula	Kuantan River; Rompin River.
		Borneo	Sungei Brunei.
SMLs 1254, 1301	Marshall	Mediterranean	Pantelleria; Beirut; Piraeus; Cyprus.

The Principal Surveys of 1947

HOME

Franklin (+ 2 SMLs)	Tripp	England, East Coast	Thames Estuary; Goodwin Sands; Harwich harbour.
Scott (+ 2 SMLs)	Bill	England, East Coast	The Humber; Approaches to Yarmouth and Lowestoft.
		Scotland, East Coast	Inverness and approaches.
Seagull	Collins	England, West Coast	Bristol Channel entrance.
		Scotland, West Coast	Kilbrannan Sound; Gareloch.
		Ireland, North Coast	N.W. Approaches to St George's Channel; Lough Foyle.
SMLs 585, 586	Royds	England, East Coast	Thames Estuary (wreck sweeping).
S.C.E.S.U.	Price	England, South Coast	Portsmouth; Portland.

ABROAD

Challenger	Southern	Persian Gulf	Qatar peninsula.
		Mediterranean	Cyprus coast.
Sharpshooter	Menzies	Malay Peninsula	Klang Strait.
		Borneo	Rajang River.
ML 1301	D.P.D.Scott	Mediterranean	Tobruk; Cyrenaican ports; Cyprus ports; Malta.

The Principal Surveys of 1948

HOME

Franklin	Connell	England, East Coast	River Medway.
Scott	Griffiths	England, East Coast	River Medway; Thames Estuary; River Stour.
Seagull	Hennessey	England, East Coast	Thames Estuary and approaches.
		Bristol Channel	Weston-super-mare to Portishead.
Sharpshooter (+ 4 SMLs)	Irving	England, East Coast	Lowestoft approaches; The Wash, Freeman Channel; East Coast NEMEDRI Route.
SMLs 585, 586	Royds	England, East Coast	attached to Sheerness M/S Flotilla.
S.C.E.S.U.	Price	England, South Coast	Solent; Portland.

ABROAD

Challenger	Southern, Sharpey-Schafer	Persian Gulf Mediterranean	Approaches to Doha. Cyprus, W & N coasts.
Dampier	Collins	Malay Peninsula	Tumpat approaches; Approaches to Klang.
		Borneo	Bintulu approaches.
ML 1301	Glen, White	Mediterranean	Zuara; Tripoli: Cyprus (attached to *Challenger*)

The Principal Surveys of 1949

HOME

Franklin (+ 1 SML)	Connell	England, East Coast	Thames Estuary and approaches.
Owen	Menzies	Scotland, West Coast	Outer Hebrides, shoal examinations.
Scott (+ 1 SML)	Griffiths	Scotland, West Coast England, East Coast	Firth of Clyde. Approaches to Colne and Blackwater Rivers.
Seagull (+ 2 SMLs)	Lowry	Bristol Channel	Worms Head to Watchet; Swansea Bay; Sker Point to Nash Point; Barnstaple and Bideford.
Sharpshooter (+ 2 SMLs)	Irving, Berncastle	England, East Coast	Blakeney to Winterton; Approaches to Lowestoft.
S.C.E.S.U. (*Meda*)	Price	England, South Coast	Portsmouth; Portland.

ABROAD

Challenger	Sharpey-Schafer	Persian Gulf	Qatar, east coast.
Dalrymple	Day, E H B Baker	Mediterranean	Malta Channel;Eastern Approaches to Malta; Grand Harbour; Tripoli (Libya).
		Persian Gulf	Northern Approaches to Bahrain
Dampier	Hennessey	Borneo	Batang Sadong and approaches; Sipitang Roads.
		Malay Peninsula	Sungei Kelantan to the Perhentian Is.

Owen, the third of the Bay class conversions, conducted work-up surveys in Scottish waters before sailing for the Persian Gulf in October. She did not start surveys in the Gulf until early 1950.

The Principal Surveys of 1950

HOME

Franklin (+ 1 SML)	Roe	England, East Coast	Thames Estuary.
Scott (+ 2 SMLs)	Griffiths, Ashton	England, East Coast	The Naze to Orfordness.
		England, South Coast	Poole Bay and western approaches.
Seagull (+ 2 SMLs)	Gordon	England, South Coast	Bolt Tail to Teignmouth; Tor Bay
Sharpshooter (+ 2 SMLs)	Berncastle	England, East Coast	Sheringham to Winterton; Winterton Shoal and Newarp Bank; Ramsgate, Cross Ridge.
S.C.E.S.U. (*Meda*)	Monk	England, South Coast	The Solent; Portsmouth.

ABROAD

Challenger	Bill, Ritchie.		World Oceanographic Voyage.
Dampier	Hennessey	Borneo	Gaya Bay and approaches; Labuan, Victoria Harbour.
		Malay Peninsula	Kuala Pahang and approaches; Pulau Tioman.
Dalrymple	E H B Baker, Irving	Persian Gulf	Approaches to Ras Tannura; N. Approaches to Qatar.
		Mediterranean	Adventure Bank
Owen	Menzies	Persian Gulf	N. Approaches to Bahrain; N. Approaches to Qatar.
		Mediterranean	Cyprus.

The Principal Surveys of 1951

HOME

Cook	Collins	English Channel	Hurd Deep.
		Scotland, West Coast	Gunna Sound; Loch Maddy; The Minches.
Franklin	Roe, Royds	Scotland, West Coast	Oban and approaches;N.W.coast of Mull; The Small Isles.
		England, East Coast	Thames Estuary.
		Ireland, North Coast	Lough Foyle.
Scott (+ 2 SMLs)	Ashton, Grattan	England, South Coast	Start Bay; Nare Point to the Manacles; Straight Point to Portland; Shoreham; Dartmouth.
Sharpshooter (+ 2 SMLs)	Gordon Penfold	England, East Coast	Harwich Harbour;Banks off Norfolk; Approaches to Lowestoft.
S.C.E.S. (*Meda*)	Monk	England, South Coast	Portsmouth; The Solent.

ABROAD

Challenger	Ritchie		World Oceanographic Voyage.
Dalrymple	Irving	Persian Gulf	Approaches to Qatar.
		Africa, East Coast	Approaches to Zanzibar.
Dampier	Connell	Borneo	Tanjong Batu to Butang Tanau; Kuala Similajau.
		Malay Peninsula	Penang; Singapore.
Owen	Menzies	Persian Gulf	N. Approaches to Qatar; Jazirat Arzanah to Jazirat Das.
		Mediterranean	Tobruk; Tripoli.

Cook and *Scott* assisted in the search for the submarine *Affray*, which sunk in the English Channel in April.

The Principal Surveys of 1952

HOME

Cook (+ 1 SML)	E H B Baker	Scotland, West Coast	North Minch; N.W. approaches to the Hebrides.
Franklin	Hall	England, East Coast	Thames Estuary.
		Scotland, West Coast	Loch Striven; Loch Linnhe.
Scott (+ 2 SMLs)	Grattan	England, South Coast	Lyme Bay; Dartmouth; Newhaven; Salcombe.
		Wales, West Coast	Milford Haven.
		North Atlantic	Oceanography with RRS *Discovery II*
Sharpshooter (+ 2 SMLs)	Penfold	England, East Coast	Thames Estuary; Skegness to Blakeney.
		Scotland, East Coast	Firth of Forth.
S.C.E.S.U. (*Meda*)	Monk	England, South Coast	The Solent; Plymouth.

ABROAD

Challenger	Ashton		World Oceanographic Voyage.
Dalrymple	Irving	Persian Gulf	Eastern approaches to Qatar.
		Mediterranean	Adventure Bank.
Dampier	Connell	China, South Coast	Hong Kong.
		Borneo	Sandakan to the Mallawallee Channel.
		Malay Peninsula	Pulau Tioman; Penang.
Owen	Roe	Persian Gulf	Eastern Approaches to Qatar.
		Red Sea	Approaches to Mohammed Qol.
		Mediterranean	Tobruk; Benghazi; Tripoli (Libya).

The Principal Surveys of 1953

HOME

Cook	E H B Baker, Connell	Bristol Channel	Flatholm to Portishead.
		Scotland, West Coast	Hebrides; Loch Shell.
		England, West Coast	Morecambe Bay.
		Africa, West Coast	Gold Coast, Tema.
Scott (+ 2 SMLs)	Hall	England, East Coast	Thames Estuary.
		England, South Coast	Lyme Bay.
		Ireland, East Coast	Strangford Lough.
		Wales, West Coast	Milford Haven.
Shackleton (+ 2 SMLs)	Paisley, Pryor	England, East Coast	Thames Estuary; Approaches to Yarmouth & Lowestoft.
		Scotland, East Coast	Firth of Forth.
		Belgium	Approaches to Ostend.
S.C.E.S.U. (*Meda*)	Monk	England, South Coast	Portsmouth; Portland; Chichester Harbour.

ABROAD

Challenger	Ashton	North Atlantic	Oceanography.
		North Sea	Oceanography.
Dalrymple	Bill	Persian Gulf	E. Approaches to Qatar.
		Africa, East Coast	Zanzibar; Dar es Salaam.
Dampier	Grattan	Borneo	Darvel Bay.
		Malay Peninsula	Tinggi to Mersing; Approaches to Penang.
Owen	Roe	Persian Gulf	E. Approaches to Qatar.
		Mediterranean	Cyprus.

Cook, *Scott* and *Shackleton* attended Queen Elizabeth II's Coronation Review at Spithead in June. *Shackleton* was *Sharpshooter* renamed.

The Principal Surveys of 1954

HOME

Cook	Connell	Scotland, West Coast	North Minch; Sound of Harris; Loch Long; Loch Fyne; Loch Ewe; Approaches to the Firth of Lorne.
Scott	Roe	England, East Coast	Thames Estuary.
		Wales, West Coast	Milford Haven.
		England, South Coast	Lyme Bay.
Shackleton	Pryor, Hatfield	England, East Coast	Thames Estuary; Skegness to Blakeney.
East Coast of England Survey Unit (4 SMLs)	Glen	England, East Coast	Approaches toLowestoft; Winterton Ness to Benacre Point; Thames Estuary.
S.C.E.S.U (*Meda*)	Monk	England, South Coast	Portsmouth; Plymouth; Bembridge harbour; Chichester harbour.

ABROAD

Dalrymple	Bill, Paisley.	Persian Gulf	Approaches to Bahrain; Western Approaches to Jazirat Yas; Jazirat Halul to Fasht Hadaid.
		Africa, East Coast	Approaches to Zanzibar.
Dampier	Grattan	Borneo	Billean to Kububan.
		Malay Peninsula	Pulau Aur to Pulau Tioman; Approaches to Penang.
Owen	Paisley, Hatfield	Persian Gulf	Northern Approaches to Bahrain; Creagh Shoal to Bu Tini.
		Mediterranean	North Coast of Cyprus.
Vidal	Collins	Scotland, West Coast	Mull of Galloway to Little Ross.
		West Indies	Kingston, Jamaica; Port Royal; Montego Bay; Belize.

Scott and *Shackleton* were part of a squadron assembled off Southend to welcome Queen Elizabeth home at the end of her Commonwealth Tour.

The Principal Surveys of 1955

HOME			
Cook	Hayter	Scotland, West Coast	Firth of Clyde; Colonsay to the Garvellachs; Sound of Islay.
Scott	Royds	England, East Coast	Thames Estuary; The Downs.
		England, South Coast	Anvil Point to St Catherine's Deep.
Shackleton	Hatfield	England, East Coast	Skegness to Blakeney.
		Scotland, North Coast	Oceanography.
E.C.E.S.U. (4 SMLs)	Glen, Hunt	England, East Coast	Fisherman's Gat; Rivers Crouch and Roach; Corton Road.
		England, South Coast	Dover; Folkestone.
S.C.E.S.U. (*Meda*)	Monk, Grattan	England, South Coast	Portsmouth; Dartmouth; Plymouth; Beaulieu River.
	ABROAD		
Dalrymple	Paisley	Africa, East Coast	Approaches to Zanzibar.
		Mediterranean	Malta, St Paul's Bay; Grand Harbour; Marsamxett. Cyprus, Famagusta.
Dampier	Roe	Malay Peninsula	Singapore, Pulau Bukum; Blair Harbour to Kuala Merchong.
		Borneo	Mallawallee Channel.
Owen	Pryor	Persian Gulf	Eastern Approaches to Bahrain; Khor Halj to Rig az Zakum; Kuwait.
Vidal	Connell	North Atlantic	Oceanography

Vidal was greatly delayed by machinery defects. While in dockyard hands in Chatham a boat party carried out surveys in River Stour and Pegwell Bay. During her North Atlantic Oceanography she landed by helicopter on and annexed Rockall.

The Principal Surveys of 1956

HOME

Cook	Hayter	Scotland, West Coast	Loch Fyne; Western Approaches to the North Channel; Sound of Islay; Oceanography.
		Wales, North Coast	Holyhead.
Scott	Hatfield	England, East Coast	The Wash, Boston Deep.
		Shetland Islands	Oceanography.
		England, South Coast	Anvil Point to Owers; Sandown Bay.
E.C.E.S.U. (4 SMLs)	Hunt, C J de C Scott	England, East Coast	Thames Estuary; Winterton Ness to Benacre Point; Harwich Harbour.
S.C.E.S.U. (*Meda*)	Monk, Paisley	England, South Coast	Portland; West Solent; Needles Channel; Devonport.

ABROAD

Dalrymple	Paisley	Mediterranean	Malta, Grand Harbour; Marsamxett; Marsaxlokk; Southern and Eastern Approaches to Malta; Suez Canal.
Dampier	Royds	Borneo	Mallawallee Channel; Tawau; Wallace Bay; Darvel Bay; Muara.
		Malay Peninsula	Port Swettenham; Dindings River; Western Approaches to Singapore.
Owen	Pryor	Persian Gulf	Creagh Shoal to Bu Tini; Las Hats Islets to Khor Duwein; Kuwait.
Vidal	Connell	West Indies	Approaches to Kingston, Jamaica; Portland Bight; Grand Cayman; Nassau Harbour, Bahamas.
Antarctic Survey Party	Wynne-Edwards		Bismarck Strait; Western Gerlache Channel; Approaches to Port Lockroy.

Dalrymple formed part of the assault force for the invasion of the Suez Canal. On withdrawal she remained with the United Nations organisation to clear the canal of wrecks and mines. *Cook*, in addition to surveys listed, carried out examinations of Scottish lochs before the visit of H.M.the Queen in *Britannia*. A party of surveying personnel, working from the *Protector* and from Falklands Islands Dependencies Survey vessels, was sent south for the first time in the southern summer of 1956/57. In this and the following tables the work carried out is listed under the year the party left Britain. *Shackleton* was under extended refit for the whole of the year.

The Principal Surveys of 1957

HOME

Dalrymple	Winstanley	Scotland, West Coast	North Channel; Tobermory.
		Ireland, North Coast	Lough Foyle.
Shackleton	C J de C Scott	England, South Coast	Sandown Bay.
		Scotland, West Coast	Loch Carnan; Firth of Lorne
E.C.E.S.U. (5 SMLs)	Simeon	England, East Coast	Thames Estuary; Approaches to Lowestoft; Winterton Ness to Benacre Point; Harwich harbour; Felixstowe to Orfordness.
S.C.E.S.U. (*Meda*)	Paisley	England, South Coast	Portsmouth; Approaches to Shoreham; Portland; Swanage Bay.

ABROAD

Cook	Hatfield	Fiji Islands	Natewa Bay; Vuya Passage.
		Gilbert Islands	Tarawa.
Dalrymple	Winstanley	Mediterranean	Malta Exercise Areas
Dampier	Royds	Malay Peninsula	Kuala Merchong to Kuala Pahang; Johore Strait.
Owen	Hall	Africa, East Coast	Pemba I, Chaki Chaki Bay.
		Red Sea	Oceanography.
Vidal	Irving	West Indies	Bahamas, Nassau harbour; Egg Reef; Long Island; Great Inagua. Jamaica, Formigas Bank; Henry Holmes Bank; Albatross Bank; Morant Cays; Mackerel Bank; Oracabessa; Savannah-la-Mar. Belize harbour. Trinidad, East Coast.
Antarctic Survey Party	Wynne-Edwards, Stumbles		South Georgia, anchorages & bays; Argentine Islands, Grandidier Channel.

Cook assisted at Christmas Island in the test of the first British hydrogen bomb. *Scott* was in extended refit for the whole year. *Dampier* entered extended refit in Hong Kong in July, leaving a party with two motor boats under Martin to survey the Johore Strait.

The Principal Surveys of 1958

HOME

Dalrymple	Haslam	England, South Coast	St Catherine's Point to Owers; River Medina.
Scott	Simeon	Scotland, East Coast	Approaches to Aberdeen; Peterhead harbour and approaches; Approaches to Wick; Firth of Forth; Oceanography.
Shackleton	D.P.D.Scott	Scotland, West Coast	Sound of Harris; Gareloch; Campbeltown Loch; Approaches to the Firth of Lorne.
		Bristol Channel	Portishead to Newport.
E.C.E.S.U. (SMLs 322, 326, 3516; *Echo*)	Green	England, East Coast	Thames Estuary; Felixstowe to Orford Haven; Approaches to Lowestoft; Goodwin Sands; Naze to Sunk Light.
S.C.E.S.U. (*Meda*)	Paisley	England, South Coast	Portsmouth; Rye Bay; Swanage Bay; Approaches to Par and Charlestown.

ABROAD

Cook	Hatfield	Solomon Islands	Lunga Roads; N and S approaches to Gizo and Honiara; New Georgia Sound.
Dampier	Haslam	Malay Peninsula	Johore Strait; Pulau Aur; S approaches to Penang; Approaches to the Dindings River.
Owen	Hall, Roe	Indian Ocean	Western Approaches to the Seychelles.
		Africa, East Coast	Pemba, Approaches to Mkoani.
Vidal	Irving	West Indies	Belize harbour; Commerce Bight; Big Creek; Navidad Bank; Trinidad, N E Coast; Grenada, St Georges.
Antarctic Survey Parties	Wynne-Edwards, Stumbles		Lemaire Channel to French Passage; South Georgia, Leith Harbour, Cumberland Bay and Grytviken.

Dampier completed her extended refit in July, and collected her Johore Strait survey party at the end of that month. *Dalrymple* entered extended refit at Devonport in May.

The Principal Surveys of 1959

HOME

Scott	Simeon	England, East Coast	Thames Estuary; Approaches to the Humber; Dogger Bank.
		Scotland, East Coast	Firth of Forth.
Shackleton	Smith RNZN	Wales, North Coast	North Eastern Approaches to the Menai Strait; Menai Strait.
		Scotland, West Coast	Vidal Bank; Sound of Iona.
Vidal	Connell	Ireland, North Coast	Approaches to Lough Foyle.
E.C.E.S.U. (*Echo, Egeria, Enterprise,* SDML 3516)	Green	England, East Coast	Thames Estuary; Naze to Sunk LV; Goodwin Sands; Approaches to Ramsgate.
S.C.E.S.U. (*Meda*)	Paisley	England, South Coast	Portsmouth Harbour & approaches; Cowes harbour.
		Channel Islands	Alderney, Braye Harbour & approaches.

ABROAD

Cook	Hatfield, Pryor.	Solomon Islands	Bina Harbour.
		Fiji Islands	Approaches to Lambasa; Vuya Passage; Moon Reef to Ovalau.
		Gilbert Islands	Tarawa, Betio; Abemama.
		Ellice Islands	Nanumanga.
Dalrymple	Ritchie	Persian Gulf	Jazirat Daz to Jazirat Halul; Jazirat Ghagha to Jazirat Dalma.
Dampier	Haslam	Malay Peninsula	Kuala Gula to Tanjong Hantu; Eastern approaches to the Singapore Strait; Kuala Pahang to Tanjong Gelang; Dindings River & approaches.
		Borneo	Sarawak, Tanjong Sirik to Mukah.
Owen	Roe	Persian Gulf	Bahrain, Khor Kaliya; Khor al Odaid to Ras Khumais.
Vidal	Connell	Atlantic Ocean	Princess Alice Bank; Marsala Bank.
		West Indies	Approaches to Bermuda; Coast of British Guiana.

Owen entered extended refit in May, *Dalrymple* completed in July. SML 3516 was rammed by a Dutch coaster in fog off Ramsgate, requiring the complete rebuilding of her bow.

Biographies

1945–1960

Vice Admiral Sir Guy Wyatt, KBE, CB
Hydrographer 1945-1950

Arthur Guy Norris Wyatt was born in 1893, the son of Arthur Norris Wyatt, and entered the Royal Navy through Osborne and Dartmouth. He began surveying in 1914, but the First World War broke out as he joined the *Triton*, Tinson. During the war he saw service with the Grand Fleet and the Dover patrol, and in 1918 commanded the destroyer *Beagle* on anti-submarine and escort duty.

Returning to surveying in the *Melisande*, Maxwell, he shared in the troubles of that unfortunate converted yacht. In 1919 he went out to the *Fantome*, Scott and later Maxwell, in Australia. Surveying was begun in boats in Port Jackson and Port Stephens, and then when the ship was ready for service she proceeded to the Torres Strait. In 1921 he came home to the *Kellett*, Harvey then Haselfoot, to do two seasons on Thames Estuary and east coast surveys, before going out to Australia again with the *Herald*, Harvey and then Silk, working in the Torres Strait and on the Great Barrier Reef.

In 1926 Wyatt was appointed to his first command, the *Ormonde*, surveying in British Guiana. From the following year he had the *Beaufort* for two years working on the west coasts of England and Scotland and on the north coast of Ireland. He returned to the *Ormonde* in 1929, working this time in the Persian Gulf and in Cyprus. In the Gulf he had trouble with some of the minor sheiks. In particular the Sheik of Khasab fired on boats, rolled rocks down the cliffs onto coastlining parties and declared that he would 'declare a Holy War and drink their blood'. Pressure from his suzerain the Sultan of Muscat and a bombardment by the SNO Persian Gulf soon changed the sheik's mind, and a later message 'hoped that the peeping nymphs of Paradise would shine on them'.

After spending 1931 at home in the *Fitzroy* on the east coast, Wyatt took the *Challenger* to the West Indies and to Labrador. Here the ship ran onto a pinnacle rock, and was only refloated with some difficulty.

After the 1935 season in the *Flinders* on the south coast Wyatt came ashore to be Superintendent of Charts until 1937, when he commissioned the *Endeavour* for surveys in New Zealand waters until the Second World War broke out. An appointment as Superintendent of Strategic Surveys did not last long, and Wyatt

173

became Assistant Hydrographer in 1940. Before this he had taken part in the rapid reconnaissance surveys of the Normandy coast before they were overrun by the German advance.

In 1942 he took the *Challenger,* now equipped with chart production equipment, out to the Eastern Fleet, making surveys and charts at Mombasa. As Fleet Hydrographic Officer he organised shore chart production facilities first in Nairobi and then at Dehra Dun, and a chart depot at Colombo from which Notices to Mariners were issued. For these services he was mentioned in despatches. In 1944 *Challenger* went to Sydney for refit, and thereafter to the Torres Strait to survey and sweep a deep channel through for the Pacific Fleet, but Wyatt was recalled to become Hydrographer in May 1945.

His five years as Hydrographer were spent at Cricklewood, where the Department had been sent in response to pressure for accommodation in Whitehall. He oversaw the return of the Hydrographic Service afloat and ashore to peacetime routines, with many staff reductions. He was promoted to rear admiral in 1945, awarded the CB in 1948, and made KBE in 1949, being promoted to vice admiral on the retired list in that year.

In retirement he settled in Tasmania, where he died in 1982.

Vice Admiral Sir Archibald Day, KBE, CB, DSO
Hydrographer 1950-1955

Archibald Day was born in 1899, the third son of Donald D.Day, FRCS, of Norwich. He entered the Navy through HMS *Conway* and Dartmouth, but was only one term at the latter due to the mobilisation of the cadets in August 1914. During the First World War he saw service as midshipman and sublieutenant in the Grand Fleet and in a destroyer in the Mediterranean. Day began surveying in 1920 soon after promotion to lieutenant, joining the *Endeavour,* Reyne and then Geary- Hill, on the north coast of Egypt. In 1922 he went to the *Fitzroy,* Woodhouse and later Silk, on the east coast of England. From 1925 to 1928 he was on the China station in the *Iroquois,* Jackson, surveying in the South China Sea and on the coasts of Malaya. From August 1928 he did a year in the Department as a naval assistant and Territorial Waters Officer. He then went back to the *Endeavour,* Law, Edgell and Rice successively, working in the Red Sea and on the coast of Palestine. For the first half of 1932 he was ashore in the Department as a naval assistant in the Chart Branch.

In June 1932 Day was appointed to his first command, the *Fitzroy,* for a year on the east coast of England and Scotland. He then went to the *Ormonde* in the Persian Gulf and in Cyprus, but the commission, during which he was promoted commander in 1934, was ended in 1935 by the Abyssinian crisis. Briefly on the Commander in Chief's staff as Maintenance Commander at Malta, he then went in charge of the survey unit at Alexandria.

He next served ashore as Superintendent of Charts during 1937 and 1938 before commissioning the new ship *Scott* at Dundee in February 1939 for work on the east coast. Earmarked for the *Endeavour*, instead on the outbreak of the Second World War Day went to the staff of Vice Admiral Dover as Staff Officer (H), becoming Chief of Staff in February 1941. He was promoted to captain in 1940, and made CBE in 1941.

In 1943 and 1944 he was Assistant Hydrographer, a period which included the Sicily and Normandy landings. In September 1944 he went via the USA and Australia, visiting their hydrographic offices, to become Fleet Hydrographic Officer Eastern Fleet, and to take command of the converted yacht *White Bear*. In 1945 he was in charge of surveys and minesweeping for the re-entry into Rangoon, and was awarded the DSO. After the Japanese surrender the *White Bear* surveyed re-occupied ports in the area, and on the west coast of Malaya, before returning to England in the summer of 1946 to pay off.

From September 1946 for two years Day was again Assistant Hydrographer, with an additional six months in the Department to write up its war history. Then in December 1948 he commissioned the *Dalrymple* for surveys in the Mediterranean. Six months later he was promoted to Rear Admiral and appointed Flag Officer British Naval Forces Germany, based in Hamburg. He served there from August 1949 until he became Hydrographer in June 1950.

Early in his time in office Day arranged for Hydrographer and a small headquarters staff to return to the Admiralty. He saw the development of the Decca Navigator into Two Range Decca, encouraged co-operation between the Navy and civil ocean scientists, and in international hydrography and oceanography. He was promoted to Vice Admiral in 1953, and made KBE in 1954. Retiring in 1955, he at once took a party of three to survey Lake Nyasa, but was soon allowed to break his contract with the East African Federal Government to join, at Royal Society instigation, the secretariat of the International Geophysical Year at Brussels where he worked from 1956 to 1958. He led the United Kingdom delegation to the Inter Governmental Oceanographic Commission from 1962 to 1965. He was the last Admiralty representative on the Port of London Authority Board, serving from 1961 until its reorganisation in 1967. He was appointed Acting Conservator of the River Mersey in 1961 and Chairman of the Dover Harbour Board in 1965.

He was invited by Irving to write the History of the Admiralty Hydrographic Service from 1795 to 1919, which was published in 1967. He also wrote widely on hydrography and its history for the periodical press. He died in July 1970.

Rear Admiral K St B Collins, CB, OBE, DSC
Hydrographer 1955-1960

Kenneth St Barbe Collins was born in 1904, son of Colonel C.B.Collins, Royal Engineers. He entered the Royal Navy through Osborne and Dartmouth Colleges. He took up surveying as a sublieutenant in 1926, joining the *Fitzroy*, Harvey and later Lockhart, working on the east coast of England. Promoted to lieutenant, he served from 1927 to 1929 in the *Ormonde*, Rice, on Indian Ocean and Malacca Strait surveys. After a short spell at home in the *Beaufort*, Rice, he was abroad again from 1930 to 1932 in the *Herald*, Maxwell and later Hardy, working on the Borneo coast, in the approaches to Hong Kong, and in the 'dangerous area' in the South China Sea.

In 1932 Collins came home to the *Flinders*, Simpson, surveying on the south and west coasts of England. He then, in 1933, went abroad to the *Endeavour*, Southern, working successively on the west coast of Africa, in the eastern Mediterranean, and on the west coasts of Siam and Malaya. After a meteorological course at the Air Ministry in 1936 he went back to the *Herald*, Hardy and later Jenks, surveying in the South China Sea and on the coasts of Borneo and Malaya.

He came ashore in 1939 to be a naval assistant in Chart Branch, and when war broke out he went as meteorological officer in the seaplane carrier *Albatross*, based at Freetown, Sierra Leone, and operating against the *Graf Spee*. He was promoted commander in 1940, and went in command of the *Scott* for two years' extremely arduous surveying with the minelaying squadron in northern waters. During this time he was involved with the raid on the Lofoten Islands, Operation ANKLET, and was awarded the DSC. From 1942 to 1944 he was on the staff of Admiral Ramsey, Allied Naval Commander Expeditionary Forces, first for the North African landings and then for those on Sicily and Normandy. He was awarded the OBE in 1945.

There followed two years as Superintendent of Charts. On promotion to captain in 1947 he went in command of the *Seagull*, surveying on the west coasts of England and Scotland and in the northern approaches to the Irish Sea, where he was among the first to make use of radar for surveying. In 1948 he took the newly commissioned *Dampier* to survey in Malaya and north western Borneo. From 1949 to 1950 he returned to the Department as Superintendent of Charts again. The following year he took command of the *Cook*, surveying on the west coast of Scotland, taking a university expedition to and from Spitzbergen and making oceanographic observations on passage. In 1952 he came ashore again to the Department, and from 1953 to 1954 was Assistant Hydrographer.

Collins' last sea command came in 1954, when he commissioned the newly completed *Vidal*. After surveys off the west coast of Scotland he took her to Washington with Hydrographic Department personnel embarked. While surveying in the West Indies later in the year the ship took a prominent part in relief work after a hurricane devastated much of Haiti, and Collins was made a commander of the 'Ordre National d' Honneur et Merite'.

Shortly after his appointment as Hydrographer in succession to Day in June 1955 Collins was made a commodore, and he was promoted to rear admiral in 1956. He was a strong advocate of the close alliance of hydrography and oceanography, and of the use of modern technology and materials both in the office and afloat.

He was made a CB in 1959, and after his retirement in 1960 became Adviser to the Canadian Hydrographic Service until 1963. He then returned to England to live in retirement near Farnham in Surrey.

Lieutenant Commander W Ashton, DSC

William Ashton joined the *Flinders*, Torlesse, on promotion to Lieutenant in 1938, surveying on the south coast of England. In June he went out to the *Herald*, Jenks and later Southern, on the China station, working on the coasts of Borneo and Malaya until war broke out. Until the end of 1939 he was in minesweepers at Singapore. He returned home by air in a flight which crashed off Taranto, where though he survived his brother officers Gage and Hocking lost their lives. He joined Day on the staff of Vice Admiral Dover until May 1940, when he went to the *Scott*, Collins, for two years in northern waters.

In March 1942 Ashton went by troopship to join the *Endeavour*, Baker, working in the Red Sea and the Canal Zone until June 1943, when he joined the port survey parties following up the army in the western desert, in Sicily and in Italy, being mentioned in despatches and awarded the US Bronze Star for his work in Naples harbour. In January 1944 he had command and charge of survey in ML 1242, continuing on port work and being awarded the DSC for his services with the salvage teams at Leghorn under heavy enemy fire.

Returning home in August 1945 after three and a half years overseas, Ashton joined the *Scott*, Bill, in October for surveys off the east coast of England. In March 1947 he took command of SML 585 for six months work with the mine clearance force on the east coast. In November 1947 he went to the *Challenger*, Southern and later Sharpey-Schafer, for two years in the Persian Gulf and the Mediterranean, and in 1949-50 he was in the *Seagull*, Lowry and then Gordon, on the west coast of England.

In March 1950 Ashton stood by and did trials in the *Cook* at Devonport, and then in August was appointed in command of the *Scott* for south coast surveys. In October 1951 he left England by sea to take over the command of the *Challenger*, then in Japanese waters, with the acting rank of commander. He continued and completed her world oceanographic cruise.

In November 1953 he joined the Department as Jacketting Officer, in which post he served until he retired at his own request at the end of 1955. For eighteen months he was marine consultant to Seismograph Services Ltd, an American oil-prospecting organisation working in the Indian Ocean, the Mediterranean and the North Sea.

From the middle of 1957 he held a number of commercial appointments, working from his home in Berkhamsted.

Captain M J Baker

Michael John Baker is the son of Captain E H B Baker, whose surveying biography is given earlier in these pages. He started surveying in January 1949 when he joined the *Seagull*, Lowry then Gordon, working on the south coast of England. When *Seagull* paid off to scrap in 1951 Baker transferred to the *Dalrymple*, Irving, in the Persian Gulf and the Mediterranean. On his return to England in January 1954 he went to the *Shackleton*, Pryor then Hatfield, for surveys in the Thames Estuary and on the east coast. During his time in the ship he had a spell in command of one of the attched MLs.

In June 1955 Baker went back to the *Dalrymple*, Paisley, Winstanley, Haslam and Ritchie successively, remaining in the ship for over five years, the last eighteen months in command as an acting commander. During this period the ship worked in East Africa, the Persian Gulf, the Mediterranean and at home, underwent a major refit and took part in the Suez operation. To his dismay, after his time in command he was appointed in June 1961 to the *Shackleton* as First Lieutenant under Nesbitt. However, on the day he joined he was selected for promotion to commander at the end of the year, and left the ship in December for shore service, first briefly in the Department as Wrecks Officer, then from May 1962 to April 1964 in the Naval Intelligence Division.

Baker returned to sea in April 1965 in command of the *Dampier*, surveying in Malayan and Borneo waters as well as making a cruise in the Indian Ocean to prospect for the site for a UK/US base and making a geophysical survey in the Solomon Islands. During the Solomon Islands survey he towed the New Zealand cruiser *Royalist*, who had broken down off Bellona Island, clear of danger. *Dampier* then had to leave her drifting in open water as she herself was in danger of running out of fuel.

Coming home from the Far East he spent a short time in RRS *Discovery* before taking charge of the Royal Naval Hydrographic School at Devonport from 1966 to 1969. From August 1969 for fifteen months he had command of the *Hydra* in the Malacca Straits, then came home to Taunton to serve as Assistant Director (Naval). He then stood by, and in 1974 commissioned, the *Herald*, but in March 1976 he had to relinquish command due to illness. He spent a last eighteen months at Taunton as Director of Hydrographic Plans and Surveys before retiring at his own request in September 1977.

Lieutenant Commander F M Berncastle, DSC*

Frank Measham Berncastle joined the Royal Navy from the Merchant Service, and in 1938 went as a lieutenant to New Zealand to join the *Endeavour*, Wyatt. On the outbreak of the Second World War Berncastle came home and was employed minesweeping from Sheerness, being awarded the DSC. In 1941 he went to the *Franklin*, Price, on the east coast. The following year he joined the staff of the Chief of Combined Operations, serving in landing craft specially adapted for measuring beach gradients at night on enemy-occupied coasts. His first operations were based on Dover, but then in 1943 he assisted at both the Sicily and Salerno landings, and then on the Normandy beaches both before and after the landings. His work was rewarded with a bar to his DSC and eighteen months accelerated promotion to lieutenant commander.

In the autumn of 1944 Berncastle went for two months to the *Franklin*, Irving, engaged in clearance surveys of north European ports, and then in October went out to the *Challenger*, Sabine, in Australia, working in the Torres Strait. Early in 1945 he fell sick and was posted ashore to the headquarters of South East Asia Command in Ceylon, where he assisted in the planning of the invasion of Malaya.

From April 1946 Berncastle was in the *Seagull*, Collins, on the west coast of the United Kingdom, until June 1947, when he went to stand by the *Dalrymple* converting at Devonport. During 1948 he was again in the *Seagull*, now under Hennessey, and in January 1949 was appointed in charge of the Surveying Motor Launches working independently on the east coast. In August he was given command of the *Sharpshooter* on east coast surveys with much wreck sweeping.

He came ashore in March 1951 to serve in the Department as Equipment Officer. From 1953 to 1955 he was lent to the Joint Intelligence Board. Then followed an appointment to the Flood Warning Service, where he remained until he retired in July 1957.

He became an assistant hydrographic surveyor with the Port of Bristol Authority on retirement. In 1964 he transferred to the Humber to be Conservator and Engineer to the Humber Conservancy Board. In retirement he now lives at Shoreham-by-Sea.

Captain R H Connell, DSC

Richard Harrison Connell started his surveying career as a sublieutenant in 1932, joining the *Beaufort*, Turner and later Tennant, working on the west coast of Scotland. Two years later he went to the *Herald*, Law and then Hardy, on the China station surveying on the east coast of Malaya, in Sarawak and in the 'Dangerous Area' in the South China Sea. In 1937 he did a season in the *Fitzroy*, Jones and then Boxall, on the east coast and in the Shetlands, and it was then that he experienced echo-sounding for the first time in ship and boats. The following year he went to the new surveying ship *Scott*, Day and then Jenks, surveying the approaches to the Tay and the supposedly blocked eastern entrances to Scapa Flow. In the Second World War Connell was first in the *Challenger*, Jenks, working on various harbour defence surveys and at the new fleet base of Hvalfjordhur in Iceland. From 1941 to 1943 he was again in the *Scott*, Collins and Sharpey-Schafer. He was awarded the DSC while she was engaged on the northern mine barrage for navigating success-fully in close proximity to a previous minelay.

In 1943 Connell went to the Mediterranean first as FHO and later as Staff Hydrographic Officer Levant and Eastern Mediterranean, and after the war commented that he did not have a shot fired at him, and only a few bombs dropped in his direction, throughout the conflict.

In 1945 he joined the *Franklin*, Irving and then Tripp, succeeding to the command himself in 1948. He was promoted commander in June 1949. Her work was chiefly in the Thames Estuary, with much wreck sweeping. In 1948 she remained in the Medway for much of the year with a reduced complement due to Navy-wide manpower shortages. In 1950 he became Equipment Officer at Cricklewood, and in 1951 went to command the *Dampier* working in Malaya and Borneo. He came home in 1953 to the *Cook*, surveying first on the west coast of Scotland and later on the west African coast.

From 1955 to 1957 Connell had command of the *Vidal*, where he was frustrated by the prolongued teething troubles with her engines and gearboxes. One of his first tasks in the West Indies was to go to Haiti to receive the awards from the Haitian government to Collins and others for their hurricane relief the previous year. *Vidal* also carried out the formal annexation of Rockall, hoisting the British flag and installing a commemorative plaque. Connell was promoted captain in December 1955. From 1957 to 1959 he came ashore to be Assistant Hydrographer (1) and Superintendent of Charts before returning to *Vidal* for his last sea command from 1959 to 1961. In 1961 he did the Senior Officers War Course before coming to the Department in Whitehall as AH(2).

He retired to Ireland, but soon found country life dull and tried to persuade the Irish government to set up its own hydrographic surveying service. Failing in this aim he started business as a compass adjuster. In 1965 he was asked to survey Sligo Bay, and this led to the setting up of his own hydrographic surveying company.

Commander J K L Dickson

John Kirkpatrick Lindsay Dickson joined the *Fitzroy*, Wyatt and later Day, in 1932 to survey off the east coasts of England and Scotland. In 1933 he went to the *Herald*, Law, for two years on the China station working on the coasts of Malaya and Borneo. In 1936 he did another season at home in the *Flinders*, Jenks, on the south coast of England, and then joined the *Stork*, Farquharson and then Jackson, to go out to

Ceylon and the Malacca Strait, remaining with her until she came home to rearm in 1939.

On the outbreak of war Dickson served as navigating officer of minelayers until September 1941, when he went to the Naval Intelligence Division for six months. Next, after four months in the *Franklin*, Stokes, on the east coast, Dickson was in July 1942 given charge of the South Coast of England Survey working out of Plymouth. From 1943 to September 1945 he served in the controlled mining ships *Atreus* and *Manchester City*.

Dickson concluded his sea time with a year in ML 586 working with the Thames Estuary minesweeping force from Sheerness. In 1947 he joined the Department, working mainly on Light Lists until he retired with the rank of commander in 1951. In retirement he lived at Northfleet, where he died in 1966.

Commander N C Glen, OBE

Nisbet Cunningham Glen, whose father served in the Department as Officer in Charge of Staff Charts in both World Wars, had his first experience of surveying when, as a midshipman in the *Malaya*, he was lent to the *Pangbourne* to help survey bombardment sites on the north coast of Africa. He began surveying formally as a lieutenant in 1943 when he joined the *Franklin*, Stokes, on the east coasts of England and Scotland. Shortly after joining he was transferred to Berncastle's unit making reconnaissance surveys of the Normandy coast, then on D Day leading in the DD tanks and later assisting in the positioning of the Gooseberry and Mulberry breakwaters.

In January 1945 Glen went to the *Challenger*, Sabine, and was detached for a survey of Keppel Harbour, Singapore on reoccupation of that port. He came home in 1946 to one of the Surveying Motor Launches attached to the *Scott*, Bill, working on the east coast of England. In February 1948 he joined SML 1301, attached to the *Challenger*, Southern, for surveys off Cyprus, but in July left to set up a beach reconnaissance team working in the Near East and later in Greece. At home in August 1949 Glen joined the experimental minesweeping squadron to help them to apply surveying techniques to their position fixing. In 1950 he went to the *Scott*, Griffiths and then Ashton, and later transferred to the *Sharpshooter*, Gordon then Penfold, working on the south and east coasts of England. In 1952 he went out to the *Dampier*, Connell and later Grattan, surveying on the coasts of Borneo and Malaya, taking command briefly while Connell was sick in Penang. Two years later he came home to take charge of the East Coast of England Survey, a grouping of all the SMLs working in the Thames Estuary and the east coast.

Glen came ashore in 1955 to the Department to become deputy Superintendent of the Tidal Branch. He suceeded as Superintendent in 1967, being promoted honorary commander on the retired list on taking up this appointment. During his long tenure of this office he was chairman of the National Tide Gauge Committee.

He finally retired in 1987, being awarded the OBE in that year. He now lives in retirement in Somerset.

Commander D L Gordon

David Leslie Gordon came to the *Stork*, Jackson and later Jones, in 1938 for surveys in the Malacca Strait and Ceylon. Coming home he was briefly in the *Jason*, Hardy, before going to the *Scott*, Day then Jenks, for the 1939 season on the east coast. Soon after the war broke out he went to the *Challenger*, Jenks, working on harbour defence surveys in the United Kingdom and in Iceland. In January 1941 he went to the *Scott*, Collins, by now working in northern waters. In May 1942 he began nearly three years in the *Challenger*, under Wyatt, Bill and Sabine in succession, beginning with surveys in East Africa, then moving to the Seychelles and Ceylon and ending with work in the Torres Strait.

From May 1945 Gordon was in the *Franklin*, Irving and later Tripp, which with attached MLs was surveying northern European ports, then the Thames Estuary and the east coast of England. In September 1947 he went again to the *Challenger*, Southern and then Sharpey-Schafer, surveying in the Persian Gulf and the Mediterranean. He took temporary command of the ship during the change- over of permanent commanding officers in 1948.

In the latter part of 1949 Gordon was in charge of the Survey Training Unit at Chatham. After short spells in the *Franklin* and in the Department he was appointed in command of the *Seagull* in March 1950, working on the south coast of England. For the 1951 season he transferred to the *Sharpshooter*, surveying on the east coast.

He came ashore in September 1951 to take charge of the Survey Training Unit again. He then joined the Department in the Tidal Branch, of which he became Superintendent in April 1956 with the acting rank of Commander. He retired from the active list on age grounds in 1959, being granted the rank of honorary commander. He continued as Superintendent of the Tidal Branch until 1967, when he retired to Majorca.

Commander J C Grattan, DSC

John Charles Grattan began surveying as a sublieutenant in 1938, and was in t.e *Challenger*, Baker, in the Red Sea and the Persian Gulf until shortly after the outbreak of the Second World War, being promoted lieutenant in 1939.

At the start of the war he served briefly in MTBs. Early in 1940 he was in the Narvik campaign survey party under Baker. From May 1940 he was for two years at Dover for survey duties, minesweeping by day and minelaying or raiding on the enemy coast by night. His services attracted the award of the DSC, two mentions in despatches and six months seniority. In May 1942 Grattan joined the *Challenger* again, which after a survey of Heysham Lake went to the Eastern Fleet for work at Mombasa, the Seychelles and in Ceylon under first Bill and later Wyatt. He was detached in the winter of 1943-44 to assist in Army operations on the Arakan coast, and was again mentioned in despatches for his part in a raid on the south bank of the Naaf River. He left *Challenger* after her transfer to Australia, and returned home in April 1945 via the Panama Canal.

In 1945 Grattan went to the *Franklin*, Irving and then Tripp, working on wreck location in German North Sea Ports and then on surveys in the Thames Estuary. From September 1946 he served again in the *Challenger*, Southern, in the Persian Gulf and in the Mediterranean. He came home in November 1947 to work on beach surveys in the United Kingdom, being injured in a serious helicopter crash in August 1948 which left him in hospital for a long time. In 1950 he went to the *Dalrymple*, Baker and later Irving, in the Persian Gulf and the Mediterranean. He moved to the *Cook*, Collins, in April 1951, taking part in the search for the sunken submarine *Affray* and in the carrying of the Universities Expedition to and from Spitzbergen.

Grattan was appointed in command of the *Scott* in 1951, surveying on the south coast and in Milford Haven, and joining RRS *Discovery* for a joint oceanographic expedition in the eastern Atlantic. Early in 1953 he went to the *Dampier* with the acting rank of commander for two years surveying on the coasts of Borneo and Malaya. In the summer of 1955 he came home to take charge of the South Coast of England Survey, and shortly afterwards was lent to the Pakistan Navy to be their Director of Hydrography until December 1957.

Retiring voluntarily in the recently established rank of honorary commander in March 1958, Grattan went to the Falkland Islands Dependencies Survey for the Antarctic seasons of 1958-59 and 1959-60. He then joined a firm of land and engineering surveyors, going in 1962 as Chief Surveyor to the Mangla Dam project in Pakistan.

Lieutenant Commander R G Green

Richard Gretworth Green started surveying as a lieutenant of two and a half years' seniority at the end of 1946 when he joined the *Seagull*, Collins for a season on the west coasts of the United Kingdom. From April 1948 for two years he was in the *Dampier*, Collins and later Hennessey, in the Far East, chiefly on the coasts of Malaya and Borneo. He came home in 1950 to command SML 324, attached to the *Sharpshooter*, Berncastle, working on the east coast of England. In 1951 and 1952 he was in the *Cook*, Collins and later Baker, on the west coast of Scotland and on the expedition to Spitzbergen.

In 1953 Green went to the *Challenger*, Ashton, for her final oceanographical work in the Atlantic and the North Sea, and when she paid off he went abroad, back to the *Dampier*, now under Grattan followed by Roe, working again in Malaya and Borneo. During 1956 he was briefly first in the Department and then in the *Scott*,

Hatfield, before going to the *Shackleton*, C J de C Scott, for the 1957 season, working on the west coast of Scotland and on wrecks in the North Sea.

In January 1958 Green was appointed in charge of the East Coast of England Survey and in command of the first of the new Inshore Survey Craft, *Echo*. He came ashore in July 1960, going first to the Naval Intelligence Division and then, in 1961, to the Joint Intelligence Bureau.

He retired at his own request in 1963, and joined the civil engineering firm Wimpeys. Later he rejoined the Department as a retired officer in the Radio Navigation Warnings section, retiring again for health reasons in 1970.

Commander R H Griffiths

Robert Henry Griffiths joined the *Beaufort*, Tennent and later Farquharson, in 1934 to survey mainly on the west coast of Scotland. In the next year he went to the *Challenger*, Jones and later Baker, for three seasons in the West Indies. In 1938 he was briefly in the *Flinders*, Torlesse, at Portsmouth, and then in the *Jason*, Hardy, on the south coast and in the Bristol Channel until the end of the year. In 1939 he went out to the *Herald*, Southern, working on the Malayan coasts until the Second World War broke out.

During the war Griffiths was with the Singapore Survey Unit, evacuating with it to Colombo in 1942 and subsequently becoming assistant to first Wyatt and then Day as FHO. He spent 1945 in the *Challenger*, Sabine, in the Torres Strait and on the China coast, being detached to survey Hong Kong in ML 1285 in the first half of 1946. A short spell in the Department was followed by the 1947 season in the *Seagull*, Collins, on the west coast including the approaches to St George's Channel.

In November 1947 Griffiths took command of the *Scott*, with SMLs attached, and surveyed in the Medway, on the east and south coasts of England and also in the Firth of Clyde, until August 1950. He then came ashore to work for the Joint Intelligence Bureau until 1952, when he joined the Department to act as Jacketting Officer.

Griffiths retired at his own request in November 1953 and joined the Nigerian Marine Department at Lagos, where he died in April 1963.

Lieutenant Commander S J Hales

Sidney John Hales entered the Royal Navy as a seaman boy in 1937, and was commissioned as an upper-yardman in 1944. He began surveying as a lieutenant in 1946, when he joined the *Scott*, Bill, on the east coast of England. In September 1946 he transferred to the *Challenger*, Southern, surveying in the Persian Gulf, Red Sea and off the coast of Cyprus. Two years later he joined the *Seagull*, Hennessey and then Lowry, working in the Bristol Channel and on the west coast of England.

34 Vice Admiral Sir Guy Wyatt, KBE, CB, Hydrographer from 1 May 1945 to 11 June 1950.

35 Vice Admiral Sir Archibald Day, KBE, CB, Hydrographer from 12 June 1950 to 12 June 1955.

36 Rear Admiral Kenneth St B. Collins, CB, OBE, DSC, Hydrographer from 13 June 1955 to 6 July 1960.

37 Rear Admiral Sir Edmund Irving, KBE, CB, Hydrographer from 7 July 1960 to 14 January 1966.

38 Rear Admiral G. Stephen Ritchie, CB, DSC, Hydrographer from 15 January 1966 to 5 February 1971.

39   Dampier, first of the Bay class, in 1948 before leaving for the Far East. Note the standard Bay class short funnel, soon to be heightened. (AUTHOR'S COLL)

40   *Owen*, the third Bay off Plymouth in 1960. She was built with a taller funnel to keep smoke from her bridge. Note also the mast for 2-Range Decca and the wooden hut for Somali seamen carried in the Persian Gulf. (AUTHOR'S COLL)

41   When the British and French seized the northern end of the Suez Canal in 1956 the surveyors were there again. A surveying boat from *Dalrymple* led the assault force.

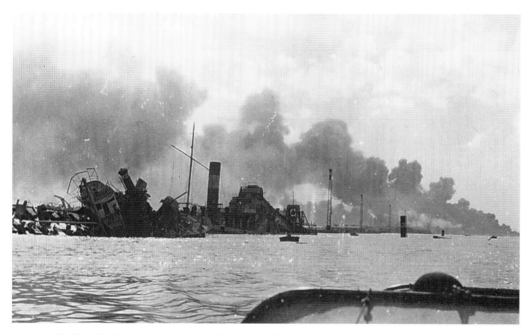

42   Port Said, taken from one of *Dalrymple's* boats the day after the assault, before the task of clearing wrecks began.

(IMPERIAL WAR MUSEUM)

43   The chartroom of *Cook* with surveying officers at work. In the foreground, with cap on, is Captain K. St B. Collins, later Hydrographer. (Imperial War Museum)

44   Landing a 2-Range Decca Station in the Persian Gulf from *Dalrymple* in 1960. Sites close to a suitable landing place were favoured.

45   *Vidal* spent much of her early life working in the West Indies. Here she is about 1955, alongside a jetty somewhere in the Caribbean (Author's coll)

46   With her helicopter, landing 2-Range Decca stations from *Vidal* was a much simpler task than from the Bays. Here is one of her stations in the West Indies about 1960.

47 At the end of the 1950s the SMLs were replaced with the three Inshore Survey Craft of the *Echo* class. This is *Echo* on trials in 1958. (AUTHOR'S COLL)

48 *Myrmidon,* one of the two Ton class minesweepers converted as interim replacements for *Scott* and *Shackleton* in the mid 1960s, alongside *Scott* for a heaving line transfer in the summer of 1964.

49   Admiral Irving (seated) examines new surveys at Cricklewood about 1963. Among the PCHOs is Marjorie Chriss, only the second woman to reach this rank. Photo courtesy of Admiral Ritchie, who appears on the extreme right.

50   In 1968 the Department came together on the Taunton site when the new building for cartography was completed, alongside the printing works in use since 1941.

51 *Hydra* the third of the *Hecla* class, in the Malacca Strait under the author's command in late 1970, flying Admiral Ritchie's flag during his tour of Commonwealth Hydrographic Offices. (Author's coll)

52 Towards the end of their first commission *Bulldog* and *Beagle*, the first pair of Coastal Survey Vessels, wintered in the Persian Gulf. *Beagle* in Khawr ash-Shamm, Oman, in January 1970. (Author's coll)

Hales spent the 1951 season in command of SML 326, working in support of the *Cook*, Collins, on the west coast of Scotland for much of the year. From November 1951 for two years he was lent to the Royal New Zealand Navy, serving in the *Lachlan*, Sharpey-Schafer and then Lowry, and surveying in Samoa and Fiji as well as in New Zealand waters.

He returned to England in January 1954 to join the *Cook*, Connell and then Hayter, working again in the Bristol Channel and on the west coast of Scotland. Two years later he went out to the *Dampier*, Royds, surveying in Malaya, the South China Sea and off the coast of Borneo. In November 1957 he joined the *Scott*, Simeon, working on the east coasts of England and Scotland.

In August 1958 he stood by and then commissioned the new Inshore Survey Craft *Enterprise*, which on acceptance became part of the East Coast of England Survey Unit. In July 1960 he became the senior officer of the Unit.

Hales then came ashore to take up his first shore appointment since 1944, as assistant to CB(N) at Cricklewood. He retired in 1967 and emigrated to New Zealand. With only a short break surveying for the Fiji Transport Survey in 1969 he was then engaged in farming activities until his death in 1988.

Rear Admiral G P D Hall, CB, DSC
Hydrographer 1971-1975

Geoffrey Penrose Dickinson Hall began surveying in 1938 as a sublieutenant when he joined the *Franklin*, Sabine, working in the North Sea. In 1939 he went to the *Scarborough*, Law, for surveys off British Somaliland and Ceylon. When she was paid off on the outbreak of war Hall spent some months in minesweepers at Singapore before being flown home at the end of 1939 to join the *Challenger*, Jenks, working first in the Orkneys and on controlled minefield surveys, then in Iceland and finally in the Gambia.

In 1942 Hall reverted to general service at his own request. He went first to the post of navigating officer to the 15th Fleet Minesweeping Flotilla, working in home waters and then back in Iceland. In 1943 he was appointed in command of a Combined Operations unit carrying out clandestine surveys of beaches possibly suitable for amphibious assault. At the end of the year he was awarded the DSC for operations off the Burma coast, and in 1944 was mentioned in despatches for similar work in northern Sumatra.

Back in England early in 1945 Hall was given command of the frigate *Bigbury Bay*, with the acting rank of lieutenant commander. He spent two years in her, mainly in 'mopping up' operations in China and Japan after the Japanese surrender.

In 1947 Hall returned to surveying, joining the *Seagull*, Collins, Hennessey and Lowry successively, working on the west coasts of England, Wales and Scotland. Towards the end of 1949 he was loaned to the Royal New Zealand Navy, commissioning the *Lachlan* in Fremantle and taking her to New Zealand for conversion for surveying. For the next two years he served in her under Sharpey-Schafer. Returning to England in 1952 he was appointed in command of the *Franklin*, working in the Thames Estuary and in the North Western Approaches. When *Franklin* paid off at the end of 1952 Hall transferred to the *Scott*, where he was promoted to commander.

In 1954 Hall went to the Department as Superintendent of the Oceanographical Branch. Command of the *Owen* followed in 1956, with surveys off the east and west coasts of Africa, in the Seychelles and off Gibraltar. From 1958 to 1960 he was again in the Department, this time as Officer in Charge of Staff Charts. He returned to *Owen* in 1960. During his second two years in her she undertook an extended oceanographic cruise in the Atlantic, spent three months surveying in South Georgia, and carried out a geophysical survey in the Indian Ocean as part of the International Geophysical Year. He was promoted captain in the middle of this appointment.

He then took the six-month Senior Officers War Course at Greenwich before going to Whitehall in 1963 as Assistant Hydrographer. In 1965 he had his last seagoing command, the name ship of the new *Hecla* class, mainly employed on North Atlantic surveys. A second two-year appointment as Assistant Hydrographer in Whitehall was followed in 1970 by transfer to Taunton as Assistant Director (Naval).

In February 1971, having been promoted rear admiral, he succeeded Ritchie as Hydrographer. He retired in September 1975 to his estate in Lincolnshire.

Rear Admiral Sir David Haslam, KBE, CB
Hydrographer 1975-1985

David William Haslam entered the surveying service as he was promoted lieutenant in the summer of 1944, joining the converted yacht *White Bear*, Sabine and then Day, as she left England for the Far East. He remained with her until December 1946, then went for a brief four months in command of SML 325 before going out to the Royal Australian Navy on loan. He took command of HMA Ships *Brolga* and *Tallarook* for passage from Sydney to Darwin and then served in the *Barcoo*, surveying in both North West and South Australia. Returning home in 1949 he was appointed to the *Scott*, Griffiths and then Ashton, working on the east coast of England. In 1951 he went to the Persian Gulf in *Dalrymple*, Irving, coming ashore in 1953 to take charge of the Survey Training Unit at Chatham. After three years he went to *Vidal* as First Lieutenant under Irving, surveying in the West Indies, being selected for promotion to commander while on detached survey in Belize.

Haslam's first command came in January 1958, when he went to *Dalrymple* again briefly before going out to *Dampier* in the Far East. Returning home in 1960 he went to the Naval Intelligence Division, in charge of Beach Reconnaisance. Here he arranged for the publication of a new 'idiot's guide' to surveying a beach, entitled 'Let's Go Beachcombing', and arranged for its illustration by the cartoonist 'Fougasse'. From 1962 to 1964 he was in command of the *Owen*, his time including the operations in East Africa after the overthrow of the Sultan of Zanzibar, for which he was awarded the OBE. His next appointment was an unusual one for a surveyor, commander of the Royal Naval Barracks, Chatham, from summer 1964 to the end of 1965, during which time he was selected for promotion to captain..

In December 1965 he went again on exchange to Australia, this time as Hydrographer, RAN. Returning home at the end of 1967, he went in command of *Hecla*, supervising the trials and first operational use of the Automatic Data Logging system. Following his time in *Hecla* he served in Whitehall for two years as Assistant Hydrographer before going out to the Far East to command *Hydra*, working mainly in the Solomon Islands, from early 1972 to the end of 1974. He received the 1974 Back Award of the Royal Geographical Society for this work.

This was his last sea command. After a year at Taunton as Assistant Director (Naval) he took the Senior Officers' War Course at Greenwich, during which he was promoted to rear admiral, and succeeded Hall as Hydrographer in September 1975. He remained in office until January 1985, thus becoming the longest-serving post-war Hydrographer.

After retirement he was for a short time Acting Conservator of the River Mersey before being elected President of the Directing Committee of the IHO in 1987. He was only able to serve one term at Monaco due to his age, and he returned home in 1992 to Bromsgrove, taking on the position of Chairman of the Trustees and Governors of Bromsgrove School.

Commander H R Hatfield

Henry Roland Hatfield specialised in surveying in January 1943 as a lieutenant. His first command was the *Owen*, in 1954 in the Persian Gulf. Later that year he moved to the *Shackleton*, surveying on the east coast of England. In late 1955 he transferred the *Scott*, where the writer remembers him as a patient instructor of his less experienced surveyors. When *Scott* entered extended refit at the end of 1956, Hatfield went to *Cook*, taking her across the Pacific to be present at Britain's first hydrogen bomb tests at Christmas Island, and afterwards working in Fiji and the Solomon Islands. Between June 1959 and July 1961 he rewrote Volume I of the Admiralty Manual of Hydrographic Surveying before going back to sea for his last command, *Dalrymple*, surveying in the Persian Gulf and off the coast of Cyprus.

In 1963 Hatfield came ashore to complete the task of rewriting the Admiralty Manual of Hydrographic Surveying and seeing it through the press. When this was completed in 1969 he went to the Naval Intelligence Division, where he remained until his retirement overage in 1974. In retirement he has developed his interest in astronomy from his home in Kent. He was President of the British Astronomical Association from 1987 to 1989.

Lieutenant Commander P J D Hayter

Peter John Danvers Hayter began surveying when as a lieutenant in 1946 he joined the *Scott*, Hennessey and then Bill, working on the east coast of England. From 1946 to 1948 he served in the *Challenger*, Southern, in the Persian Gulf and the Mediterranean, and then joined a small party working on beach surveys round the United Kingdom.

In 1950 he went out to the *Dampier*, Hennessey and later Connell, working off the coasts of Malaya and Borneo and in Hong Kong. He came home in 1952 to the *Sharpshooter*, Penfold, for surveys on the east coast of England. From 1953 to 1955 he was in the *Dalrymple*, Bill and then Paisley, working on the east coast of Africa and in the Persian Gulf.

In 1956 he came home to command the *Cook*, surveying off the west coast of Scotland. After a short spell in the Department he was lent to the Pakistan Navy from 1958 to 1960 as Director of Hydrography. On his return in 1960 he entered the Department in charge of Chart Branch (N). On the move to Taunton he transferred to the Notices to Mariners Branch where he remained until his retirement in 1980, when he became a reviser of Sailing Directions.

Commander F W Hunt, MBE

Frank William Hunt began surveying as a sublieutenant in January 1942 when he joined the *Franklin*, Price followed by Stokes, engaged on surveys in the Thames Estuary. In June he left England by sea to join the *Endeavour*, Baker, in the Red Sea. *Endeavour* was paid off in 1943 and Hunt was attached to a party set up to survey ports, bays and beaches for the invasions of Sicily and Italy. In December 1943 he took charge of one of the units carrying out occupation surveys of ports on both shores of the Adriatic.

After a brief spell as temporary Fleet Hydrographic Officer at Naples following the death of Jenks, Hunt took command of SML 324, attached to the *Franklin*, Irving, for surveys of northern European ports, and later worked in the Thames Estuary. In March 1946 he joined the *Seagull*, Collins, newly converted for surveying, working on the west coasts of England and Scotland.

Early in 1948 Hunt was lent to the Royal Australian Navy for two years, when he served in the *Barcoo*, surveying on the north-west and south coasts of the continent. In 1950 he returned to England to take charge of the Survey Training Unit at Chatham until, late in 1951, he was attached to the Falkland Islands Dependencies Survey for work in the Falklands, South Georgia and the Dependencies further south. In 1952 he went to the *Scott*, Grattan and later Hall, working on the west and south coasts of England. The following year he went to the *Owen*, Hatfield and then Pryor, working in the Mediterranean and the Persian Gulf. While in the Gulf in 1954 he transferred to the *Dalrymple*, Paisley.

On his return home in 1955 he went in charge of the East Coast of England Survey Unit, working mainly in the Thames Estuary. At the end of 1955 he was promoted to commander. In the middle of 1956 Hunt went out to New Zealand to command the *Lachlan* and as Staff Hydrographic Officer. After over three years he came home to the Department at Cricklewood as Superintendent of the Oceanographic Branch. In 1962 he went to the Far East in command of the *Cook*, working in the islands of the South Pacific. After she grounded on the reefs off Vatu Ira in the Fijis he was court-martialled and returned to England. He became Superintendent of Staff Charts, a post he held until his voluntary retirement in February 1967.

After retirement he worked from 1967 to 1969 as Marine Superintendent of the British Service in the New Hebrides. He later joined the New Zealand Marine Department, where he remained until his final retirement in 1981. He now lives in New Zealand.

Captain C C Lowry

Colin Courtenay Lowry joined the *Fitzroy*, Hughes, as a sublieutenant in 1934, working mainly in the Shetlands. At the end of the year he went to the *Challenger*, Jones, in the West Indies. At the end of 1936 he volunteered for exchange service in Australia, and did four years in the *Moresby*, Little, Martin and Hunt in succession, the principal surveys being on the north coast and in the Great Barrier Reef.

When the Second World War broke out he served in a minelayer off New Caledonia and then made independent surveys of potential fleet bases in Fiji and New Zealand, returning home in mid 1943 after an absence of six and a half years. Lowry then went as SO(H) at Dover, planning various operations until at the end of 1944 he joined the *Franklin*, Irving, working from Cherbourg to Antwerp behind the advancing Allied armies.

Late in 1945 Lowry stood by the *Seagull*, converting at Chatham, and was temporarily in command of her for the first half of 1946 working in the Hebrides, and thereafter continuing in the ship under Collins. He spent 1947 making a documentary film on the surveying service and compiling instructional film strips. Early in 1948 he joined the *Sharpshooter*, Irving, sweeping east coast wrecks, and in mid-year obtained charge of surveys as senior officer of the East Coast SMLs. Lowry was promoted to commander in December 1948, and spent 1949 in command of the *Seagull* in the Bristol Channel. In 1950 and 1951 he was in the Department, first as Officer in Charge of Staff Charts and then in Chart Branch (N). In 1952 he was back in New Zealand in charge of the Hydrographic Service and in command of the *Lachlan*. He worked on the east coasts of both islands and also in Fiji and Samoa, and under him *Lachlan* acted as senior officer, inshore escort for HM the Queen's visit in December 1953.

Promoted captain, Lowry came home to be AH2 in Whitehall until retirement at the end of 1957, in which year he stood for a directorship of the IHB, but failed to gain election. He then began three years as Hydrographic Surveyor to the Sarawak Marine Department, but had to resign in 1960 owing to ill health. He returned to North Devon, where he still lives in retirement.

Captain H Menzies

Henry Menzies had done two years in the submarine service before he began surveying as a lieutenant of four years seniority when, in 1934, he went to the *Herald*, Law, for two years on the China station, working in Malayan and Borneo waters. In 1936 and 1937 he was in the *Flinders*, Jenks, on the south and west coasts of England, and in 1938 joined the *Jason*, Hardy, working on the south coast of England and in the Bristol Channel.

On the outbreak of war in 1939 Menzies was briefly in the *Challenger*, Baker, working on the east coast war channels, and then in 1940 went to the staff of Captain M/S Grimsby. In 1941, on Beech Thomas's death, he was sent to take charge of the Singapore Survey Unit. At the fall of Singapore the unit made its way via Java to Ceylon, where its major task became the survey of an area destined to be a Landing Craft Training School in south India.

In 1942 Menzies was promoted to commander, and as SOH SEAC initiated arrangements for the production of charts at New Delhi in co-operation with the Survey of India at Dehra Dun; arrangements which were later transferred to Ceylon. Returning to England towards the end of 1943, he was employed in the Department, being engaged in the developing applications of radar. Then, soon after VE Day in May 1945, Menzies, with Dr J.N.Carruthers, went to Hamburg to re-activate the Deutsche Hydrographisches Institut.

In 1946 and 1947 Menzies had command of the *Sharpshooter*, the only *Halcyon* class surveying ship to spend any considerable time abroad, working in Malaya and in Borneo. He came ashore in February 1948 to serve as Officer in Charge of Staff Charts in Whitehall. From July 1949 he commanded the *Owen*, carrying out surveys in the Persian Gulf and the Mediterranean. He was promoted captain in 1950. His sea career ended in 1952 when he was appointed AH(1) and Superintendent of Charts.

He retired in 1954 to take up the post of Naval Professional Officer at the Ministry of Transport, a post he held until 1972.

Commander W B Monk

William Bonnar Monk was a lieutenant of one year's seniority in 1929 when he joined the *Kellett*, Hardy, on Thames Estuary surveys. He soon went to the *Ormonde*, Wyatt, working in the Persian Gulf and off Cyprus for two years. In 1931 he went to the *Flinders*, Simpson, surveying on the west coasts of England and Scotland, and then in 1933 moved to the *Challenger* for two years working in the West Indies and off Labrador.

Monk joined the *Fitzroy*, Hughes, early in 1935, but her complement was reduced in August due to the Abyssinian crisis, so he went for the 1936 season to the West Coast of Scotland Survey, under first Farquharson and then Sabine. In 1937 he was appointed to the *Endeavour*, Wyatt, for surveys in New Zealand waters, until her recall to Singapore and paying off on the outbreak of war.

Monk commanded the minesweeper *Bagshot* for three months before being flown home to join the *Challenger*, Jenks, in northern waters. In 1941 he was moved to the controlled minelaying ship *Manchester City*, working first in northern waters, then off South Africa and in the Indian Ocean. In 1944 he was brought home to join the Interservices Topographical Division at Oxford. He spent a short time in the Department in 1946, then returned to what was now the Joint Intelligence Bureau from 1947 until his retirement at the end of 1949.

On retirement as a commander Monk was given charge of the South Coast of England Survey Unit, where he remained until ill-health forced his resignation in 1956. From 1958 to 1975 he revised Sailing Directions from his home in Hampshire.

Lieutenant Commander J K T Paisley

John Keith Taylor Paisley joined his first surveying ship, the *Jason*, Jones, in 1939, shortly before his promotion to lieutenant, but the outbreak of war soon intervened, and he was back in general service for a year. In 1940 he returned to surveying in the *Scott*, Collins and then Sharpey-Schafer, for two years work with the minelaying squadron on the northern barrage, with a break in 1941 when for a few months he went to the *Challenger*, Jenks, working in the Gambia. From 1943 to 1946 Paisley was in the Mediterranean, first in North Africa and then in surveying units on the west coast of Italy and later in the Levant.

He came home in 1947 to the *Franklin*, Tripp, on the east coast and later served in the *Scott* under Griffiths. In 1951 he went out to the China station to the *Dampier*, Connell. After a short spell in the Joint Intelligence Bureau at the end of 1952 Paisley was appointed in command of the *Sharpshooter*, soon to be renamed *Shackleton*, working on the east coasts of England and Scotland, and also attending the Coronation Review.

In 1954 he went to the *Owen* in the Persian Gulf, but shortly afterwards transferred to the *Dalrymple* with the acting rank of commander, and worked for two years first on the east coast of Africa at Zanzibar and later in the Mediterranean off Cyprus. He took over charge of the South Coast of England Survey in 1956, continuing in post after his formal retirement in 1963 until 1977.

Commander D N Penfold, DSC

David Neil Penfold entered the Royal Navy from the Merchant Service as an acting lieutenant in 1938 when he was briefly in first the *Fitzroy* and then in the *Scott* before going for the 1939 season to the *Jason*, Jones, working in the Bristol Channel and off Milford Haven.

On the outbreak of war in September 1939 he went to the re-armed *Stork* on convoy duty and in the Norwegian campaign. By November 1940 he was back surveying in the *Challenger*, Jenks, working first in Iceland and then in the Gambia. During the summer of 1942 Penfold was in the *Gulnare*, Passmore, on the Clyde. Then, until July 1943, he was sent to the *Scott*, Sharpey-Schafer, with the northern minelayers. He next went to the *Franklin*, Stokes and then Irving, for surveys of Scapa Flow and Rosyth, later taking part in the Normandy landings and surveys on the French coast.

In October 1944 Penfold joined the *White Bear*, Sabine and later Day, on surveys of Chittagong and the Burma coast until, after surveying various rehabilitated ports subsequent to VJ Day, the ship ended up working on the west coast of Malaya. Penfold was working with the minesweepers in the operation to re-enter Rangoon. He tells a good story of the flotilla when ordered to destroy magnetic mines laid by the RAF to make a safe channel available in 48 hours. A sporting element was introduced by opening a book for all officers and men on the ship to explode the first or the most mines, the total number swept, and so on. In fact, owing to one of the flotilla dragging her anchor the previous night the spare ship took her place and exploded the first mine as a 20 to 1 outsider. The concern for their bets helped young and inexperienced personnel to forget to be nervous. For his work in this operation Penfold was awarded the DSC.

In 1946 and early 1947 Penfold was with 'Party Sandstone' making operational port surveys. Later in 1947 he joined the *Franklin*, Tripp and later Connell, on Thames Estuary surveys and Decca trials. He went south in the Antarctic summers of 1947-48 and 1950-51 in the Falkland Islands Dependencies Survey ship *John Biscoe*, taking charge of the Survey Training Unit at Chatham in the interval between the two.

In August 1951 Penfold was appointed in command of the *Sharpshooter*, surveying in the Wash and in the Firth of Forth. He came ashore in February 1953 to serve in the Department, taking charge of Chart Branch (N) with the acting rank of commander from June 1955. Retiring in 1958 as an honorary commander, he remained in CB(N) until September 1960, when he resigned to succeed Lowry as Hydrographic Surveyor to the Marine Department of Sarawak. He returned to the

Department in 1968 to become Notices to Mariners Officer, from which post he finally retired in 1976. He died in 1991.

Commander J S N Pryor

John Stoneman Nelson Pryor was attracted to the surveying service by meeting E H B Baker while both were prisoners of war. He was appointed to the *Franklin*, Tripp, in January 1946, working in the Thames Estuary. A year later he was sent to Portsmouth as Command Surveying Officer, mainly employed in verifying the depths over wrecks dispersed by explosion.

Early in 1948 Pryor went to the newly converted *Dampier*, Collins, which on commissioning steamed out to start 19 years' continuous service in the Far East. Returning home in mid 1950 he was appointed to the *Franklin*, Roe, again, but soon transferred to the *Cook*, the last of the four new ships, to stand by and then to commission her, again under Collins' command. He spent the summer of 1951 on Seaward Defence duties at Plymouth, then in September went to the *Owen*, Roe, then about to depart for the Persian Gulf.

In October 1953 Pryor was appointed in command of the *Shackleton* for surveys in the Thames Estuary. A year later he went back, this time in command, to the *Owen*, bound again for the Persian Gulf. From July 1956 to February 1959 Pryor served in the Department as Superintendent of the Oceanographic Branch, then returned to sea in command of the *Cook*, surveying in the islands of the south Pacific. In 1960 he was in the Department again as Officer in Charge of Staff Charts. From 1962 to 1964 he was in the *Dampier*, working in Borneo, Malaya and Hong Kong. On his return to England he went to the Director of Naval Intelligence's division for beach surveys from 1964 to 1965. He then spent almost three years as Assistant Hydrographer with the acting rank of captain.

On the Department's move to Taunton in April 1968 Pryor reverted to commander's rank and became Superintendent of Sailing Directions, a post he retained on retirement from active service in 1969 until December 1983. In retirement he lives in Suffolk, keeping his hand in at surveying by forwarding to Taunton regular surveys of the River Ore and Alde.

Captain C R K Roe, DSC

Charles Richard Kelsey Roe joined the *Beaufort*, Farquharson, in 1934, working on the west coasts of England and Scotland. In the following year he went out to the *Endeavour*, Southern, at first working on the west coats of Malaya and Siam, but later on the Arabian coast and acting as guardship at Aden during civil disturbances. For a short period during the Abyssinian crisis he was appointed to the minesweeper *Bideford*, then later in 1936 went to the new surveying ship *Stork*, Farquharson, then

Jackson, steaming out from England to survey on the west coast of Siam and in Ceylon.

In 1938 Roe was appointed to the *Franklin*, Sabine, working on the south and east coasts of England with a short season in Labrador. On the outbreak of war the ship was engaged in supporting the laying of the Dover mine barrage and then, from March 1940, in route clearance on the east coast, with surveys of fleet bases in Scotland and the Faeroe Islands. In 1941 he went to the monitor *Erebus* as navigator for the long pasage to the Mediterranean via the Cape. At Mombasa he left the ship to set up a surveying unit working in East African ports.

In 1943 he was lent to the Royal Australian Navy, serving in the *Wyalla* and *Shepperton*, latterly in command of that ship and then of the *Benalla* and later the *Moresby*. Serving with the US 7th Fleet, the ships surveyed anchorages, routes and landing areas in New Guinea and the off-lying islands. Returning to England in 1945, Roe had command of HDML 1053, attached to the *Scott*, Hennessey and later Bill, opening up north European ports. In 1946 he transferred to *Scott* herself, until in 1948 he left to stand by the new conversion *Dalrymple*, commissioning her in 1949 under Day and later E H B Baker for surveys in the Mediterranean and the Persian Gulf.

In 1950 Roe was appointed in command of the *Franklin*, surveying in the Thames Estuary and on the west coast of Scotland. He was promoted commander at this time. In 1951 he moved to the *Owen*, working in the Persian Gulf and off Cyprus. At home from 1953 to 1955 he was in the *Scott*, before going out in 1955 to the *Dampier* in the Far East. His first shore appointment came in 1956, to the Department as Officer in Charge of Staff Charts. Then in 1958 he went again to the *Owen* in the Persian Gulf, being promoted captain that year. Two years from 1959 to 1961 were spent in the Department as Assistant Hydrographer (2) before he went to the Senior Officers War Course in 1961.

Roe returned to sea in 1961 in command of the *Vidal*, surveying in the West Indies. Another spell in the Department followed from 1963 to 1967, first in Whitehall then at Cricklewood. Finally, in 1967, he went back to sea for his last command, *Vidal* again, this time surveying in the Persian Gulf and the Indian Ocean. He retired in 1968, and now lives in Devon.

Lieutenant Commander N D Royds

Nigel Denis Royds joined his first surveying ship, the *Scott*, Collins, as a newly promoted lieutenant in 1942, and saw service with the minelaying squadron operating between Iceland and the Faeroes. In 1943 he went to the *Franklin*, Stokes, working on the east coasts of England and Scotland, and in 1944 he went abroad in the *White Bear*, Sabine and later Day, surveying off Chittagong. Later Royds was sent on detached surveys on the Burma coast including Rangoon, and finally in re-occupied Singapore. After the war and after visiting various ports in the Far East *White Bear* worked on the west coast of Malaya until her return to England in 1946.

From 1946 to 1948 Royds was in command of ML 586, working with minesweepers in the Thames Estuary. Then followed a short period in the *Franklin*, Connell, working on surveys in the Medway while the ship was manned with a reduced complement owing to manpower shortages. From 1949 to 1951 he was in the *Dalrymple*, Day, E H B Baker and Irving successively, working in the Mediterranean and the Persian Gulf.

In 1951 he went to the *Franklin*, Roe, working on the west coast of Scotland, succeeding to the command for the later part of the season. From 1952 to 1955 Royds was in the Department as Equipment Officer at a time when the first trials of Two Range Decca were being carried out. For the season of 1955 he went in command of the *Scott* on the south and east coasts of England, doing much wreck sweeping. This was followed by his last command, *Dampier*, with the acting rank of commander from 1956 to 1957, surveying on the coasts of Borneo and Malaya.

On return from sea in 1957 Royds joined the newly formed Flood Warning Organisation at Dunstable which later became the Storm Tide Warning Service at Bracknell. He continued to serve there until his retirement in 1971.

Lieutenant Commander C J de C Scott

Charles James de Courcy Scott joined the surveying service as a lieutenant in 1944 when he went to the *Franklin*, Irving, working, after the Normandy landings, in north west European ports. In 1946 he moved to the *Sharpshooter*, Menzies, working on the coasts of Borneo and Malaya. He continued with her in the 1948 season on her return home, in command of one of her attendant MLs, sweeping wrecks on the east coast.

During 1949 Scott served with the Hydrographic Mission to Turkey, working from an LCT on the south coast of Asia Minor. For security reasons, in Turkish waters the vessel wore no ensign and the ship's company shifted into the suits at that time being issued to men being demobilised. His recollections from this unusual assignment include arrest by Turkish villagers, shooting expeditions, and the gypsies who made baskets out of wire, preferring to filch five-core submarine detector cable rather than the local telephone wire. The survey was of special interest because Beaufort's charts of 1811-12 were in use. Scott was astounded at the accuracy and completeness of the original surveys. The principal difference was found in the values of longitude where Beaufort had interrupted his work to take refugees to the island of Kos.

From April 1950 to February 1951 Scott was in the *Seagull*, Gordon, on the south coast of England, but he was detached for a flying visit to test the suitability of the Monte Bello Islands for atomic bomb trials. In 1951 he went to the *Dalrymple*, Irving, in East Africa and the Persian Gulf, transferring to the *Cook*, E H B Baker, for the latter half of 1952 to work on the west coast of Scotland. During 1953 and 1954 Scott was in the *Dampier*, Connell and then Grattan, working again on the coasts of Malaya and Borneo, and then came home to work on east and south coast surveys in ML 3516 , and then in first *Shackleton* and later *Scott*, both under Hatfield.

In August 1956 he was appointed in charge of the East Coast of England Survey Unit, then throughout 1957 commanded the *Shackleton* for surveys on the east and south coasts of England and the west coast of Scotland.

Coming ashore in 1958, Scott was in the Department in charge of handling wreck information until his retirement in 1962. Since then he has been a reviser of Sailing Directions from his home in Somerset.

Lieutenant Commander D P D Scott, MBE

Desmond Patrick Dehany Scott joined the *Franklin*, Irving, in 1944 as a sublieutenant and took part in the surveys of north European ports after the Normandy landings. In 1945 he went to the Mediterranean and for three years served in SMLs surveying in the Adriatic, Greece, North Africa and Cyprus.

After a spell on beach surveys in the Mediterranean and the United Kingdom, Scott went back to the *Franklin*, now under Connell, during 1949 for work in the Thames Estuary. Then in 1950 he went on exchange service to the Royal Australian Navy, where he was engaged, among other tasks, in the surveys of the Monte Bello Islands for the first British atomic bomb tests. Coming home in 1952 Scott went to the *Cook*, E H B Baker, working on the west coast of Scotland. In 1953 he joined the newly completed *Vidal*, Collins then Connell, for over three years of varied work from the West Indies to the Barents Sea. In 1954 he was awarded the Order of Honour and Merit of the Republic of Haiti for his work on hurricane relief, and in 1955 he led the team which landed on and took possession of Rockall.

After a year at the Survey Training Unit Scott was appointed in command of the *Shackleton* in 1958 for surveys on the west coast of Scotland and in the Bristol Channel. In 1960 he transferred to the *Scott*, working on the south and east coasts of England.

In 1961 Scott came ashore, to become Deputy Superintendent of the Oceanographic Branch with special responsibility for liaison with the Royal Naval Scientific Service and the National Institute of Oceanography. When in 1968 the Cricklewood establishment moved to Taunton Scott transferred to Whitehall in the new post of Oceanographic Planning and Liaison Officer. He was appointed MBE in that year. Scott became Secretary of the Intergovernmental Oceanographic Commission of UNESCO in October 1972, holding a nominal appointment under the British Naval Attaché in Paris until his retirement in February 1973. He left the IOC post in 1980, but continues active in international oceanography, and particularly bathymetric charting, from his home near Chichester.

Lieutenant Commander G J B Simeon

Geoffrey John Barrington Simeon joined the *Franklin*, Irving and later Tripp, in 1946 for a season in the Thames Estuary. From 1946 to 1948 he was in the *Challenger*, Southern, in the Persian Gulf and the Mediterranean, then in 1948 and 1949 had command of MLs attached first to the Thames Estuary minesweeping flotilla and then to the *Seagull*, Lowry, working in the Bristol Channel. In 1950 he went to the *Sharpshooter*, Berncastle, working on east coast surveys and wreck sweeping.

Later in 1950 Simeon went to the *Challenger*, Ritchie followed by Ashton, for her world oceanographic voyage. There followed a season at home during 1953, again in the *Sharpshooter*, now under first Penfold and then Paisley, in the Thames Estuary. He then went to the *Cook*, Connell, working on the Gold Coast of Africa and on the west coast of Scotland.

In 1955 and 1956 Simeon was Equipment Officer in the Department, then in 1957 he was appointed in charge of the East Coast of England Survey Unit. From 1958 to 1960 he had command of the *Scott* on the east coasts of England and Scotland, during which time he took the Hydrographer, Collins, on a visit to Stavanger and in a separate incident lost the ship's asdic dome on an unexpected shoal on the Cant in the Thames Estuary.

From 1960 until his retirement in 1963 Simeon was assistant to the Officer in Charge of Staff Charts in Whitehall. From 1963 to 1966 he was with the Southampton Harbour Board. In 1966 he went to Fiji to set up a hydrographic service under the auspices of the United Nations. He remained there until 1975, when he returned to England.

Lieutenant Commander J C E White

Jeremy Charles Ellinthorpe White joined the *Franklin*, Tripp, in 1947 as a lieutenant, when she was working in the Thames Estuary with two SMLs. The next year he was himself in SML 1301, first under Glen and then himself in command, working as a tender to the *Challenger*, Sharpey-Schafer, in the Mediterranean. In 1948 and 1949 he served in *Challenger* herself, both in the Mediterranean and in the Persian Gulf.

From 1949 to 1951 White was back in the *Franklin* under Roe, working with attached SMLs on the east coast of England, in the Thames Estuary and on the west coast of Scotland. In 1951 he went with Roe to the *Owen*, working once more in the Mediterranean and the Persian Gulf. He came home in 1952 to serve in the *Scott* under Grattan, Hall and Roe in succession, surveying on United Kingdom coasts and on the east coast of Ireland.

White went again to the *Owen*, Pryor, in 1955-56, back in the Persian Gulf and the Mediterranean, then spent a brief time in the *Cook*, Hayter, on the west coast of Scotland, before going to the Department as Equipment Officer from 1957 to 1958.

In 1959 he went to the South Pacific in the *Cook*, Hatfield, then in 1960 was appointed in command of the *Shackleton* to work on the west coast of Scotland.

After two years in the Department from 1961 to 1963 White retired at his own request to join Kelvin Hughes, surveying for commercial interests at home and abroad. In June 1967 he became Hydrographic Officer to the Port of London Authority.

Captain J D Winstanley, CBE

John Davenport Winstanley joined the Merchant Service in 1938. As a reservist he was called up on the outbreak of war, transferred to the Royal Navy in 1945, and joined the surveying service two years later as a lieutenant, being appointed to the *Seagull*, Collins, working in Scottish and Northern Ireland waters. In 1949 he joined the new surveying ship *Dalrymple*, Day then E H B Baker, when she commissioned for work in the Mediterranean and the Persian Gulf. He returned home in 1951 to the *Scott*, Ashton and later Grattan, surveying along the south coast of England. Two years later he went back to the Persian Gulf in the *Owen*, Roe, then joined the *Cook*, Connell, in 1954 for surveys mainly on the west coast of Scotland.

Winstanley was appointed to his first command, the *Dalrymple*, in 1956, for surveys in the Mediterranean, but within a few months the ship was required, firstly to stand by in Tobruk ready to rescue King Idris of Libya, and then to form part of the spearhead of the allied forces in the Suez Canal operation. On the withdrawal of the allies *Dalrymple* remained at Port Said under the United Nations flag to assist in the clearing and salvage work required to re-open the canal.

From 1958 to 1960 he was employed in the Department at Cricklewood, and was promoted commander before taking command of the *Dampier*, engaged in surveys in Malaysian waters. He returned to the Department, this time to Whitehall, in 1962, and two years later was attached to the staff of the Commodore Superintendent Contract Built Ships for work on the design and building of the *Hecla* class and the conversion of *Mermaid*, *Myrmidon*, *Woodlark* and *Waterwitch*. He acted as Admiralty Master for the trials of the first of the new class, *Hecla*, then took command of the second, *Hecate*, on first commissioning in 1965, spending the next two years mainly on Atlantic Ocean surveys.

He went back to the Department at Cricklewood as Superintendent of Charts shortly before it transferred to Taunton, and after the move became the first Assistant Director (Naval). A further commission in *Hecate* followed. Working mainly off the west coast of the British Isles, it was during this appointment that one of the ship's surveying motor boats was blown up by the IRA during a survey of Baltimore Harbour in County Cork. In 1972 he took up the post of Assistant Hydrographer in Whitehall, and three years later returned to Taunton to the renamed post of Director of Hydrographic Plans and Surveys. He retired in 1976, being made CBE in that year.

His several appointments to the Department carried with them a number of NATO and international tasks. At the 1958 Copenhagen meeting of the International Council for the Exploration of the Sea he was a UK Adviser. In 1962 he became Executive of the International Routing and Reporting Authority. In 1969 he was chairman of the NATO Hydrographic Conference at the Hague, and in 1976 was chairman of the NATO Maps and Charts Working Party conference in Brussels. He was instrumental in establishing the World Wide Radio Navigational Warning system, and the transfer of the RN Radio Navigational Warning organisation from Whitehall to Taunton.

In retirement he lived in Somerset until his death in 1992.

CHAPTER EIGHT

Modernisation and Metrication
1960–1970

Rear Admiral Sir Edmund Irving, KBE, CB, 1960–1966

Rear Admiral G S Ritchie, CB, DSC, 1966–1971

'Egg' Irving, as he was always known, took over from Collins on 7 July 1960. A big man with a beaky nose and a bluff manner which masked a razor-sharp intellect, he brought a breath of fresh air to the Department as soon as he took over. He made it plain to the surveying fleet that they were part of the Navy, not the private service which they had all too often given the impression that they considered themselves. He also cultivated both the political and scientific establishments, and achieved good relations with important members of both which served the Hydrographic Service, both ashore and afloat, well.

He encouraged both naval and civilian staff to 'sell' the Service both to the Navy and to the world beyond. He continued and further developed the more informative style of Annual Report started by Collins, and articles on aspects of surveying and charting began to appear in the scientific and popular press. He also continued the 'Hydrographer's Messages' to his own people ashore and afloat which his predecessor had started, and cultivated good relations between his naval staff and the civilians at Cricklewood and Taunton, which had often been hostile in the past.

It fell to 'Steve' Ritchie, who succeeded Irving in January 1966, to reap where he had sown, five years being nothing like long enough for procurement plans, either for buildings or ships, to be formulated, approved and come to fruition. A sturdy man with a florid complexion and a happy nature which endeared him to all and sundry, he maintained the contacts developed by Irving, completed the projects started by him and initiated others of his own. From his time in command of *Challenger* during her world oceanographic cruise in the '50s he had developed many contacts with the civil scientific community which he used to good effect as Hydrographer. A keen historian and writer, his books on the Admiralty Chart in the Nineteenth Century and HMS *Challenger* and his autobiography have been of great help to the author of this work.

Shortly after Ritchie took over the Whitehall offices of the Hydrographic Department were moved from the Admiralty Archway Block to the Old War Office, where they occupied a fine set of rooms on the principal floor. Hydrographer himself was installed in an impressive circular office at the north east corner of the building. This was, in fact, part of a general reshuffle of office accomodation in Whitehall in all three services as a consequence of Mountbatten's decision to move the operational staffs to a single Ministry of Defence Main Building, the former Air Ministry. The move brought Hydrographer (Whitehall) nearer the Naval Staff than he would have been had he remained in Archway Block.

At the beginning of Irving's time in office the home surveying ships were down to two, *Scott* and *Shackleton*, with the East Coast of England Survey Unit, soon to be renamed the Inshore Survey Squadron, of the three *Echos*, on the east coast; and the last two SMLs working as independent units, *Medusa* out of Devonport with a Naval crew and *Meda* out of Portsmouth with a civilian crew under a retired surveyor. Abroad, with the cycle of major refits continuing, three of the four Bays and *Vidal* continued the pattern of West Indies, Gulf, Indian Ocean and Far Eastern surveys.

The first break in this pattern came in the autumn of 1960, when *Owen*, under Hall, having completed her long refit in Gibraltar and then worked up in home waters, left for the South Atlantic for an oceanographical cruise combined with three months surveying in South Georgia. Here a dwindling but still energetic whaling industry had been reporting uncharted dangers, and it was considered desireable both on safety and on political grounds to pay some hydrographic attention to a neglected area. Much useful work was achieved by the ship and by detached boat parties, mostly at the north-western end of the island, before *Owen* returned home at the end of May 1961.

At Plymouth after her South Atlantic adventure *Owen* was fitted with the first sea gravimeter to be taken afloat in one of the Hydrographer's vessels. This, together with other geophysical equipment and a Precision Depth Recorder for use with her deep echo sounder, were to enable her to take part in the International Indian Ocean Expedition, a co-ordinated effort by world-wide scientists to probe the secrets of an ocean which was seen by the scientific comunity to have been neglected since the days of the *Mabahiss* in the early 1930s. From October 1961 to the end of May 1962 *Owen* made traverses across the seas between Mombasa, the Seychelles, Bombay and Karachi. Meanwhile her boats were detached to resurvey parts of the Kenya coast not charted since the great surveyor after whom she was named had worked in the same waters in the early years of the previous century.

With the development of inertial navigation, which works by sensing the earth's gravitational field, there came a need to know the anomalies and wrinkles in that field, at sea as well as on land. The early sea gravimeters required careful nursing. The problem was that they were trying to measure tiny variations in gravity which were masked by much larger forces generated by the motion of the ship both horizontal and vertical. The experience gained in *Owen's* first geophysical cruise convinced Hydrographer's staff both that there was a defence need to measure gravity and that a great deal more experience would have to be acquired before the Hydrographic Service was capable of making the necessary observations without the help of civilian scientists. The Askania gravimeter in *Owen* was therefore purchased from its owners, the Department of Geodesy and Geophysics of Cambridge University, in 1963 and its use continued, still at first under Cambridge supervision. As a quid-pro-quo, *Owen's* Indian Ocean surveys in subsequent years contained a substantial amount of purely scientific work. In the autumn of 1963, for instance, she conducted a seismic programme with RRS *Discovery* between Mombasa and the Seychelles.

Vidal was also fitted with geophysical equipment during 1963, ready to start a very broad brush survey of the whole North Atlantic known as NAVADO. This comprised a traverse across the ocean every 3° of latitude from 10° North to the edge of the Arctic ice, both taking continuous geophysical observations and making oceanographic stations at regular intervals. With the participation in 1965 of the Dutch surveying ship *Snellius*, and with a closer examination of the approaches to the Straits of Gibraltar, an area of particular bathymetric and geological complexity, by *Vidal* and *Owen*, the operation was completed in 1966, and provided a framework on which to base the more detailed oceanic surveys carried out by the *Hecla* class during the last years of the decade and beyond.

The life of the foreign-going surveying ships was not without its excitement. In January 1964 *Owen*, under Haslam, was ordered to Zanzibar, where a coup had taken place ousting the Sultan. After a week acting as a steadying influence discouraging action by the new government against the British High Commission or the numerous British nationals on the island, 150 civilians were evacuated to Mombasa, with another 40 embarked via *Owen's* boats in the Royal Fleet Auxiliary *Hebe*. No sooner had she landed her refugees than she was embarking troops from the Gordon Highlanders to stand by to quell the mutiny of elements of the Tanganyikan army at Dar es Salaam. By this time there was a considerable British squadron in the area, *Victorious*, *Albion*, *Diana*, *Salisbury*, *Rhyl* and *Eskimo* all being involved at one time or another. It was not until the end of February that Haslam was able to concentrate on his surveying tasks without keeping a weather eye open for orders to drop everything and to go off in support of the civil power. This was in fact the last period *Owen* spent in the Indian Ocean, as she returned home at the end of April 1964 and spent her last year west of Gibraltar on NAVADO II. She finally paid off in September 1965, a large proportion of her surveyors going to man the *Hydra*, then fitting out at Yarrows.

Cook emerged from her major refit at Singapore in March 1961, and resumed her work in the south western Pacific, mainly in Fiji but with working visits to the Gilbert and Ellice Islands and recreational and maintenance visits to New Zealand. She had her own brand of excitement when, on 1 October 1963, she grounded on a coral head off Vatu Ira in the channel between the two main Fijian islands. Though she was refloated by her own efforts her bottom was badly damaged. A false bottom was patched onto her over the damage by the Fijian Public Works Department on a patent slip at Suva, but without echo-sounders she did no more surveying. She was brought home early in 1964 and laid up, to be sold for scrap in 1968.

Dalrymple continued working in the Persian Gulf in the winters, withdrawing to the Mediterranean, and for refits back to England, in the summers. She too carried out oceanographic and magnetic observations over the Murray Ridge, in the Indian Ocean south of the south east Arabian coast, in 1962 and 1963. She returned to Devonport from her last foreign deployment in May 1963. For the remainder of her life in the Royal Navy she was employed on surveys off the west coast of Scotland, with regular voyages further out into the Atlantic for oceanography. She finally steamed up the Hamoaze with Hydrographer embarked on 19 November 1965 to pay off. She was sold to Portugal, where she enjoyed a second incarnation as their surveying ship *Afonso de Albuquerque*, remaining in service until 1979 and even after that acting as an accomodation hulk at Lisbon, thus being the last survivor of the surveying Bays.

Dampier remained on her usual beat between Singapore and Hong Kong, surveying on both coasts of the Malay Peninsula and in the waters of the formerly British parts of Borneo. In the autumn of 1965 she went east to work off the Solomon Islands, where she embarked a team of scientists from United States universities with a gravimeter, magnetometer and Precision Depth Recorder for a coarse-grained geophysical survey. During this period she towed the New Zealand cruiser *Royalist*, which had broken down, into clear water away from Bellona Island before having to leave her to fuel. She then spent some months in Fiji and the New Hebrides, carrying out priority work which had been earmarked for *Cook* before that ship's grounding and subsequent withdrawal. After final surveys in Malayan waters and a last oceanographical cruise in the Indian Ocean *Dampier* left Singapore on 5 October 1967 to return home to pay off after 19 years continuously on the Far East station. When she hauled down her pendant at the end of the year she was the last of her class, as she had been the first, in the Naval service.

Before devoting her time to oceanography and geophysics *Vidal* too had her share of excitement over and above the routine of surveying. In October 1961 she was sent to Belize in the aftermath of Hurricane Hattie, where as well as providing relief food and building materials to settlements devaststed by the high winds and waves, she assisted in the refloating of the Royal Mail cargo liner *Essequibo*. This ship had grounded in the approaches to Belize while entering through the reef channel whose marks and beacons had been destroyed in the hurricane. In December of the same year *Vidal* had again acted as communications link for the second meeting of the Prime Minister and the US President, now Kennedy, at Bermuda. It was during her NAVADO survey, in May 1966, that *Vidal* was involved in a collision in mid-Atlantic with the merchant ship *Hong Kong Fair*, which inexplicably altered course across *Vidal's* bows at close quarters on a clear, star-lit night. Both ships were damaged, though both made port safely under their own power.

After *Vidal's* NAVADO surveys she was deployed for her last years to the Persian Gulf, where her helicopter proved its worth not only to her own survey parties but also in assisting *Bulldog* and *Beagle* in their Trucial Coast surveys. She was finally paid off after the end of our period, in 1971, to be replaced by *Herald*, the fourth Ocean Survey Ship.

Early in 1961 Irving turned the thoughts of his staff towards the replacement of *Scott* and *Shackleton*, both well over 20 years old. By the end of the year the Naval Staff had been brought into the process, and design studies for a new small surveying ship had been put in hand. But by the end of 1962 the increasing interest in defence oceanography, the commissioning of the United Kingdom's first fast, deep-diving nuclear submarine, and the ever-increasing complexity of the design of even a 'small' surveying ship to full Naval Staff requirements led to a review of the way ahead for the surveying fleet.

Irving persuaded Lord Carrington, the First Lord of the Admiralty, of the need for a new surveying fleet designed to carry out the surveys and oceanography required by the Navy in the most economic and efficient way. In a speech to the Royal Geographical Society on 10 June 1963 Carrington made an unprecedented public acknowledgement of the importance of hydrography to the Navy and the nation, and gave his personal endorsement to the new look fleet.

The outcome was approval for nine new ships, three Ocean Survey Ships with a design based on the Royal Research Ship *Discovery*, and six coastal surveying vessels to work on 'traditional' surveying tasks, either at home or in pairs overseas. All were to be built to 'best commercial standards' rather than to full Naval specifications.

Scott and *Shackleton*, meanwhile, were almost beyond further nursing along, and were paid off at the end of 1964 and 1962 respectively. To bridge the gap until the first of the new coastal survey vessels commissioned, two Ton class minesweepers were given a very basic surveying conversion. *Edderton* and *Sullington* became *Myrmidon* and *Mermaid*, and entered service in their new role in 1964. They only remained in the surveying fleet for four years, paying off at the end of 1967 in time to release their officers and men to commission the *Bulldog* class Coastal Survey Vessels in 1968. *Myrmidon* gained a new lease of life when she was bought by the Royal Malaysian Navy for their hydrographic service and became KD *Perantau* in 1969.

Using the *Discovery* hull as a model the three Ocean Survey Ships were designed and built by Yarrows on the Clyde. By Naval standards they were short, fat ships, with a length of 230 feet overall and a beam of 49 feet. Their single screw, transverse bow thruster and diesel-electric machinery were designed to give them flexibility in operation, and particularly to allow the long periods at very slow speed (or even holding the ship stopped) required for oceanographic observations in the ocean depths. They were fitted with a flight deck aft and a hangar for a Wasp helicopter, and with Askania gravimeters and towed magnetometers for the geophysical observations which inertial navigation now required.

The first of class, *Hecla*, entered service in September 1965, followed by the second, *Hecate*, in December. The North Atlantic in the autumn provided a testing first cruise for the new ship, and it was soon discovered that the class, though very stable and seaworthy, had a motion for which 'lively' was a distinct understatement. It was quickly approved to fit passive stabiliser tanks, which were built into the third ship, *Hydra*, before her completion and acceptance, which occurred at the end of May 1966.

As the *Hecla*s commissioned they all took up more detailed oceanic surveys in the North Atlantic in the wake of *Vidal's* NAVADO work. *Hecla*, under Hall, working south of Iceland, sent a boat party to assist the Icelandic gunboat *Thor* in surveying the newly risen volcanic island of Surtsey in the summer of 1967. In the same year *Hydra*, under Nesbitt, took part in NATO military oceanographic observations off the Azores and further oceanography in the upwelling zone off the west coast of Africa with scientists from the Ministry of Agriculture and Fisheries laboratories at Lowestoft. In 1969 *Hydra* took part, with ships from the Federal Republic of Germany and the United States, in the Atlantic Trade Wind Experiment, a 15-day drift with a helium-filled balloon carrying instruments above the ship and a buoy tethered to the ship carrying more instruments below her. She also undertook surveys on the coast of Sierra Leone.

At the end of 1969 *Hydra* was sent out to the Far East under M J Baker to begin a complete resurvey of the Malacca Strait for the safe passage of deep-draught vessels, the first Royal Naval surveying ship to go east of Suez since *Dampier's* withdrawal over two years previously.

Six Coastal Survey Vessels were at first planned for, and the names *Albatross*, *Albacore*, *Barracouta*, *Bulldog*, *Fawn* and *Fox* put forward. The first three were soon changed to *Pelican*, *Porcupine* and *Beagle*, as the two 'A' names were thought to be too close phonetically, and Hydrographer wished to revive the historic surveying name of *Beagle*. However, when approval was given to go out to tender in 1964, it was only for four vessels. The design competition was won by Brooke Marine of Lowestoft, and in 1966 orders for all four were placed with that yard. Of the collection of names the 'B' and 'F' pairs were chosen, and the class named the *Bulldog* class.

At 1080 tons full load displacement the *Bulldog*s are actually bigger ships than the *Halcyon*s of the late 1930s, though with a hull of similar proportions to the *Hecla*s they appear much smaller, being only 189 feet long compared to the *Halcyons'* 230. Four Lister Blackstone diesels coupled through gearing to two variable pitch propellors can drive them at a nominal 15 knots, with bridge control of both engine revolutions and propellor pitch. They were fitted with Hi-Fix, precision ranging radar and dry-paper echo-sounders.

Bulldog, the first of the class, was launched in July 1967, and entered service in March 1968. All four were in commission by the end of 1968. They are highly efficient and economical surveying units. Their fitness for surveying world wide was well proven when, before the end of their first commission, *Bulldog* and *Beagle* were sent round the Cape of Good Hope to spend the 1969-1970 winter working in the Persian Gulf.

At the same time as approval was given to seek tenders for the *Bulldog*s, it was approved to replace the remaining two SMLs with converted Inshore Minesweepers. *Yaxham* and *Powderham* were taken in hand at the end of 1964, and entered surveying service as *Woodlark* in December 1965 and *Waterwitch* in March 1966. They had enclosed bridges, a more modern electronics fit and a slightly different internal layout, but were otherwise identical to the *Echo* class.

Though not strictly a surveying ship, Ritchie and his equipment officer, Lieutenant Commander C J C Wynne-Edwards, were closely involved in the purchase of the *Anita Dan* in April 1967 and her conversion at Harland and Wolff, Belfast into the Ice Patrol Ship *Endurance*. She entered service in October 1968, and carried a team of specialist surveyors as part of her ship's company. It had been hoped by Ritchie that she would be commanded by a surveying officer, and it was a disappointment to Read, who had been earmarked for this interesting post, when it was ruled that she would have a general service captain.

Finally, though properly outside the period covered by this book, it should be mentioned that a fourth, slightly modified *Hecla* was ordered in November 1971 to replace *Vidal*. Though only a bare 20 years old, *Vidal's* very large engine-room complement militated against her retention and in favour of a fourth *Hecla*. The new ship was built by Robb Caledon at Leith, named *Herald*, and entered service in 1974 to complete the replacement of the immediate post-war surveying fleet by modern purpose-built ships.

The four *Bulldog* class took up the home surveys, both the routine resurveying of the shifting banks of the southern North Sea and elsewhere round the coasts of the British Isles.

The increasing size of the largest merchant ships, and the way in which commercial pressures required them to be operated with little regard for safety margins under their keels, was an increasing worry for the Hydrographers of all the major maritime nations as the 1960s wore on. For none was it of more concern than those of the countries round the southern North Sea, where the shifting sandbanks required constant monitoring even for conventional shipping, and the seabed was strewn with the detritus of two major wars. In 1969 Ritchie told the Chart Users' Panel of VLCCs already over 200,000 tons, with an expectation before long of even bigger ships of 500,000 tons drawing over 80 feet. Under the aegis of the North Sea Hydrographic Commission, set up in 1962 following the Eighth International Hydrographic Conference, areas of surveying responsibility were agreed between the member nations*. Surveys under this dispensation for designated deep draught routes through the southern North Sea were the first task for *Bulldog* and *Beagle* on commissioning under Read and Morris respectively.

In the autumn of 1969 *Bulldog* and *Beagle*, as has already been mentioned, were sent out to the Persian Gulf round the bottom of South Africa to spend the winter surveying off the coast of what was then Trucial Oman, now the United Arab Emirates. *Fox* and *Fawn*, when they commissioned under Dathan and Robinson, were employed mainly on the west coast of the United Kingdom, working both in Scotland and Wales. In the winter gales of 1969 in the Minch *Fox*, anchored in Loch

---

*Norway, Sweden, Denmark, Federal Republic of Germany, Netherlands, United Kingdom, later joined by France and Belgium.

Bay, dragged and went aground on Mingay Island. After drying out at low water she was got off on the rising tide by *Fawn* in a fine piece of ship handling by Robinson. That a docking found her undamaged showed how stoutly built the Coastal Survey Vessels are. After the 'B's returned from the Gulf in the spring of 1970, the 'F's were sent out to the West Indies for the winter of 1970-71. For some years it became the practice for one pair of Coastals to be deployed abroad each winter.

By 1960 all the major surveying units were fitted with Two Range Decca, and Lambda, with its lane identification facility, was coming into service. The equipment, though, was heavy and ponderous, requiring a 100-foot mast at the slave stations, and having an accuracy of not much better than 100 metres. Decca developed a smaller, higher frequency and so more accurate version on the same basic principles, named HiFix. Roberts, in *Scott*, carried out successful trials of the new equipment in the approaches to the Firth of Forth in conjunction with the 100th Minesweeping Squadron. By 1964 HiFix had been acquired and was being used operationally by *Mermaid* in the waters between Northern Ireland and the Hebrides, and by the Antarctic Survey Party in RRS *John Biscoe* in the Bismarck Strait.

With the position of the ship now being fixed continuously in all weathers by electronic means and with new echo-sounders recording the depths on dry paper without the distortion or fading of the old wet iodide rolls, thought was directed to the possibility of scanning between the lines of soundings to detect wrecks and rock pinnacles which might otherwise be missed. Kelvin Hughes had developed a 'Fisherman's Asdic' which was designed to allow fishing vessels to search for and find shoals of fish by obtaining asdic returns from their swim-bladders. After trials in 1961 sets were fitted in the *Echo* class during their 1961-92 winter lie-up, and later in *Mermaid* and *Myrmidon* and the *Bulldog* class. Neither the 'Fisherman's Asdic' or the old Type 144 fitted in the larger ships up to this time did more than provide some indication when large objects existed between sounding lines, and only a very alert and experienced operator could provide a rough idea of what that large object might be. The tediousness of sitting at the sonar set for long hours militated against any operator remaining alert, and many wrecks were missed during sonar sweeping.

In 1969 research on the development of a surveying sonar was contracted to the Committee for Marine Technology of the Ministry for Technology. The specification asked for a set which would both detect small objects (the target was an object 1 metre square projecting one metre above the sea bed) and give their height above the seabed. This eventually came to fruition with the HYDROSEARCH set fitted first in *Bulldog* and then in *Roebuck* in the 1980s. Though it performed well it was a cumbersome and very expensive piece of equipment which could never have been put into service throughout the surveying fleet. A much more promising line of development was the towed sidescan sonar, in principle very much the same as the old Type 162 'Cockchafer', but towed astern of the ship much closer to the bottom, and with a higher frequency giving much clearer definition. First trials of an EG&G sonar of this type took place in *Fawn* in 1971. Within a year or two sidescan sonar became a standard fit, and with it the surveyor could at last look between his sounding lines with confidence, and say that his whole survey area had been well and truly covered.

When the *Hecla*s entered service and began to measure gravity as a standard part of their surveying task, the problems of reducing the observed gravity measurements to the more meaningful Bougier Anomalies in the earth's gravitational field became evident. While the heave of the ship in a seaway was eliminated by 'damping' the meter, the effect of the ship's movement through the water, of its course and speed, known as the Eötvös Correction, had to be calculated and applied to the raw readings. To do this by hand was a slow and tedious business, replete with opportunities for error. The answer was to automate the process. Automatic Data Logging equipment was procured from Elliott Bros, with the first set given trials in *Hecla* in the summer of 1968. It included not only sensors to log electronically the navigational aids, gravity meters and magnetometers and to make the necessary calculations to determine the Eötvös Correction every few minutes, but also a flat-bed Kingmatic plotter to provide a graphic output to aid in error detection and control of the surveys. The first surveys were rendered on punched tape recorded by the Elliott system in 1969. Though the original purpose of the ADL system was to reduce gravity readings, once it had been fitted a whole range of other uses were found, from drawing borders for fair survey sheets to plotting HiFix lattices for boat surveys, as well as plotting the ship's track for conventional surveys.

In the oceanographic field, a new echo-sounder capable of recording depths down to 4,500 fathoms was introduced throughout the Fleet in 1962, with a helical Precision Depth Recorder for accurate sounding to be fitted in surveying ships only. At the same time a bathythermograph (a towed device for recording the temperature of sea water against depth on a glass slide) reading down to 250 fathoms was also introduced. To collect, compile and publish the greatly increased volume of data which it was hoped would flow from this new equipment, a British Oceanographic Data Centre was established by the Department at Cricklewood. Serial water data from physical sampling by bottle casts as well as bathythermograph data were to be recorded on punched cards, with gravity, magnetics and bathymetry recorded on plotting sheets at a scale of 1:1 million.

All this collection of data would be of no use unless it was digested and published in a form that both oceanographic scientists and the military could understand and use. A large number of specific inquiries for data were answered, and a series of Oceanographic Atlases as well as charts and diagrams for submarine navigation began to be issued - an ongoing process, though much digested data is now presented in digital form.

In inshore waters much attention was given to the study of siltation and the movement of sandbanks. The existence of sand waves, very large ripples or ridges within a sandy area, usually where there is also a strong tidal stream, was a cause of concern since many sand wave fields were found in areas where deep draught traffic was passing close to the seabed, particularly in the Dover Strait and southern North Sea but also in the Malacca Strait and elsewhere. Opinions varied as to how mobile these waves were, and detailed, repeated surveys of selected critical areas were made to try to determine their movement. In 1969 research into coastal sedimentation was devolved to the National Environmental Research Council, and a Coastal Sedimentation Unit set up in a purpose-built set of offices in the Hydrographic Department's grounds at Taunton.

The surge of interest in oceanography led to increasing co-operation between the Department and the Naval Weather Service. Instructor officers qualified in Meteorology and Oceanography served regularly in surveying ships, and the connection between the weather above the surface of the sea and that below it was increasingly being appreciated. Board approval was given in 1965 for the Naval Weather Service to be brought under Hydrographer's aegis, a merger which took effect in February 1966. The NWS's title was changed at the same time to the Meteorological and Oceanographic Service.

To compensate for this acquisition (though not strictly connected to it) Hydrographer in 1965 lost the responsibility for the Astronomer Royal which Beaufort had assumed in 1831. This was transferred to the Science Research Council as part of the Wilson government's shake-up of the administration of science.

The Fleet's need for predictions of oceanographic conditions had been recognised for some time, and an Anti-Submarine Warfare Environmental Prediction Service (ASWEPS) established in 1963 to provide predictions for particular exercises. This was soon seen not to be enough. A two day seminar was held in London in the autumn of 1966, attended by both Naval and civilian oceanographers, in which much useful information on oceanographic prediction was exchanged. In 1967 the generic name for the service was shortened to the simpler Oceanographic Forecasting Service. At the same time the service was made routine rather than particular, and both it and the provision of normal weather forecasts to the Fleet were transferred to a new Fleet Weather Centre in the Fleet's headquarters at Northwood. Trial OFS units were also set up at Malta and Singapore, the former under the NATO headquarters there. In 1971 the Malta unit moved to Naples, and a new oceanographic and meteorological centre was set up in the NATO headquarters at Lisbon.

With the advent of so much electronic equipment it was seen that more training in the potential and use of it was needed for officers. This was pointed out in Irving's Annual Report for 1961. Putting plans to achieve this into effect was held back by the move of the Hydrographic School from its huts in St Budeaux Camp to the West Battery in HMS *Drake* early in 1966, but later in the same year a revised officers' training package was brought in. The new scheme allowed for a short basic course on entry into the specialisation, then an intermediate course after a few years' experience and last an advanced course at the level of 1st Class Assistant. At the same time the Royal Institution of Chartered Surveyors agreed to recognise the School's courses and to exempt from their examinations students who had passed all three officers' courses.

Besides the Royal Naval students at the Hydrographic School a number of foreign students were trained. In 1970, a typical year, 1 Pakistan Naval officer and one Pakistani civilian were on the Advanced Course; one Royal Malaysian Naval officer, one Royal New Zealand Naval officer and one Guyanan civilian were on the Intermediate Course, and four Royal Malaysian Naval ratings on the SR 2 course. As a number of universities and polytechnics began to offer surveying courses with a hydrographic element, so the number of British civilians attending the Hydrographic School dropped away. Many of these civilian courses were staffed by former Royal Naval surveyors.

In February 1961 a symposium on the Admiralty Chart was held at the Royal Institute of Navigation, as a result of which Irving set up a Chart Users' Advisory Panel. This comprised representatives of about 45 shipping companies, who were consulted by Chart Branch staff when planning new chart schemes or considering changes in current charting. As a result of discussions with the CUAP a series of Routeing Charts were introduced. These were small scale charts covering the whole of one ocean, showing great circle tracks between major ports, prevailing winds, weather and current information, and the seasonal limits of load lines, with a different chart for each month of the year. After a modest start with four charts of the North Atlantic issued at the end of 1961, the series has gone from strength to strength, and now covers the whole world and all the months of the year in each ocean.

A series of special charts for yachtsmen, printed on foolscap size paper and with simple sailing directions printed on the backs, was also started in 1961. Though moderately popular, when pressure of work grew later in the decade effort could not be devoted to maintaining them, and they were withdrawn in 1970.

To avoid unnecessary duplication of effort and to share the load of compiling charts negotiations were entered into with the Australian and New Zealand hydrographic services in 1962 for them to assume complete responsibility for the charting of their own waters, with Taunton receiving reproduction material and printing facsimile copies of Aus and NZ charts. Aus and NZ Notices to Mariners would be reprinted in the Admiralty series so that users who obtained the charts through the Admiralty system could correct their charts without having to take two more sets of Notices. Charting agreements along these lines were signed by Irving on his Commonweath tour early in 1963, and entered into force on 1 August of that year. Even now not all British Admiralty charts of these two nations' areas of responsibility have been replaced by national ones, but the agreements have been highly successful since the start.

Irving's lobbying of the First Lord, Lord Carrington, not only resulted in the new surveying fleet being give a fair wind from the top. An inspection of the Department in 1961 had recommended that Chart Branch should be co-located with Production Branch, but in the way of these things the report was gathering dust in a Whitehall pigeonhole. In 1962 Lord Carrington visited both Cricklewood and Taunton, was quickly convinced that it was high time that the inefficiency of running a Department with two interlocking halves separated by some 180 miles ceased, and directed that an examination be put in hand to determine the possibility of moving the whole Cricklewood establishment to Taunton.

The Director General of Navy Works estimated that a building to take the Cricklewood operations could be provided on the Taunton site for about £300,000. It was now that the foresight of Llewellyn in 1938 in buying enough land to take the whole Department paid off, since the fact that land was already available on the site adjacent to the printing works removed what would otherwise have been a major obstacle. A further windfall occurred for the Admiralty when, in discussions about the provision of the new building, the Ministry of Public Buildings and Works offered to provide it as a charge to their votes and not to the Navy's. Board approval was given in June 1963, and work started in 1964. At that time it was stated in response to a query from the Staff Side that any move was unlikely to take place away from Cricklewood before 1966 or 1967.

In the event there were delays, and Ritchie made the decision early in 1968 to move in April whether the building was ready or not. This concentrated minds wonderfully, and the first occupants moved in on 16 April with the building to all intents and purposes complete. The remainder of the Cricklewood staff arrived over the next three weeks. A great deal of help was received from the Taunton civic authorities to settle the large number of incoming people. At an Open Day held shortly after the arrival to show the working places to the families of staff the Mayor of Taunton attended and declared all the incomers 'instant citizens' of the borough. Special travelling allowances were paid to those who did not move their homes to Somerset, but most of the staff moved, and the Department has been very happy in Taunton ever since.

Ritchie took the opportunity offered by the move to initiate a complete restructuring of the Department. He himself had offices both in Taunton and Whitehall. The Whitehall end of the Department, under a captain (H) as Assistant Hydrographer, kept responsibility for surveying personnel and for the appointing of (H) officers. Territorial Waters Officer; the Hydrographic Information Officer, with responsibility for publicity and responding to external queries except those specifically on charting matters; the Directorate of Meteorological and Oceanographic Services, which was an independent Directorate under Hydrographer; and a small registry, comprised 'Hydrographer (Whitehall)'.

At Taunton the establishment was controlled by three Assistant Directors. The Assistant Director (Naval), a captain (H), was responsible for planning the operations of the surveying fleet and monitoring the standard of its work, for Sailing Directions, for Notices to Mariners (which now included Radio Navigational Warnings), for Light Lists and for the Tidal Branch.

The Assistant Director (Professional), the Chief Civil Hydrographic Officer, was responsible for the collection of data, and for its compilation and cartography, up to the point where the chart compilation was ready to be redrawn to production standard to be transferred onto a printing plate.

The Assistant Director (Administration and Supply), a Grade 5 Administrative

Organisation after move to Taunton in 1968
(Surveying Ships not shown)

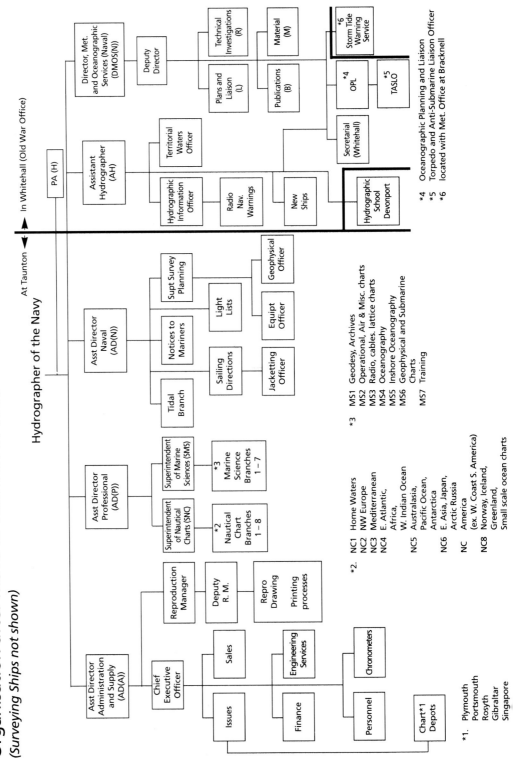

Hydrographer of the Navy

In Whitehall (Old War Office)

At Taunton

PA (H)

Director, Met. and Oceanographic Services (Naval) (DMOS(N))
- Deputy Director
  - Technical Investigations (R)
  - Material (M)
  - *6 Storm Tide Warning Service
  - Plans and Liaison (L)
  - Publications (B)
  - *4 OPL
  - *5 TASLO
- Secretarial (Whitehall)

Assistant Hydrographer (AH)
- Territorial Waters Officer
- Hydrographic Information Officer
- Radio Nav. Warnings
- New Ships
- Hydrographic School Devonport

Asst Director Naval (AD(N))
- Tidal Branch
- Notices to Mariners
- Sailing Directions
- Supt Survey Planning
- Light Lists
- Jacketting Officer
- Equipt Officer
- Geophysical Officer

Asst Director Professional (AD(P))
- Superintendent of Nautical Charts (SNC)
  - *2 Nautical Chart Branches 1–8
- Superintendent of Marine Sciences (SMS)
  - *3 Marine Science Branches 1–7

Asst Director Administration and Supply (AD(A))
- Chief Executive Officer
  - Issues
  - Sales
  - Finance
  - Engineering Services
  - Personnel
  - Chronometers
  - Reproduction Manager
    - Deputy R. M.
      - Repro Drawing
      - Printing processes
- Chart *1 Depots

*4 Oceanographic Planning and Liaison
*5 Torpedo and Anti-Submarine Liaison Officer
*6 located with Met. Office at Bracknell

*3 MS1 Geodesy, Archives
MS2 Operational, Air & Misc. charts
MS3 Radio, cables, lattice charts
MS4 Oceanography
MS5 Inshore Oceanography
MS6 Geophysical and Submarine Charts
MS7 Training

*2. NC1 Home Waters
NC2 NW Europe
NC3 Mediterranean
NC4 E. Atlantic, Africa, W. Indian Ocean
NC5 Australasia, Pacific Ocean, Antarctica
NC6 E. Asia, Japan, Arctic Russia
NC America (ex. W. Coast S. America)
NC8 Norway, Iceland, Greenland, Small scale ocean charts

*1. Plymouth
Portsmouth
Rosyth
Gibraltar
Singapore

civil servant, was responsible for the reproduction and printing of the charts and publications, for issues to the Fleet and for sales to the general public, and for the domestic arrangements of the establishment.

Before the move to Taunton the number of sections in Chart Branch had grown to no less than fourteen. In the new location AD(P)'s division was organised into eight Nautical Chart Branches, NC 1 to NC 8, each responsible for a geographical area, the world being divided to give each branch a similar workload; and seven Marine Science Branches, with responsibilities ranging from Geodesy, the Archives and Photogrammetry (MS 1) to Geophysical and Submarine Charting (MS 6), the seventh branch being responsible for all Professional Division training. Two new posts at ACCHO level were created in the reorganisation to supervise the Nautical Chart Branches and the Marine Science Branches respectively. The first Superintendent of Nautical Charts was Miss Margaret Hall, BSc, who had been the first woman Cartographer when she joined the Department in 1935 and was now the first woman ACCHO.

For some years before 1966 successive Hydrographers had been looking into the need to modernise the Admiralty Chart series, which by the early 1960's contained charts in a variety of styles from ornately engraved Early Victorian to comparatively simple and modern. Through a series of committees and working parties a concensus developed on a new style, with clearer and simpler lettering and symbology and with colour washes in place of stippling to denote land areas. Charts in this modern style would be very much easier to keep up to date than the mix of older styles, and would also be marginally easier to produce in the first place. It had been planned to introduce the new style charts in 1967. In 1966 the Wilson government committed the United Kingdom to converting to metric units. Metres had always been the preferred unit of the IHB for charting, though as with everything connected with that organisation there was no absolute compulsion on member states to comply. Ritchie appreciated that if a change from fathoms and feet to metres as the units for the Admiralty Chart was to be made the moment when the new style was introduced was an opportunity which would not recurr. In October 1966 he set up a Metrication Committee to look into the implications of 'going metric', to report to him by the end of January 1967.

The Committee consisted of one Naval officer (Weeks), a PCHO (I D Kember) and a Senior Draughtsman (D F Saunders) from Professional Division, two senior men from the Production Section (R E Clarke and E T Earp), and the Superintendent of Sales (D W Collins). Recognising that a major modernisation of the whole Admiralty Chart series was essential anyway if the Department was to remain competitive in the international market, the Committee recommended very strongly that the Department should 'go metric' at the same time. Of the various ways in which the charts could be converted it came down heavily for the combination of changing the units of measurement with the complete re- planning of chart provision and cover, which had in any case been envisaged in the modernisation. The change should be planned in 'blocks', specific areas being converted at one fell swoop. It recognised that extra staff would be needed to implement the change within a reasonable time frame, but argued that they would be paid for by the increase in sales which would result from the need of all mariners to buy the new charts. A period of fifteen years (originally ten, but it was recognised even then that ten would simply not be realistic) was given as the length of time beyond which the change-over should not be allowed to drag out.

The decision to metricate and modernise was taken in 1967, and widely publicised. It was recognised that there would inevitably be confusion among users during the change-over period. To minimise this Ritchie decreed that only charts in metric units would be produced in the new style. This, with buff land tint and a much greater use of blue washes for shallow water as well as with a simpler and cleaner set of type faces for letterpress and names, was quite distinct from any of the older styles, so the fact that a chart was a metric chart could be seen at a glance. The change of units did not meet with universal approval, though it is fair to say that objections came more from those attached to the fathom by ties of affection rather than from practical seamen. That eminent humorist and yachtsman A P Herbert threatened to form a society of 'Friends of the Fathom', though sadly he died before he could do so.

The conversion programme started slowly. In 1968 nine metric charts were produced, and only nineteen more in 1969. A new Chart Branch, NC 9, was formed in 1969 to concentrate on the programme, and in 1970, with a large intake of new CHOs and draughtsmen, a second metrication branch was formed. However, the fifteen year programme was soon seen to be unduly optimistic. In fact it was only in 1989, over twenty years after the change had started, that the half-way point was reached! Only rigid adherence to the rule that no chart with depths in fathoms would be produced in the new buff land tint style has made the extension of the conversion period acceptable to the mariner. The fact that the rule of thumb for conversion of 'one fathom equals two metres' is roughly correct but errs on the side of safety has also helped.

It is in some ways unfortunate that the metrication aspect has loomed so large in the presentation of the modernisation programme. Far more significant for the long term has been the complete reassessment of the needs of the mariner, and the re-ordering of what had become over the years since Dalrymple produced the first Admiralty charts in 1795 a very haphazard collection into a logical and practical series of related charts. The new scheme would result in the overall number of charts in the series being reduced by some 15%, with improved cover in many areas. The new style charts are also much easier to maintain than the old ones, the simple style lending itself to the removal of out-of-date information and the insertion of new in a way that was difficult and time-consuming with the complex if artistically attractive Victorian engraved work on many older charts.

One snag with the new style charts is, paradoxically, their uniformity. With the old series, the general appearance gave an indication of the date, and hence of the reliability, of the particular chart, at a glance. A new metric chart may be based on information no later than that on the early nineteenth century chart it replaces, but since it appears modern in style and presentation it will seem to a user who does not read the small print of the title block to be up to date and reliable. Experience indicates that all too few users do read the small print and appreciate the limitations of charts which are the best possible but are based on scanty or ancient data.

The Department's other publications followed the charts. Tide Tables would be published in metric units (forecast heights in metres and decimetres) from 1972. Echo-sounders converted to metric units began to be supplied to the surveying fleet in 1968. Other instruments also had to be re-provided for surveying in metric units, and a major programme was set in hand and carried out by the Equipment Officer, Myres and his long-serving and indefatigable Equipment Clerk, Jack Ballard. By 1970 all surveys were being rendered in metres.

For some time there had been concern that while other products of the Department were moving forward with new forms and content suitable for the last quarter of the twentieth century, the volumes of the Sailing Directions still maintained the format and language of the nineteenth. When Pryor took over as Superintendent of Sailing Directions from Hennessey in 1968 he set up a committee to review the format and content of the books. It reported in 1969, recommending that the books be printed in A4 paper size rather than the old quarto, and that the style of text become much more succinct, with a bolder printing of headings and subdivision to make the salient points easier to extract from the verbiage. This was combined with the change to metric units, and all volumes taken up for revision in 1970 and after were written in the new style of text, in metres, for publication in A4 size.

The new coloured style of chart was only possible with the use of new four-colour offset printing machines, the first of which were installed in 1967. There were at that time no less than seven different trades unions represented in the works at Taunton, and it took a considerable amount of negotiation before rates could be struck for all the staff operating the new machines. Once introduced they greatly simplified printing, one pass through the machine being all that was required for a basic chart, with a second pass for a three-colour Decca lattice, for which a total of seven passes would have been required in the old one-colour machines.

With the new style of charts came a review of the chart pricing structure. To encourage users to buy the new charts a single price was introduced for all charts in the navigational series, with another single price, slightly higher, for latticed charts. The price was set at a rate which would notionally recoup the costs of printing and production, though not as yet to make any contribution either to the cost of compilation or of surveying. The price charged for the basic chart was ten shillings (50p) in 1968, rising to eleven shillings (55p) in 1969. Only with another review of pricing policy in 1970 was the cost of compilation, now taking place at the same establishment as printing, considered in setting the price to the customer.

Soon after the move to Taunton the Department took delivery of its first automatic plotting machine. At first this and its accompanying computer were designed only to be able to process the tapes being received from the *Hecla* class's ocean surveys, but as in the ships the possibilities for other uses soon became apparent. Chart borders and electronic navigational aid lattices were soon being plotted automatically, with a great saving in draughtsmen's time. In 1970 the Department's own computer, an ICL 1902A, was delivered. It was used on a bureau basis by both the Professional Division and by the accountants for commercial work. A new Marine Science branch was formed to take responsibility for automatic cartography, though the main developments in this field have taken place after the end of the period considered in this book.

In the international field there were significant developments in the status of the IHB. It will be remembered that the Bureau had originally been set up as a dependency of the League of Nations, but a strictly non-political one. With the demise of that body in the course of the Second World War, the Bureau's legal position had disappeared as well. In the years immediately after the war this had not concerned the Hydrographers attending the quinquennial conferences. However, with the entry into membership of states who were not originally concerned in the foundation of the Bureau, some of them it must be confessed taking up legalistic and even political attitudes, the question of the Bureau's legal position was raised at the 1962 conference.

It was agreed that the position was anomalous, and that it needed rectifying. Direct attachment to the United Nations was objected to by many Hydrographers as being 'too political'. No clear decision was reached at the conference, other than to agree to have a draft Convention to present to the 1967 conference for the agreement of member states. Irving, together with representatives from the Foreign Office legal department, drew up a form of words, and took it to Monaco for discussions with the Directing Committee in 1964, and a Convention establishing an International Hydrographic Organisation as a legal entity, largely based on the British draft, was laid before the 1967 conference and adopted. It would, once ratified by two thirds of the member states at the time, come into force and constitute the IHO as an intergovernmental body in international law. By the end of 1967 ratifications were coming in fast, and the Convention entered into force on 22 September 1970, 28 states having ratified it. The Bureau, or Organisation as it now became, had grown from just 12 states at its nadir during the slump of the 1930s to 41 in 1967. It was to continue to grow in the years ahead until at the beginning of 1994 it stands at no less than 59.

The terms were much as in the original convention of 1920. The changes were mainly in the conditions of service of the employees. In particular, with the number of distinguished but elderly directors who had died in post in mind, both an upper age limit on election and a maximum of two five-year terms in office was imposed on the Directors. That this provision was very much needed was underlined by the fact that at the 1967 there were only two Directors of the outgoing Directing Committee present, Rear Admiral C Pierce, USCGS having died in office in July 1965. Ritchie himself was elected President of the Directing Committee in 1972, after his retirement as Hydrographer, as was Haslam in 1987.

It was not only between Commonwealth countries that the scope for co-operation in the avoidance of unnecessary duplication of effort was recognised. At the 1967 Conference member states agreed on the principles for an International series of charts, each chart to be compiled by one nation (the Producer Nation) with reproduction material made available to any national hydrographic office who wished to print it (Printer Nations). Initially the series would be confined to small scale oceanic charts, and an International Chart Commission was set up to work out the details under the chairmanship of Ritchie. The specifications, which were very similar to the new British Admiralty style, were soon agreed, schemes for world cover at a scale of 1:10 million and 1:3.5 million were drawn up, and Producer Nations allocated for both series. Within ten years almost all the charts had been produced, and the International Chart taken forward into coastal areas on larger scales.

A most important bilateral international initative started in June 1964 when three Soviet oceanographical vessels called at Southampton. The Group Commander, Captain 2nd Rank Petrov, called on the Hydrographer in Whitehall, and invited him to visit the ships when they put in to Glasgow in July. He did so, and the exchange led to Irving taking the *Vidal* to Leningrad in September for a most successful visit to the Soviet Hydrographic Office and its head, Vice Admiral Rassokho. The following year Rassokho visited London in the Soviet oceanographical vessel *Nikolai Zubov*. The exchange of visits established an excellent rapport with the Soviet Hydrographic Office, and unlocked the supply of Russian charts which had ceased for several years previously and which had never been particularly free-flowing. As a result the policy of attempting to maintain British Admiralty chart cover of areas for which no Soviet chart was available to the public was abandoned. Only areas for which Soviet charts were available were charted in the Admiralty series, since only they could be kept up to date from information received from Leningrad. When, much later, similar relations were established with the Chinese Hydrographic Office in Shanghai, a comparable policy was adopted for Chinese waters.

When Ritchie came to write his last Annual Report at the end of 1970 he summed up the position of the Hydrographic Service as it was at the end of his term of office. The surveying fleet was entirely composed of new, purpose-built ships, with all the old conversions scrapped or sold and the only intermediate type remaining, *Vidal*, approved for replacement. Geophysics observation and Automatic Data Logging were general in the larger ships, and satellite navigation was being introduced. The whole Department was co-located at Taunton, had been re-equipped with modern printing machines, and had begun to employ computers for draughting and cartography. The Admiralty Chart series was being modernised and metricated. Meteorology and Oceanography were firmly under Hydrographer's aegis. The Service had celebrated its 175th birthday. He could well be satisfied with the position. There were clouds, though, on the horizon, and Hall and his successors in the '70s and '80s would have a much rougher ride. But that, as Sheherezade said to the Caliph of Baghdad, is another story.

The Principal Surveys of 1960

HOME

Owen	Hall	Scotland, West Coast	Stanton Banks.
Scott	D P D Scott	England, South Coast	Dungeness to the Goodwin Sands.
		England, East Coast	Approaches to the Humber.
Shackleton	White	Scotland, West Coast	Inner Sound; Sound of Harris; Sound of Iona; Bute Sound to Holy Loch.
E.C.E.S.U. (*Echo, Egeria, Enterprise*)	Green, Hales	England, East Coast	Thames Estuary; Goodwin Sands; Approaches to Lowestoft; River Deben
		Ireland, East Coast	Belfast Lough and Bangor Bay.
S.C.E.S.U. (*Meda*)	Paisley	England, South Coast	Portland; Approaches to Weymouth.
		Channel Islands	SW approaches to Jersey.
SDML 3516	David	England, South Coast	Approaches to Plymouth; Looe harbour; Fowey; Approaches to Falmouth.

ABROAD

Dalrymple	Ritchie, M J Baker	Persian Gulf	Bahrain, Sitra Channel; Ras Kumais to Jaza'ir Yasat; Jazirat Halul to Rig Kareinein; Strait of Hormuz.
Dampier	Haslam, Winstanley	Malay Peninsula	Johore Strait;Port Dickson and approaches; Tanjong Gelang to Dugun.
		Borneo	Darvel Bay.
Owen	Hall	Atlantic Ocean	Oceanography.
Vidal	Connell	West Indies	British Guiana coast; Tobago to North Coast of Trinidad.

Cook spent the whole year in long refit in Singapore. *Vidal* paid off for refit in Chatham in July. *Owen* recommissioned at Gibraltar on 16 May after long refit. After a period surveying in the North Western Approaches she sailed in September for the South Atlantic. SDML 3516 was detached from the East Coast of England Survey Unit to Plymouth, to work in the South West and to provide sea experience for classes from the Hydrographic School. She was renamed *Medusa* in August.

The Principal Surveys of 1961

HOME

Scott	Roberts	England, South Coast	South Foreland to Dungeness.
		England, East Coast	Orfordness to Lowestoft; Approaches to the Humber; Outer Dowsing.
Shackleton	Nesbitt	England, South Coast	Mevagissey.
		Bristol Channel	Watchet to Hinkley Point.
		Scotland, West Coast	Approaches to theFirth of Lorne.
		England, West Coast	Barrow Channel.
		Channel Islands	The Swinge.
Inshore Survey Squadron (*Echo, Egeria, Enterprise*)	Benson	England, East Coast	Thames Estuary; Lowestoft; Yarmouth;Caister Road.
		England, South Coast	Salcombe.
S.C.E.S.U. (*Meda*)	Paisley	England, South Coast	Yarmouth (Isle of Wight); Bexington; River Exe and approaches.
		Channel Islands	SW approaches to Jersey.
Medusa	David	England, South Coast	Bigbury Bay; Falmouth; Salcombe.
		Bristol Channel	Padstow.
		Wales, West Coast	St Tudwal's Roads

ABROAD

Cook	Paton	Fiji Islands	Sau Sau Passage to Ringgold Channel; Langa Langa River to Tilangitha Pass; Tasman Strait; Savu Savu Bay.
		Gilbert Islands	Abaiang.
		New Hebrides	Vila harbour.
Dalrymple	M J Baker Hatfield	Persian Gulf	Strait of Hormuz; Approaches to Abu Dhabi; Bahrain, Sitra Channel.
		Mediterranean	Adventure Bank.
Dampier	Winstanley	Malay Peninsula	Approaches to the Perak River; Western approaches to Singapore; Pulau Aur exercise area.
		Borneo	Usukan Bay to Pulau Silad;
Owen	Hall	South Atlantic	Oceanography; South Georgia, western end.
		Indian Ocean	Geophysics and Oceanography.
		Africa, East Coast	Approaches to Lamu, Manda and Patta Bays
Vidal	Roe	West Indies	Jamaica, Approaches to Portland Bight.

The completion of *Vidal*'s long refit in September concluded the programme of modernisation of the surveying fleet. Immediately on her arrival in the West Indies she was involved in relief work after Hurricane Hattie struck Belize. In December she acted as United Kingdom communications link for the conference between President Kennedy of the United States and Prime Minister Macmillan of Great Britain.

The Principal Surveys of 1962

HOME

Scott	Roberts, Powell	England, East Coast	Orfordness to Southwold; Sizewell Bank; N.E.approaches to the Wash.
		Scotland, East Coast	Wee Bankie.
Shackleton	Nesbitt	England, East Coast	Approaches to Tynemouth.
		Bristol Channel	Avonmouth to Sharpness; Approaches to Watchet; Watchet to Weston.
		Scotland, West Coast	Sound of Jura; Firth of Clyde, Bute Sound.
		Channel Islands	N. approaches to Alderney.
I.S.S. (*Echo, Egeria, Enterprise*)	Beazley	England, East Coast	Thames Estuary; North Shipwash; Approaches to Lowestoft and Yarmouth.
		Scotland, West Coast	Sound of Jura.
Medusa	Mackay	Bristol Channel	Avonmouth to Sharpness; Middle Ground.
		Wales, West Coast	Caernarvon Bay.
		England, South Coast	Salcombe.
S.C.E.S.U. (*Meda*)	Paisley	England, South Coast	Portsmouth and the Solent; Teignmouth; Christchurch Bay.
		Channel Islands	Approaches to St Helier.

ABROAD

Cook	Paton, Hunt	New Hebrides	Vila Harbour.
		Fiji Islands	N.E. approaches to Ringgold Channel; Natewa Bay; Wainunu Bay and approaches.
		Gilbert Islands	Abaiang; Nonouti; Oceanography.
Dalrymple	Hatfield	Persian Gulf	Approaches to Abu Dhabi; Jazirat Sir Abu Nu'air.
		Indian Ocean	Murray Ridge, Oceanography.
		Mediterranean	Cyprus, Cape Andreas.
Dampier	Winstanley, Pryor	Malay Peninsula	Approaches to Penang.
		Hong Kong	Western approaches to Hong Kong Harbour.
		Borneo	Labuk Bay; Lahad Datu and approaches.
Owen	Hall, Haslam	Africa, East Coast	Approaches to Lamu, Manda and Patta Bays.
		Indian Ocean	Oceanography and Geophysics.
Vidal	Roe	West Indies	Barbados; St Lucia, Port Castries; Trinidad, north coast; Tobago, Man-of-War Bay; British Guiana, offshore waters; Jamaica, Portland Bight.

The Principal Surveys of 1963

HOME

Dalrymple	Hatfield	Ireland, North Coast	Western Approaches to the North Channel. Lough Foyle. Oceanography.
Scott	Powell	Ireland, North Coast	North Channel to Lough Foyle; Portrush; Portstewart.
		England, East Coast	N.E. approaches to the Wash; Outer Silver Pit.
		Scotland, East Coast	Arbroath & approaches.
I.S.S. (*Echo, Egeria,* (*Enterprise*)	Hammick, Mackay, Weeks	England, East Coast	Thames Estuary; Coquet Island to Whitby; Approaches to Lowestoft and Yarmouth
		Scotland, West Coast	Loch Ewe.
Medusa	Robinson	England, South Coast	River Yealm and Wembury Bay; Nares Head to Downend Point.
		Bristol Channel	Middle Ground; Godrevy Island to Trevose Head; Falmouth.
S.C.E.S.U. (*Meda*)	Paisley	England, South Coast	Portsmouth.
		Channel Islands	Guernsey, Herm and Sark.

ABROAD

Cook	Hunt	Fiji Islands	Bligh Water.
		Gilbert Islands	Tabiteuea; Nonouti; Oceanography.
Dalrymple	Hatfield	Persian Gulf	Approaches to Abu Dhabi; Kuwait.
		Mediterranean	Cyprus, Cape Melissakros to Cape Eloea.
Dampier	Pryor	Malay Peninsula	Singapore, Keppel Harbour; Singapore Strait, Jodoh to Tanjong Ayam.
		China, South Coast	Western approaches to Hong Kong.
		South China Sea	Geophysics
		Borneo	Sungei Brunei; Darvel Bay.
Owen	Haslam	Africa, East Coast	Kenya, Lamu harbour; Manda Bay and approaches; Manda Bay to Ras Chiambone; Mambrui to Ras Tenewiati; Formosa Bay; Approaches to Malindi.
		Indian Ocean	Geophysics.
Vidal	Roe	West Indies	British Guiana coastal waters; Trinidad to Tobago; Approaches to Port of Spain.
		North Atlantic	NAVADO, oceanography and geophysics.
Antarctic Survey Party	Dixon	Antarctic Peninsula	Adelaide Island; Bismarck Strait; Discovery Bay.
		Falkland Islands	Eagle Passage.

Dalrymple returned from the Middle East in May and recommissioned for Home Sea Service, on which she was employed for the rest of her time.

Cook grounded and was badly damaged in Vatu Ira Channel, Fiji, on 1 October. Though she was got off and made seaworthy to steam home, she was never fully repaired, and was sold for scrap in 1968 without doing any further surveying.

The Principal Surveys of 1964

HOME

Dalrymple	Powell	Ireland, North Coast	Portavogie to Craiganadam; Lough Foyle.
		North Atlantic	MILOC 64; Rockall Oceanography.
		Bristol Channel	Approaches to Cardiff.
Scott	Martin	England, South Coast	Portland Exercise Areas.
		England, East Coast	Outer Silver Pit; Southern North Sea.
		Scotland, East Coast	Approaches to Leith; Montrose.
Mermaid	Read	Scotland, West Coast	North Western Approaches.
Myrmidon	Dixon	England, East Coast	River Roach; Southern North Sea.
I.S.S. (*Echo, Egeria, Enterprise*)	Weeks	England, East Coast	Thames Estuary; Coquet Island to Whitby; Shipwash; Harwich harbour & approaches; Goodwin Sands; Approaches to Ramsgate.
		Wales, West Coast	Cardigan Bay, seismics.
Medusa	Morris	England, South Coast	Dodman to Fowey;Approaches to the River Yealm.
		England, West Coast	Approaches to Heysham.
		Wales, West Coast	Barmouth; Tremadoc Bay.
S.C.E.S.U. (*Meda*)	Paisley	England, South Coast	Portsmouth and the Solent; Portland; Approaches to Langstone Harbour.
		Channel Islands	St Peter Port; Little Russel and approaches.

ABROAD

Dampier	Pryor, M J Baker	Malay Peninsula	Port Swettenham; Penang to Langkawi.
		Indian Ocean	Base Recce Surveys.
		China, South Coast	Southern approaches to Hong Kong.
Owen	Haslam, Paton.	Africa, East Coast	Kenya, Formosa Bay.
		Red Sea	Perim.
		Atlantic Ocean	Western Approaches to the Strait of Gibraltar.
Vidal	Ritchie	North Atlantic Ocean	NAVADO Oceanography and Geophysics.
Antarctic Survey Party	Bradley, Wynne-Edwards	Falkland Islands	Falkland Sound.
		South Orkney Islands	Signy I, Borge Bay; Approaches to Signy.
		Antarctic Peninsula	Argentine Islands.

Owen spent much of January at Zanzibar after the coup which toppled the Sultan, finally evacuating British officials and civilians to Mombasa.

The Principal Surveys of 1965

HOME

Dalrymple	Martin	Ireland, North Coast	Guns Island to Craiganadam; N.W. approaches to the North Channel.
		North Atlantic Ocean	Oceanography.
Hecla	Hall	Irish Sea	Seismics.
		North Atlantic Ocean	Ocean survey N.W.of Scotland
Mermaid	Stumbles	Bristol Channel	Breakstone to Peterstone Flats.
		Scotland, West Coast	Stanton Banks to Islay; Skerries to Fair Head. Southern Approaches to the Clyde.
Myrmidon	Benson	England, East Coast	Outer Approaches to the River Thames; Orfordness to Southwold; Well Bank to Swarte Bank.
I.S.S. (*Echo, Egeria, Enterprise*)	Weeks	England, East Coast	Thames Estuary; Approaches to Lowestoft and Yarmouth; Goodwin Sands.
		Scotland, East Coast	Newburgh to Stonehaven.
Medusa	Morris	England, West Coast	Barrow Channel.
		Bristol Channel	N.W.Elbow to Walton Bay; Godrevy Island to Trevose Head; Approaches to Cardiff.
S.C.E.S.U. (*Meda*)	Paisley	England, South Coast	Portsmouth; Solent; Outer approaches to the Nab Channel; Portland.
		Channel Islands	Guernsey, Herm and Sark.

ABROAD

Dampier	M J Baker	Borneo	Darvel Bay.
		Malay Peninsula	Singapore Roads.
		South China Sea	Oceanography.
		Solomon Islands	Thousand Ships Bay; Oceanography.
Owen	Paton	Atlantic Ocean	Western Approaches to the Strait of Gibraltar; MILOC; Western Approaches to the Bay of Biscay.
Vidal	Ritchie	Atlantic Ocean	NAVADO
		West Indies	Jamaica, Port Kaiser; Montego Bay; British Guiana coastal survey.
Antarctic Survey Party	Cheshire	South Orkney Islands	Signy I.
		Antarctic Peninsula	Marguerite Bay; Cape Kater triangulation.

The Principal Surveys of 1966

HOME

Hecate	Winstanley	North Atlantic Ocean	Ocean Survey Programme; MILOC
		Africa, West Coast	Oceanography.
Hecla	Hall	North Atlantic Ocean	Ocean Survey Programme.
		South Atlantic Ocean	Oceanography.
		Ireland, West Coast	Killybegs.
		Celtic Sea	Seismics.
Hydra	Paton	North Atlantic Ocean	Ocean Survey Programme.
		North Sea	Wreck Search.
Mermaid	Stumbles	England, South Coast	Approaches to the Dodman.
		Scotland, West Coast	North Western Approaches; Southern approaches to the Clyde; Gareloch; Loch Gilp.
Myrmidon	Bradley	North Sea	Indefatigable Banks to 53 N.
		Scotland, East Coast	Firth of Forth.
		England, East Coast	Thames Estuary.
I.S.S. (*Echo, Egeria, Enterprise*)	Mackay	England, East Coast	Thames Estuary; Goodwin Sands; Approaches to Lowestoft and Yarmouth.
		Scotland, East Coast	Stonehaven to Montrose.
Woodlark	Pugh	England, West Coast	Walney Channel; Morecambe Bay.
		Bristol Channel	various small areas.
		England, South Coast	Wembury Bay; Approaches to Mevagissey.
S.C.E.S.U. (*Waterwitch*)	Paisley	England, South Coast	Approaches to Portsmouth; Approaches to Chichester Harbour; St Catherine's Deep.
		Channel Islands	Approaches to St Peter Port.

ABROAD

Dampier	M J Baker, Cardno	New Hebrides	Malekula; Eromanga. Fiji Islands Vanua Levu, North Coast.
		South China Sea	Oceanography.
		Borneo	Labuan.
Vidal	Cooper, R.A.N.	West Indies	Guyana coast.
		North Atlantic Ocean	NAVADO
		Scotland, West Coast	Firth of Clyde.
Antarctic Survey Party	Cheshire	Antarctic Peninsula	Cape Kater triangulation; Western Approaches to French Passage.
		South Shetland Islands	Northern Entrance to English Strait.

The Principal Surveys of 1967

HOME

Hecate Rathlin	Winstanley	Scotland, West Coast	North Western Approaches; to Islay; Raasay Sound.
Hecla	Hall	North Atlantic Ocean	Ocean Survey Programme.
		Iceland	Surtsey.
		Scotland, West Coast	Sound of Raasay.
		Ireland, West Coast	Killala Bay.
Hydra	Nesbitt	North Atlantic Ocean	Ocean Survey Programme; MILOC.
		Ireland, West Coast	Burtonport and approaches.
		Africa, West Coast	Oceanography.
Mermaid	Dathan	Wales, West Coast	Cardigan Bay.
		Scotland, West Coast	Firth of Clyde; North Western Approaches wrecks.
Myrmidon	Bradley	Scotland, East Coast	Firth of Forth.
		Southern North Sea	Fairy Bank to the Sandettie Bank.
		England, East Coast	Norfolk banks; Approaches to Boston.
I.S.S. (*Echo, Egeria, Enterprise*)	Mackay	England, East Coast	Thames Estuary; Goodwin Sands; Approaches to Lowestoft and Yarmouth; River Crouch; Gunfleet Sand.
Woodlark	Pugh	England, South Coast	Plymouth Sound; Scilly Islands.
		England, West Coast	Walney Channel; Approaches to Liverpool.
		Bristol Channel	Padstow; Middle Ground.
S.C.E.S.U. (*Waterwitch*)	Paisley	England, South Coast	Portsmouth and approaches; Chichester Harbour; Portland Bill to St Albans Head.
		Channel Islands	Approaches to St Peter Port; Approaches to Guernsey.

ABROAD

Dampier	Cardno	Malay Peninsula	Langkawi Strait; Singapore Strait; Malacca Strait, Cape Rachado Shoals.
		South China Sea	Oceanography.
		Indian Ocean	Oceanography.
Vidal	Roe	Indian Ocean	Oceanography; Diego Garcia; Aldabra.
		Persian Gulf	Northern Approaches to Jazirat Daz.
Antarctic Survey Party	Odling Smee	Falkland Islands	North West Passage;
		South Orkney Islands	Port Stanley

Dampier returned home to pay off on 23 December after 19 years continuously on the Far Eastern Station. *Mermaid* and *Myrmidon* also paid off at the end of the 1967 season, having satisfactorily bridged the gap between the demise of the *Scott* and *Shackleton* and the arrival in service of the *Bulldog* class.

The Principal Surveys of 1968

HOME

Hecate	Osborn, R.A.N.	North Atlantic Ocean Ireland, West Coast	Ocean Survey Programme. Killala Bay; Broadhaven Bay.
Hecla	Haslam	North Atlantic Ocean Ireland, North Coast Scotland, West Coast	Ocean Survey Programme. Inishtrahull to Tory Island. Sound of Raasay.
Hydra	Nesbitt	Bristol Channel Scotland, West Coast Africa, West Coast	Approaches to Perranporth. Clyde, Rhu Narrows; Benane Head to Culzean; North Western Approaches. Sierra Leone, Sherbro River; Jong River.
Vidal	Cardno	North Sea Scotland, East Coast Persian Gulf	Indefatigable Banks to Dogger Bank. Firth of Forth. Ras Hanjura to Ras Ghanada; Northern Approaches to Jazirat Das.
Beagle	Morris	Southern North Sea Scotland, East Coast	Deep Draught Routes. River Tay to Montrose.
Bulldog	Read	Southern North Sea England, East Coast	Deep Draught Routes. Approaches to the River Swale.
Fawn	Robinson	Scotland, West Coast	North Minch.
Fox	Dathan	Scotland, West Coast	Northern Approaches to Inner Sound; North Minch.
I.S.S. (*Echo, Egeria, Enterprise*)	Margetts	England, East Coast	Thames Estuary; Approaches to Ramsgate; Goodwin Sands; Approaches to the Humber; Approaches to Lowestoft and Yarmouth.
Woodlark	Campbell	England, South Coast England, West Coast Bristol Channel	Approaches to Plymouth. Walney Channel. N.W.Elbow to Walton Bay; Approaches to Barry.
S.C.E.S.U. (*Waterwitch*)	Paisley	England, South Coast Channel Islands	Portsmouth and approaches; Solent; Approaches to Selsey Bill. Approaches to Guernsey.
Endurance	Dixon	South Shetland Is Antarctic Peninsula	Deception Island. Western Approaches to the Argentine Is.

Endurance commissioned in October with surveyors as a part of her ship's company, the senior surveyor being her First Lieutenant. Her normal pattern of operation was to leave England in the autumn, spend the southern summer in the Antarctic, and return north in April. In this and subsequent years her surveys are listed under the year in which she left for the south. With the return of *Dampier* the distinction between ships surveying at home and abroad becomes meaningless, and has been abandoned in the tables from this year.

The Principal Surveys of 1969

HOME

Hecate	Osborn, R.A.N.	North Atlantic Ocean	Ocean Survey Programme.
		Ireland, West Coast	Blacksod Bay; Broadhaven Bay.
Hecla	Haslam	North Atlantic Ocean	Rockall Plateau.
		Scotland, West Coast	Southern Approaches to the Minch; Kyles of Loch Alsh.
		Irish Sea	Seismics.
Hydra	Nesbitt, M J Baker	Mediterranean	Oceanography.
		Atlantic Ocean	Atlantic Trade Wind Experiment (GATE).
		Africa, West Coast	Approaches to Sierra Leone; Jong and Sherbro Rivers.
Vidal	Cardno, Paton	Persian Gulf	N.E. approaches to Jazirat Das; E. approaches to Jazirat Halul; Khor Ghurabi.
Beagle	Morris	Scotland, East Coast	River Tay to Montrose; Firth of Forth.
		Persian Gulf	Mina Rashid to 'Ajman.
Bulldog	Read	Southern North Sea	Deep Draught Routes.
		Persian Gulf	Jebajib Bay to Umm al Qaywayn.
Fawn	Robinson	Wales, West Coast	Cardigan Bay; Aberystwyth.
		Scotland, West Coast	Sea of the Hebrides.
Fox	Dathan	Wales, West Coast	Cardigan Bay; Port Cardigan; Newquay.
		Scotland, West Coast	Sea of the Hebrides.
I.S.S. (*Echo, Egeria, Enterprise*)	Margetts	England, East Coast	Thames Estuary; Goodwin Sands; Approaches to Lowestoft and Yarmouth; Approaches to Harwich.
Woodlark	Campbell, Myres	Bristol Channel	N.W.Elbow to Walton Bay; Approaches to Barry.
		Scotland, West Coast	Loch Indaal.
		England, West Coast	Lune Deep; Approaches to the River Dee.
S.C.E.S.U. (*Waterwitch*)	Paisley	England, South Coast	Approaches to Langstone Harbour; Approaches to Selsey Bill; Beachy Head to Hastings.
		Channel Islands	Approaches to Guernsey.
Endurance	Campbell	Falkland Islands	Port Salvador; Falkland Sound.
		Scotia Sea	Geophysics.
		Antarctic Peninsula	Approaches to French Passage.

The Principal Surveys of 1970

HOME

Hecate	Winstanley	North Atlantic Ocean	MILOCSURVNORLANT; Ocean Survey Programme.
		Ireland, West Coast	Baltimore.
		England, South Coast	Scilly Islands.
Hecla	Haslam, Robinson	North Atlantic Ocean	MILOCSURVNORLANT; JASIN
		Scotland, West Coast	Sea of the Hebrides; S Approaches to the Minches; Loch Boisdale; Kyles of Loch Alsh.
Hydra	M J Baker Morris.	Malay Peninsula	Malacca Strait.
Vidal	Paton	Persian Gulf	Deep Draught Tanker Routes; Khawr Essadayat to Ras Hasa.
		South Atlantic Ocean	St Helena.
Beagle	Morris, Dixon	Persian Gulf	Mina Rashid to 'Ajman; Umm al Qaywayn.
		England, East Coast	Northern Approaches to the Dover Strait.
Bulldog	Read, Halliday	Persian Gulf	Jebajib Bay to Umm al Qaywayn.
		England, East Coast	Northern Approaches to the Dover Strait.
Fawn	Robinson, Davidson, R.A.N. Calder, R.A.N.	West Indies	Jamaica, Pedro Bank; Anguilla to Antigua; CICAR.
Fox	Hope	West Indies	Jamaica, Pedro Bank; Anguilla to Antigua; CICAR.
I.S.S. (*Echo, Egeria, Enterprise*)	Margetts, Merriman	England, East Coast	Thames Estuary; Southern Approaches to the Thames Estuary; Falls Gap; South Falls Tail; Approaches to Lowestoft and Yarmouth; Blyth to Hartlepool.
		Scotland, East Coast	Firth of Forth, Middle Bank.
Woodlark	Myres	England, West Coast	Walney Channel.
		Scotland, West Coast	Little Minch; Harris, East Loch Tarbert.
		Wales, West Coast	Cardigan Bay.
		Bristol Channel	Newport Deep to Redcliffe.
S.C.E.S.U. (*Waterwitch*)	Paisley	England, South Coast	Portsmouth and Approaches; The Solent.
		Channel Islands	Approaches to Guernsey.
Endurance	Campbell	Antarctic Peninsula	Western Approaches to Bismarck Strait and French Passage; Argentine Islands.
		Falkland Islands	Bull Roads.

Biographies

1960–1970

Rear Admiral Sir Edmund Irving, KBE, CB
Hydrographer 1960-1965

Born in British North Borneo, Edmund George Irving, always known as 'Egg', entered the Navy through the Royal Naval College, Dartmouth in 1924, going to sea as a midshipman in the battleship *Royal Oak* in 1927. He began surveying in 1931, joining the *Kellett* Southern, on east coast of England surveys. He obtained his first command, the hired vessel *Gulnare*, working on harbour surveys for berthing and floating docks, in 1941.

After only a short time he was sent out as First Lieutenant of the *Endeavour*, which had escaped from Singapore manned by survivors from the *Repulse* and *Prince of Wales*, and was now engaged in surveying possible fleet anchorages in the Red Sea as the Axis armies threatened the Nile delta. When the pressure on the Egyptian theatre eased after Alamein the old ship was paid off. He and the other surveying officers from *Endeavour* were formed into survey units for various tasks round the Mediterranean. After the capture of Sicily Irving was tasked with providing leading marks for the allied forces crossing the Straits of Messina to assault the Italian mainland. This he did with three pairs of mobile searchlights surveyed into the Royal Artillery triangulation.

Irving was next appointed in command of the *Franklin*, in which he supported the Normandy landings and subsequently took part in port clearance surveys. Appreciating the importance of Antwerp for supplying the allied armies as they struck deeper into Germany, he sent one of his sounding boats through the canals to Terneuzen before the mouth of the Schelde was clear, so shortening the time before which the port was surveyed clear for shipping. He was awarded the CBE for his services in *Franklin*.

After the war, in the *Sharpshooter*, Irving carried out some of the early trials with the Decca Navigator which resulted in the Two Range Decca system for surveying. From 1950 to 1952 he commanded the *Dalrymple* in the Mediterranean, the Persian Gulf and on the east African coast. After service in the Department he went back to sea in 1957 in command of the *Vidal* in the West Indies. He came ashore for the last time at the end of 1958, returning to the Department, where he succeeded Collins as Hydrographer in 1960.

His period as Hydrographer was notable for incident and activity. He was able to persuade Their Lordships that it was both more economic and more efficient to build specially designed surveying ships rather than to use converted warship hulls, and the result was the *Hecla* and *Bulldog* classes. He also persuaded the First Lord, Lord Carrington, that it was time that the Department was concentrated at Taunton and that Cricklewood should be abandoned. He made a notable visit to his Russian opposite number at Leningrad in the *Vidal*. He was appointed CB in 1962, and KBE just before his retirement in 1966.

He remained active in maritime affairs in retirement. For a number of years he was a consultant for Decca. He was a Trustee of the National Maritime Museum, a member of the Management Committee of the Royal National Lifeboat Institution and chairman of its boat committee from 1969 to 1978, and was President of the Royal Geographical Society from 1969 to 1971. He was Acting Conservator of the River Mersey, and perhaps the tribute which sums him up best came from a tugmaster to whom he had presented a medal. The man said afterwards 'I've often heard of gentlemen, but I had never met one until I met Sir Edmund Irving today'.

He died on 1 October 1990 aged 80, four days after he had been present at the naming of a new lifeboat at Ramsgate.

Rear Admiral G S Ritchie, CB, DSC
Hydrographer 1966-1971

George Steven Ritchie was born in Burnley, Lancashire, of Scottish parents. He entered the Royal Navy through the Royal Naval College, Dartmouth. Through his father, then Secretary to the Port of London Authority, the young Steve met Sir Frederick Learmonth and became hooked on surveying. As a promising young officer his efforts to volunteer for the hydrographic service were thwarted until, commanding officer of his own armed trawler on the Palestine patrol in 1935, he forwarded his own name.

Early in 1936 he joined the *Herald*, Hardy then Jenks, in Hong Kong for surveys on the coasts of Malaya and Borneo. In 1939 he came home to the *Jason*, Jones, but within a few months transferred to the *Franklin*, Sabine, for surveys in Labrador. The American surveys were cut short by the outbreak of war, and *Franklin* returned to provide the control for the laying of the Channel Mine Barrage. Early in 1942 Ritchie was sent by sea round the Cape to join the *Endeavour* at Suez for surveys in the Red Sea and Gulf of Suez. After Alamein had lifted the threat to Egypt *Endeavour*'s surveyors were dispersed in Mobile Survey Units, surveying ports as they were captured to open them for shipping.

In 1944 Ritchie joined the *Scott*, Hennessey, for surveys in support of the Normandy landings, and then port opening work along the north European coast. Early in 1946 he was appointed to stand by the conversion of the *Sharpshooter* for surveying, and on her commissioning by Menzies went out to the Far East as her First Lieutenant. Returning from Borneo Ritchie was appointed to the Department at Cricklewood as Officer in Charge of Notices to Mariners. Two years later he was sent to Chatham to set up the Surveying Training Unit for the training of surveying recorders.

In 1949 Ritchie returned to sea in the newly completed *Owen*, Menzies, for deployment to the Persian Gulf. In June 1950 he was promoted commander and appointed to his first command, *Scott*. Before taking up this appointment it was changed, and Ritchie was flown out to Bermuda to take over *Challenger* from the invalided Bill and to continue her world oceanographic cruise. He left *Challenger* at the end of 1951 to become Superintendent of the Oceanographic Branch at Cricklewood. This lasted until 1954, when he was lent to the Royal New Zealand Navy for two years as commanding officer of HMNZS *Lachlan* and as head of the New Zealand Hydrographic Service. He was promoted captain while in New Zealand, and came back to London in 1957 as Assistant Hydrographer (2).

After two years in Whitehall Ritchie went back to sea in the *Dalrymple*, surveying in the Persian Gulf. In 1960 he became Assistant Hydrographer (1) at Cricklewood, where he was to serve for three years before going to his last sea command, *Vidal*, in September 1963. The ship was engaged in Operation NAVADO, a series of geophysical traverses across the North Atlantic Ocean. Also during this commission *Vidal* became the first British naval vessel to visit the Soviet Union for eleven years when she took the Hydrographer, Irving, to Leningrad.

Ritchie left *Vidal* in August 1964, was promoted rear admiral and took over as Hydrographer in January 1966. During his period of office the whole Department was finally concentrated at Taunton, as had been planned by Edgell in 1938. Chart metrication was started, together with the four-colour printing of Admiralty charts, and the new ships of the *Hecla* and *Bulldog* classes came into service. He retired from office and from the Navy in February 1971.

In 1967 Ritchie had led the United Kingdom delegation to the Ninth International Hydrographic Conference. At the Tenth Conference in 1972 he was elected President of the Directing Committee of the International Hydrographic Organisation. He spent the next ten years in Monaco, being re-elected for a second term in 1976.

On leaving Monaco in 1981 Steve, as he is always known, retired to his family home in Aberdeenshire, where he remains active as an author and petanque player.

Commander P B Beazley, OBE

Peter Bryan Beazley specialised in surveying in 1948, when he joined the *Sharpshooter*, Irving, spending some months in command of one of the ship's attached SMLs only months after joining. In 1949 he went to the *Owen*, Menzies, on her first commissioning for service in the Persian Gulf, and subsequently served in the *Franklin*, Hall, then *Cook*, Hatfield, and on loan service with the Royal New Zealand Navy.

Following a spell in the Department in the Notices to Mariners section he was appointed in command of the *Echo* in December 1960, becoming Senior Officer of the Inshore Survey Squadron in 1962.

In 1963 he was appointed Officer in Charge of Staff Charts (2), issuing radio navigational warnings, and in the following year he moved to Territorial Waters Officer, a post he was to occupy for the next twenty years. On his arrival in post the effects of the First United Nations Conference on the Law of the Sea, held in 1958, were beginning to be felt. Both the British law on territorial waters and the boundaries between our continental shelf and that of our neighbours required much revision and negotiation, in which Beazley was heavily involved.

He retired from active service in 1970, but continued in post, and was granted Honorary Commander's rank. From 1973 to 1982 he was an adviser to the UK delegation to the Third UN Conference on the Law of the Sea. He was also chairman of the IHO Commission set up in 1973 to establish a world wide system of Radio Navigational Warnings.

On his final retirement from government service in 1983 he was made OBE. In retirement he remains active as a consultant expert in territorial waters delimitation and law from his home in Somerset, and was appointed Commander of the Norwegian Order of Merit in 1993.

Lieutenant Commander D R Benson

Donovan Roy Benson began his surveying career when he was appointed to the *Scott*, Bill, in January 1947 for surveys on the east coast of Great Britain. A year later he went to commission *Dampier* under Collins for her passage out to and then surveys in the Far East. Returning home in 1950 he commanded SML 325 for two years working under the control of Berncastle in *Sharpshooter* before returning to the Far East and *Dampier*, now under first Roe and then Grattan. Service in *Sharpshooter* again, by now renamed *Shackleton* and in *Owen* followed before Benson was given his next command, *Egeria* in October 1960. He became Senior Officer of the Inshore Survey Squadron in March 1961. After a short spell attached to the Department for book-writing he became Hydrographic Information Officer from 1962 to 1965.

His last sea command was the *Myrmidon*, working on the east coast of England and taking part in a North Sea Hydrographic Commission survey off the coast of

Denmark in April and May 1965. He came ashore in 1966, and after a spell in Whitehall became Wrecks Officer at Taunton. He retired in 1975, taking up farming on the Devon/Somerset borders.

Lieutenant Commander E M Bradley

Edgar Michael Bradley, known to his contemporaries as Joe, took up surveying in 1953 as a lieutenant, joining the *Cook* under first E H B Baker and then Connell for surveys in home waters, including attendance at the Coronation Review. Service in the *Dampier* in the Far East under Grattan and Roe, and then in the *Scott*, Hatfield, at home, followed before he joined the *Cook*, again under Hatfield, for the passage out to the Pacific and participation in the Hydrogen bomb trials in the Monte Bello islands and surveys in the south Pacific from 1957 to 1960.

In 1961 Bradley went to *Dalrymple*, M.J.Baker and then Hatfield, for surveys in the Persian Gulf and off Cyprus, taking temporary command when Hatfield had to return home for family reasons. From 1962 to 1964 he was in charge of the Hydrographic School, during which time formal courses for officers were introduced. He then went south in charge of the R.N. Antarctic Survey Party, operating from, among other ships, RRS *John Biscoe* from which he made the first use of Two Range Decca in Antarctic waters.

At the end of 1965 he was appointed in command of the *Myrmidon*, surveying on the east coast. He came ashore to the Department at Taunton in 1968 as Wrecks Officer, retiring at his own request in 1969.

Joining the Port of Bristol as a hydrographic surveyor, he worked his way up the hierarchy to become Haven Master of the port from 1981 to 1994.

Captain R J Campbell, OBE

Richard John Campbell joined the Navy through the Royal Naval College, Dartmouth in 1946. He was drafted into submarines in the aftermath of the *Affray* disaster, but finally specialised in surveying in 1956, going to the *Dalrymple*, Winstanley, in time to participate in the Suez operation, and in the subsequent clearing up under the United Nations flag.

In 1958 he qualified as a Free Diver (H), a new qualification introduced at that time, before going to the *Vidal* for surveys in the West Indies under Irving. After service in *Dampier*, *Dalrymple* and again in *Vidal* he was sent to Devonport to take charge of the Hydrographic School in July 1964. In 1966 he returned to *Dampier* for her last eighteen months as her First Lieutenant. On her final voyage home he was in charge of the diving team which secured her propellor when the shaft parted, and then aided and abetted Cardno in rigging sails to speed her passage home.

In March 1968 he was appointed in command of the *Woodlark*, working on the west coasts of the United Kingdom. In September 1969 he went to the *Endurance* as both her First Lieutenant and in charge of surveys. He was promoted commander while in this post. Returning from the Antarctic in 1971 he was given command of the *Beagle* and was senior officer of the 'B' pair of coastals, working in the Indian Ocean. In the Maldives he carried out the last set of astronomical observations for geographical position made by a naval surveyor.

He returned to Devonport and to the Hydrographic School, by now in the West Battery of the barracks and a commander's post, for rather more than two years before going in command of the *Hydra* in 1975. In 1977 he attended the Senior Officers' War Course before taking up the post of Assistant Hydrographer with the acting rank of captain. Reverting to commander's rank he went back to *Hydra* for almost three years, before coming ashore to take up the post of Superintendent of Sailing Directions at Taunton at the end of 1982. He retired with the honorary rank of captain in 1983, remaining as SSD, a post which he still holds. He was appointed OBE in 1983.

Commander P G N Cardno

Peter George Noel Cardno joined the surveying service in January 1956, being appointed to the *Vidal*, Connell then Irving, where he was soon sent in command of a detached party surveying Oracabessa on the north coast of Jamaica. After two years he moved briefly to the *Shackleton*, Smith, before spending two years in the Far East in the *Dampier*, Haslam. His enthusiasm for observing and collecting was infectious, but could verge on the disastrous. He returned on board from a day's work on one occasion with two highly venomous sea snakes in his binocular case, and then wondered why the Medical Officer, as the ship's biologist, was not as keen as he was! He went in 1960 for two years to the *Owen*, Hall, before returning to the *Dampier*, this time under Pryor, as First Lieutenant.

In 1964 he was appointed in command of *Echo* and as Senior Officer of the Inshore Survey Squadron. When observing from one of the beacons in the Thames Estuary he and his party were trapped by heavy seas, two were washed away and drowned, and Cardno himself was commended by the subsequent inquiry for his bravery in his efforts to save them. He was then selected for early promotion to commander, in which rank he supervised the building of the *Hecla* and *Bulldog* classes on behalf of Hydrographer.

In 1966 he went back to *Dampier* yet again, this time to command her for her final commission. When she fractured her port propellor shaft in the Bay of Biscay on the way home he rejected all suggestions that she should put into another port, and not arrive at Chatham, her home port, in time for Christmas. By rigging awnings and boats' sails to augment the power of her one remaining screw she just made the lock entrance in the River Medway before the Yard closed for the holiday.

Cardno's last command was the *Vidal*, where he was commended for his handling of an ugly political incident when he made the first visit by a British warship for some years to Iraq.

He retired at his own request in 1969, and took the post of Chief Hydrographic Surveyor in Sarawak. With his customary enthusiasm and energy he turned out as much work, often almost single-handed, as a whole ship full of surveyors. He died in Kuching in February 1982 from injuries sustained in a fall in a building being prepared for him to occupy as his office.

Captain P J E Cheshire

Peter John Edward Cheshire joined the Navy in May 1954 as a National Service Ordinary Seaman. After successfully passing Upper Yardman training and being made Temporary Midshipman RNVR he transferred to the regular service in 1955.

Cheshire joined surveying in 1959, spending a year in *Shackleton* Smith then White, on the west coast of Scotland. He then went for two years to the *Dalrymple*, M.J.Baker then Hatfield, surveying in the Persian Gulf and the Mediterranean, before joining *Cook*, Hunt, in the south west Pacific in 1962. Here he spent much of his time in detached parties both in Fiji and the Gilbert Islands. In November 1963 he was in charge of a team which salvaged the 20-ton yacht *Fjord III* which had run aground on a reef in Nairai, one of the smaller islands in the Koro Sea.

Returning to England after *Cook's* grounding, Cheshire next stood by the conversion of the coastal minesweeper *Stubbington* into the surveying ship *Mermaid* and became her First Lieutenant under Read on commissioning in July 1964. Read had arranged her adoption by the Mermaid Theatre, and the union was sealed at a grand adoption party in the Pool of London with an impressive guest list of theatrical and naval luminaries.

In 1965 he was appointed in charge of the Royal Naval Antarctic party, based on the Ice Patrol Ship *Protector.* Two years later he went to the *Hydra*, Nesbitt, first as navigating officer and later as First Lieutenant. His time in her spanned both ocean surveys in the North Atlantic and work off the west coast of Africa. From October 1968 for two and a half years he was First Lieutenant of the Hydrographic School under first M.J.Baker than Nesbitt, and after that returned to the Antarctic as the First Lieutenant and charge surveyor of the *Endurance, Protector's* successor as the Antarctic Patrol Ship.

In 1974 Cheshire was appointed in command of the *Beagle* and as senior officer of the 'B' pair of Coastal Survey Vessels with the acting rank of commander, which was confirmed a year later. Further commands, including two and a half years in charge of the Hydrographic School, followed until he came ashore for the last time to the Department at Taunton as Director of Hydrographic Plans and Surveys, having been promoted captain in 1981. In 1984 he became the first Captain, Hydrographic Surveying Flotilla, controlling the operations of the surveying ships from offices in the old Master Ropemaker's House in Devonport Dockyard. He returned to the Department as Assistant Hydrographer before retiring on age grounds in 1990.

Lieutenant Commander R Dathan

Robin Dathan joined the surveying service as a lieutenant in February 1952, being appointed to the *Scott*, Grattan, working on the south coast of England. A year later he went to the *Dalrymple*, Bill, surveying in the Persian Gulf, the east African coast and the Mediterranean, where he carried out a survey of St Paul's Bay, Malta, in charge of a detached party. In 1956 Dathan joined the *Cook*, Hayter, working on the west coast of Scotland. Trials with Two Range Decca were followed by the use of this system for regular surveys, allowing the work to be progressed in poor visibility and at night, an aspect more welcome to the Hydrographer ashore than to the surveyors in the field.

For 1957 he was given command of SML 326, operating in the Thames Estuary and off East Anglia as part of the East Coast of England Survey Unit. The next three years were spent in the *Vidal*, Irving and then Connell, working in the West Indies and returning yearly to Chatham to lie up and to draw charts. In 1961 Dathan was appointed to the Department as Equipment Officer. Here he was involved in the procurement of oceanographic equipment following the upsurge of interest in that science, in the specifications for the design of the new surveying fleet ordered under Irving, and in the introduction of desk top computers to surveying chartrooms. Dathan returned to sea in 1963 as First Lieutenant first of *Vidal* under Ritchie, then of the brand new *Hecate* under Winstanley.

He obtained his first command, *Mermaid*, in 1967, surveying on the west coasts of Wales and Scotland. When she paid off at the end of the year he, together with many of his ship's company, transferred to *Fox* completing at Lowestoft. On commissioning in July 1968 *Fox* took over the work of *Mermaid* on the west coasts of the United Kingdom.

Dathan retired at his own request in January 1970, and has since held a variety of posts in the commercial surveying field both at home and abroad.

Lieutenant Commander J B Dixon

John Barry Dixon joined the surveying service in 1954, spending two weeks at the Survey Training Unit before being appointed to the *Owen*, Hatfield, surveying in the Persian Gulf. After serving in the *Dampier* and the *Dalrymple* he returned to the *Owen*, this time under Hall, in 1960. He was in charge of the shore party sent down to South Georgia ahead of the ship to put in control and survey the coastline at the western tip of the island.

A spell in the West Indies in Vidal under Roe followed before he returned to the

Antarctic in the *Protector* for the southern summers of 1962-63 and 63-64. In July 1964 he took command of the newly-converted *Myrmidon*, working her up and then surveying in conjunction with *Scott* in the southern North Sea. After a short time in the Department at the end of 1965 he went to Australia for two years from January 1966. On his return he stood by the *Anita Dan* in Harland and Woolffs yard in Belfast during her conversion to the Ice Patrol Ship *Endurance*, and became her first First Lieutenant on commissioning and in charge of her surveys.

In 1969 he came ashore to Whitehall for a year as Hydrographic Information Officer before going to command the *Beagle* and as senior officer of the 'B' pair with the acting rank of commander. He retired from the Navy at his own request in July 1971, and worked as a free-lance surveyor until a serious road accident incapacitated him.

Commander B S Dyde

Brian Sidney Dyde specialised in surveying as a lieutenant in 1959, spending a year and a half in the *Vidal*, Connell, on surveys in the North Western Approaches and in the West Indies. He was then sent to the School of Military Survey at Hermitage, Berkshire, for the School's officers' surveying course. On completion of this he went to the south Pacific, to the *Cook*, Paton, for 1961 and 1962. After two years at home in the *Scott*, Powell and then Martin, he returned to the Far East as the navigating officer of the *Dampier* under M.J.Baker. As well as her regular surveying round Malaysia and Hong Kong he was involved in her foray into the Indian Ocean to investigate possible sites for the UK/US base which, partly as a result of *Dampier's* work, was established on Diego Garcia.

He returned in 1966 to the new *Hecate*, Winstanley, transferring shortly after to the *Hydra*, Paton, for surveys in the North Atlantic. The following year he was put in charge of a large party surveying the approaches to Burtonport and Aran Island on the Donegal coast.

Dyde was given his first command at the end of 1967, the *Enterprise*, working as one of the Inshore Survey Squadron in the southern North Sea based at Chatham. In 1969 be began two years as Equipment Officer at Taunton, followed by six months in *Hydra*. Command of *Woodlark*, *Fawn* and *Hecate* followed, in the acting rank of commander from November 1973. He came ashore to his last post, Superintendent of Surveying Equipment, in February 1976. He retired at his own request, with the honorary rank of commander, in 1979.

In retirement he set up practice as an independent surveyor in Antigua, where he also acted as an Admiralty Chart Agent. He is now engaged in writing as a full-time occupation.

Commander R I C Halliday

Robert Ian Charles Halliday's introduction to surveying came in 1960 when he was appointed to the *Dampier*, Haslam, working in Malaya and Borneo. He came home in 1961 to the *Scott*, Roberts then Powell, surveying on the east coast of England. In 1962 he was back under Haslam's command in the *Owen* in the Indian Ocean for two years before going on loan service to New Zealand from 1964 to 1967.

On his return from New Zealand he went for six months to RRS *Discovery* before spending the next year in the Department. In February 1969 he was appointed in command of the *Enterprise*, followed in June 1970 by commanding the *Bulldog*, for two years in the Indian Ocean. Returning home in 1972, he took command of the *Echo* and was Senior Officer of the Inshore Survey Squadron, being promoted to commander in 1974. He then served in charge of the Hydrographic School from 1975 to 1977. He went back to sea in command of the *Hydra,* mainly in Iranian waters, from 1977 to 1979, then came into the Department at Taunton from 1979 to 1981, followed by command of the *Herald* from 1981 to 1982, in the Red Sea and Oman and taking part in the Falklands campaign, before he came ashore in 1982 to serve as Territorial Waters Officer until 1985. His last active appointment was Queen's Harbourmaster, Gibraltar, where he served until 1988 before retiring on the grounds of age in 1989.

Captain G L Hope

Geoffrey Lewis Hope joined his first surveying ship, *Dalrymple*, Winstanley, at the start of the Suez campaign in 1956. Towards the end of 1957 he transferred to the *Owen*, Hall, for surveys in the Indian Ocean and then, under Roe, in the Persian Gulf. In 1959 he returned to the *Dalrymple*, now under Ritchie, for more Persian Gulf surveys. Service at home in the *Shackleton*, Nesbitt, was followed by eighteen months in the Far East in the *Dampier*, Pryor then M.J.Baker. While *Dampier* made an oceanographical cruise in the Indian Ocean, Hope was left in charge of a boat party carrying out a survey of the Brunei River. This was during the Indonesian confrontation, and gave rise to the unusual situation that Hope and his party qualified for the award of the Naval General Service Medal (Borneo clasp) while their parent ship did not.

After a spell in the *Vidal* during which Hope took temporary command between Ritchie's departure and the arrival of Captain A. Cooper, RAN, he was appointed to the staff of the Hydrographic School as officers began to be trained there. He returned to sea at the end of 1968 for a year in *Hecla* under Haslam, engaged in North Atlantic surveys.

In December 1969 Hope gained his first command, *Fox*, taking her to the Caribbean early in 1970. After two years in *Fox* he was promoted to commander and transferred to the *Hecate*. Further commands, interspersed with periods in the

Department, culminated in command of the *Hecla* during the Falklands conflict. His last appointment was as Captain, Hydrographic Surveying Flotilla, from late 1985 to 1987.

In retirement he took up the post of Superintendent of the Tidal Branch at Taunton, which he still holds.

Commander J M Mackay, OBE

John Macdonald Mackay started surveying as a lieutenant in the *Sharpshooter*, Gordon then Penfold, in 1951, working on the banks off the Norfolk coast. After a number of appointments at home and abroad he was given command of the *Medusa* in October 1961. Just over a year later he went to the *Echo* as Senior Officer, Inshore Survey Squadron. Early in 1964 he went out to Australia for two years exchange service with the RAN, returning in April 1966 for a second spell as SOISS, this time commanding the *Enterprise*.

He came ashore in 1967 to act as Hydrographer's representative on the staff of the Commodore Superintendent Contract Built Ships, looking after the later stages of the building of the *Bulldog* class, and the conversion of *Endurance*. In this post and later as Superintendant of Survey Equipment he was involved in the initial planning for *Herald* and the commissioning and acceptance of the new computer-based surveying systems. In 1974 he retired with the honorary rank of commander into the post of Light Lists Officer. Two years later he left this to become the General Manager to the Northern Lighthouse Board, the general lights and buoyage authority for Scottish waters.

Lieutenant Commander J M Margetts

John Michael Margetts entered the surveying service in May 1955, spending a brief period in SML 324 surveying in the Downs before being appointed to the *Owen*, Pryor, for surveys in the Persian Gulf, Aden, both coasts of Africa and the Mediterranean. There followed service in the *Shackleton*, D.P.D.Scott, and *Scott*, Simeon, in home waters before he was sent out to the *Dampier*, Haslam, for surveys in the Malay Peninsula, Borneo and Hong Kong. Returning to England in 1961, he went back to *Scott* as navigating officer under Roberts until in March of the following year he went out to Australia for two years exchange service with the Royal Australian Navy. For much of this Margetts was in command of the converted lighter *Paluma*, surveying on the south coast of Papua-New Guinea, in New Britain and in Arnhem Land.

Back in England Margetts spent two and a half years in the Department in Whitehall in change of Radio Navigational Warnings. He then went back to sea, taking command of the *Echo* in November 1966 and becoming Senior Officer,

Inshore Survey Squadron in March 1968. His last sea command ended in January 1970, when he joined the Defence Intelligence Staff in London. He continued with Defence Intelligence as a civilian Intelligence Officer after his retirement from the Navy in 1980.

Lieutenant Commander R P F Martin

Rodney Peter Frank Martin started surveying as a lieutenant in 1950, joining the *Seagull*, Gordon, working off the south coast of England. In 1957 he was left in charge of *Dampier's* boats in Singapore to survey the Johore Strait while the ship was undergoing a major refit in Hong Kong, becoming her navigator when she emerged. After a spell in the Department's work study team at the beginning of 1961 he went to the *Owen*, Hall, for surveys in the Indian Ocean. Returning to England, he went in the summer of 1963 to the *Scott*, briefly as First Lieutenant to Powell before taking command himself in September. He paid *Scott* off for disposal at the end of 1964, then went to the *Dalrymple* for her last year and paying her too off for disposal, gaining something of a reputation in the service as a ship-breaker.

He went on an oceanographic cruise in RRS *Discovery* in the spring of 1966 before joining the Department at Cricklewood for three months. In September 1966 he was lent to the Royal Malaysian Navy to set up their hydrographic service and to command KD *Perantau*, the former *Myrmidon*.

He retired at his own request in April 1969, and was employed for some years in charge of Decca's survey operations in the Far East.

Lieutenant Commander A G Merriman

Anthony Gordon Merriman specialised in surveying in 1956, being appointed to *Dampier*, Royds, working in Borneo and off the west coast of Malaya. On his return from abroad in the summer of 1957 he spent some time drawing charts at Cricklewood before joining *Dalrymple*, Haslam, for surveys round the Isle of Wight until May 1958, when she entered refit. He spent the remainder of 1958 in *Shackleton* under D.P.D.Scott, then transferred to the *Vidal*, Connell, for a year's surveying in the West Indies.

A course at the School of Military Survey at Hermitage was followed by another two years in the Far East in the *Dampier* under first Winstanley and then Pryor. Returning home he obtained his first command, *Enterprise*, in April 1963, working on the east coast of England in the Inshore Survey Squadron under Mackay. In September 1963 Merriman went back to *Dalrymple*, now as First Lieutenant under first Hatfield and then Powell, working on the west coast and on oceanography in the North Atlantic.

He next spent two years, 1965 and 1966, back in the Inshore Survey Squadron, this time in command of *Echo*. Appointments as First Lieutenant of *Vidal* under Roe and Cardno and then of *Hecate* under Osborne* followed, until he was advanced to Charge Surveyor and appointed to *Echo* again, this time as Senior Officer, Inshore Survey Squadron, in January 1970. He remained as SOISS for three years, then after a year in command of *Beagle* as an acting commander came ashore at the beginning of 1974 to the Storm Tide Warning Service at Bracknell.

Merriman retired at his own request in 1977 to take up the post of Reviser of Tidal Literature, which he pursues from his home in Sussex.

Rear Admiral R O Morris, CB
Hydrographer 1985-1990

Roger Oliver Morris grew up within sight of Devonport Dockyard, and joined the Navy through the Royal Naval College, Dartmouth in 1946. He specialised in surveying in 1956, taking part in the SR2 course at the Survey Training Unit under Haslam before joining the *Scott*, Hatfield, for surveys in the Wash and on the south coast.

In 1957 he went to *Dampier*, Royds, in the Far East, remaining in Singapore with Martin on the Johore Straits survey while the ship was refitted in Hong Kong. After a course at the School of Military Survey he went to the *Owen*, Hall in 1960 in time to be sent with Dixon to spend three months under canvas on South Georgia. He served under Hunt in *Cook's* last commission in the south Pacific before being appointed to his first command, *Medusa*, in 1964, ranging the west coast from Plymouth to Barrow in Furness. Paying *Medusa* off to disposal in 1966 Morris then stood by the third Ocean Survey Ship, *Hydra*, building at Yarrows on the Clyde, and became her First Lieutenant on commissioning under Paton and then Nesbitt.

In 1968 he was given command of the brand-new *Beagle* working first in the North Sea and then wintering in the Persian Gulf. After a brief spell in Whitehall as Hydrographic Information Officer he went to command *Hydra* in the Malacca Strait, joining the relief operations after the East Pakistan cyclone soon after his arrival. Promoted to commander at the end of 1971, he spent from May to December 1972 in command of *Fawn* before coming ashore to to Taunton as Superintendent of Survey Planning.

Command of *Hecla* followed for three years surveying off the west coast of Scotland, during which time Morris was promoted to captain and took the ship to the Jubilee Review at Spithead. He then went to the Royal College of Defence Studies before returning to *Hydra* as senior officer of the squadron working on the coast of

---

*Captain J.Osborne, RAN, on loan to the Royal Navy.

Iran, where he quickly became involved in the evacuation of westerners from Bandar Abbas following the overthrow of the Shah.

Morris came ashore for the last time in 1980 to go first to Taunton as Director of Hydrographic Plans and Surveys and then to Whitehall as Assistant Hydrographer before being promoted to Rear Admiral and succeeding Haslam as Hydrographer in February 1985. He retired in 1990, and now lectures and writes on Naval Historical affairs from his home in Somerset.

Rear Admiral J A L Myres, CB
Hydrographer 1990-1994

John Antony Lovell Myres first became aware of hydrography when, as a sublieutenant, he was given the task of bringing up to date his ship's chart outfit which had not been corrected for six months. His first surveying appointment was to *Scott*, Simeon and later D.P.D.Scott, in October 1959, surveying in the North Sea and the Dover Strait. From August 1960 for a year he went to the *Dalrymple*, M.J.Baker, in the Persian Gulf, including involvement in the salvage of the burning tanker *Polyanna*. Two years in *Vidal* under Roe and, at the end, Ritchie followed, mainly engaged in surveys in the Caribbean.

In June 1963 Myres returned to *Scott*, Powell and then Martin, for a year, then went back to *Vidal*, still under Ritchie but later under Cooper (RAN), in time to take part in her Leningrad visit flying Irving's flag. He came ashore in 1967 to serve as Equipment Officer, first in Whitehall and then at Taunton. This period included the procurement of all the instruments needed to convert the surveying fleet from working in feet and fathoms to metric units.

In the summer of 1969 Myres was appointed to his first command, the *Woodlark*, surveying up and down the west coasts of the United Kingdom. He moved to the *Fox* at the beginning of 1972, and it was during his time in command, on her West Indies deployment in 1973, that HRH The Prince of Wales spent a month in the ship as a sublieutenant, the first member of the Royal Family to have served in a surveying ship. Myres was promoted to commander in June 1973. Three successive periods in command of *Hecla* were separated by two at Taunton as Superintendent of Survey Planning, during the second of which he was promoted to captain.

Starting in April 1982 he was lent for three years as Hydrographer RAN. Before going out to Australia he attended the XII International Hydrographic Conference in Monaco as an observer in the delegation of his temporary country. He returned in 1985 to serve first as Director of Hydrographic Plans and Surveys at Taunton and then as Captain, Hydrographic Surveying Flotilla before succeeding Morris as Hydrographer in February 1990. He retired in February 1994.

Commander R A G Nesbitt

Robert Alexander George Nesbitt joined the surveying service as a lieutenant in 1948. After a mixture of home and foreign appointments, including two years exchange service with the South African Navy, he went to the *Dampier*, Royds, as navigator in 1957. He was left in command of her during her long refit in Hong Kong the following year. After two years as Equipment Officer at Cricklewood from 1959 to 1960 he was appointed in command of the *Shackleton* in January 1961, working in the Irish Sea, the English Channel and the Channel Islands. A year later he went in charge of the Hydrographic School, then at St Budeaux, for eighteen months before being given a roving commission with an oceanographic flavour, spending time in RRS *Discovery* and on board the submarine *Grampus*.

He was promoted to commander in June 1963, and put his oceanographic experience to good use for two and a half years from August 1964 as Superintendent of the Oceanographic Branch at Cricklewood. Command of the *Hydra* followed, first on North Atlantic surveys and then off West Africa. In August 1969 Nesbitt returned to the Hydrographic School, now in HMS *Drake*, for a second time in charge. His last sea command was the *Hecla* from 1972 to 1974. Coming ashore for the last time he went to the Defence Intelligence Service for two years before retiring at his own request to take up the post of Superintendent of Notices to Mariners at Taunton. He was still in this post when he was tragically killed in a road acident while coming to work in July 1979.

Commander J Paton, OBE

John Paton took up surveying in 1947, being appointed as the second officer in SML 585. In 1948 he joined the newly converted *Dampier* under first Collins and then Hennessey, going out in her to the far East where she was to spend all her working life. He returned to England in 1951 to the *Franklin*, Royds, working on the west coast of Scotland and in the Thames Estuary. A year later he went back to the *Dampier*, now under Connell and working in the channels round the north-east tip of Borneo. Service at home in *Cook* and *Shackleton* followed before he was attached to the team preparing for Operation GRAPPLE, the testing of the UK's hydrogen bomb at Christmas Island. After serving as Resident Naval Officer, Christmas Island he returned to *Cook* for surveys in the SW Pacific.

He obtained his first command, the *Echo*, in June 1960, and was promoted commander at the end of that year. Leaving *Echo* on promotion, he spent a short time in the Office before being appointed in command of the *Cook* in March 1961. Towards the end of 1962 he came home to become Superintendent of the Oceanographic Branch for two years, after which he went in command of the *Owen* for her last year, working mainly in the approaches to the Straits of Gibraltar. With many of *Owen's* people he moved to the new *Hydra* for a year before he returned to

Cricklewood as SOB for the second time. His last sea command was the *Vidal* from the middle of 1969 to the end of 1971. He then went to the Hydrographic School at Devonport before retiring at his own request to take up the post of Naval Professional Officer at the Department of Transport, from which he retired in 1989.

Lieutenant Commander W M Powell

William Mason Powell started surveying in the spring of 1950 as a lieutenant. After junior appointments at home and abroad he spent a year from the summer of 1959 to August 1960 in the Department in Whitehall. He then went to the *Shackleton*, White, working o the west coast of Scotland. In July 1961 he went out to the *Dampier*, Winstanley, working in Malaya and Borneo.

On his return home he was appointed to his first command, the *Scott*, in July 1962, working on the east coast of England. In the autumn of 1963 *Scott* took the Hydrographer to Helsinki for an exhibition 'Navigare '63'. Early next year Powell moved to the *Dalrymple*, mainly working off Northern Ireland but with oceanographic cruises to Rockall and a NATO military oceanographic operation.

He came ashore in 1965, and after two years in Whitehall went to the Tidal Branch at Cricklewood, remaining there and then at Taunton even after his retirement on age grounds in 1977. He finally retired from the Office in 1992.

Captain R C Read, CBE

Richard Chester Read started surveying in 1952 after having served in submarines. After service in *Scott*, Grattan, in command of SML 326, and *Owen*, Hatfield, he was lent to the Royal New Zealand Navy from January 1957 for two years, during which he served in the *Lachlan* and in command of the SML *Takapu*. Returning to England in 1959 he spent a year in the *Dalrymple*, Ritchie, bringing her out of extended refit and going out to the Persian Gulf, where Read was involved in an observation programme to connect the Musandam Peninsula on the eastern horn of Arabia to the mainland of Iran across the Straits of Hormuz.

In 1960 Read was appointed in charge of the Hydrographic School, returning to the *Dalrymple*, this time under Hatfield, for more Persian Gulf and Indian Ocean surveys in 1962. After a year in *Owen*, Haslam, during which he was involved in the Zanzibar affair, he was given his first charge command, the newly converted *Mermaid*, in July 1964. Read arranged for the ship's adoption by the Mermaid Theatre, and the ship made a memorable visit to the Pool of London to seal the adoption. He was promoted to commander at the end of 1964.

A spell in the Directorate of Naval Intelligence was followed by command of the first of the new Coastal Surveying Vessels, *Bulldog*, from early 1968. After surveys in the southern North Sea Read took the pair of Coastals round the Cape to the Persian

Gulf for the winter of 1969-70. On their return in 1970 he went to Taunton as Superintendent of Survey Planning, being promoted to captain before going to the Senior Officers' War Course in 1973. Two years in command of the *Hydra* in the Pacific followed, after which Read returned to Whitehall as Assistant Hydrographer. He moved to Taunton as Director of Hydrographic Plans and Surveys in September 1977. He had been selected to suceed Haslam as Hydrographer in April 1980, but ill health forced his early retirement in November 1979.

Lieutenant Commander W J M Roberts

William John Mervyn Roberts was one of the large intake of officers into the Hydropgraphic Service at the end of the Second World WAr, joining the *Scott*, Bill, in September 1946, working on the east coasts of England and Scotland. In the following year he took command of one of her attached MLs, 585. In December 1948 he went to the *Dalrymple*, Day, then completing her conversion, for surveys in the Mediterranean and the Persian Gulf. He next served in the *Cook*, Collins then E.H.B.Baker, at home, before starting two years loan service with the Royal Australian Navy in 1953.

Returning home in 1955, after a series of short appointments he went to the *Owen*, Hall, as First Lieutenant in May 1956. After two years working mainly in the Indian Ocean Roberts came ashore to take responsibility for Radio Navigational Warnings in Whitehall. In 1960 he had a season in the Inshore Survey Squadron in command of the *Egeria* then in 1961 took command of the *Scott*, working on the east coast. This was his last sea appointment, and he came back to the Department in July 1962 as Officer in Charge of the Wrecks Section.

He retired at his own request in 1964 to take up an appointment with Decca's Survey Division. He remained with Decca until his untimely death in December 1988.

Commander C E K Robinson

Christopher Elgar Kemp Robinson joined the surveying service in December 1954, being appointed to the *Vidal*, Connell, surveying first in the northern Atlantic and then in the West Indies. He took command of SML 322 for his second appointment, in the East Coast of England Survey Unit. He next went to the *Dalrymple*, Hatfield, working first in the Persian Gulf and then in home waters. In 1963 he went back to Motor Launches when he was given command of the *Medusa* (the former HDML 3516), surveying independently up the west coast of England and Wales.

In 1965 he was sent out to the *Dampier*, M.J.Baker, working in Malaya and Borneo, with a foray into the Indian Ocean. Returning from the Far East in 1966 he was appointed in command of the *Egeria*, now part of the Inshore Survey Squadron under Mackay. In 1968 he was advanced to charge surveyor and promoted to commander. He went to the *Fawn* as her first commanding officer and as senior officer of the 'F' pair of coastals, surveying on the west coasts of the United Kingdom. When Fox went aground in a gale in the Minch he towed her off without outside assistance.

In 1970 Robinson moved to *Hecla*, mainly employed on North Atlantic deep ocean surveys. From February 1972 for two years he was Assistant Queen's harbourmaster at Chatham, an unusual general service post for a surveyor at that time. Returning to surveying in 1974 he went in command of the *Hecate* for a year before going to Whitehall as Assistant Hydrographer with the acting rank of captain. In 1976 he went back to sea in command of the *Herald*, working on the west coast of the United Kingdom and in the Atlantic.

He then came ashore to another general service post, as Deputy Captain Naval Drafting at Gosport from 1978 to 1980. In the summer of 1980 he returned to Taunton to the post of Superintendent of Notices to Mariners. Since his retirement in 1986 he has been involved in local government in the Taunton area.

Lieutenant Commander C G McQ Weeks

Colin George McQueen Weeks started surveying in 1950 as a lieutenant. After a range of appointments in surveying ships he was trained in work study techniques before heading the Hydrographic Staff Work Study team from March 1959 to March 1961. He then went to the *Vidal*, Roe, as First Lieutenant, where he brought his work study expertise to bear on the ship's maintenance schedules.

In the autumn of 1963 he was appointed in command of the *Enterprise* and as Senior Officer, Inshore Survey Squadron. In 1966 he came ashore to Cricklewood, where he was one of the Committee on Metrication. He retired at his own request in July 1967.

After working for the Decca Navigator Company and heading their surveying operations in the southern United States working out of Houston, Texas, he became a free-lance surveying consultant. He remains based in the USA.

APPENDIX 1

Principal Posts and their Holders

HYDROGRAPHER OF THE NAVY
1914 Parry; 1919 Learmonth; 1924 Douglas; 1932 Edgell; 1945 Wyatt; 1950 Day; 1955 Collins; 1960 Irving; 1966 Ritchie; 1971 Hall.

ASSISTANT HYDROGRAPHER (From 1951 to 1968 AH(2), Whitehall)
1919 Douglas; 1921 Glennie; 1924 Nares; 1928 Edgell; 1930 Nares; 1931 Edgell; 1932 Jackson; 1936 Law; 1939 Hardy; 1940 Wyatt; 1942 Southern; 1943 Day; 1944 Southern; 1946 Day; 1948 Southern; 1950 E.H.B.Baker; 1951 Hennessey; 1953 Collins; 1954 Irving, Lowry; 1957 Ritchie; 1959 Roe; 1961 Connell; 1963 Hall; 1965 Pryor; 1968 Hall; 1970 Haslam.

ASSISTANT HYDROGRAPHER (Bath)*
1939 Jackson; 1942 Nares.

SUPERINTENDENT OF CHARTS (From 1951 AH(1) and Superintendent of Charts at Cricklewood; from 1968 Assistant Director (Naval) at Taunton.)
1917 Edgell; 1920 Nares; 1923 Edgell; 1925 Haselfoot; 1928 Maxwell; 1929 Jackson; 1931 Law; 1933 Hardy; 1935 Wyatt; 1937 Day; 1939 Hardy, Jones; 1942 Jenks; 1944 Southern, Collins; 1946 E.H.B.Baker; 1949 Collins; 1951 E.H.B.Baker; 1952 Menzies; 1954 Irving; 1956 Connell; 1959 Irving; 1960 Ritchie; 1963 Roe; 1966 Cooper (RAN); 1968 Winstanley; 1970 Hall.

SUPERINTENDING CARTOGRAPHER (From 1949 Chief Civil Hydrographic Officer, from 1968 Assistant Director (Professional))
1917 H.H.Underhill, OBE; 1924 J.W.Atherton, ISO; 1933 H.Moody; 1935 G.B.Stigant, OBE; 1951 N.Atherton, OBE; 1962 L.N.Pascoe, OBE; 1972 D.W.Newson.

SUPERINTENDENT OF SAILING DIRECTIONS
1920 Davy; 1928 Reyne; 1944 Shearme, Jones; 1956 Hennessey; 1968 Pryor.

---

*See page 110 for the confused numbering of the two AHs during the War.

SUPERINTENDENT OF NOTICES TO MARINERS
1920 Grant; 1928 Harvey; 1944 Tennent; 1952 Lansdown; 1968 Penfold.

SUPERINTENDENT, OCEANOGRAPHIC BRANCH (from 1968 Superintendent of Survey Planning)
1952 Ritchie; 1954 Hall; 1956 Pryor; 1959 Winstanley; 1961 Hunt; 1963 Paton; 1965 Nesbitt; 1967 Paton; 1970 Read.

APPENDIX 2

Details of Surveying Ships

Condor class Sloop
Mutine   Built by Lairds, Birkenhead
Launched 1 Mar 1900, converted for surveying 1907, paid off for disposal
1925
980 tons.   180 × 32 ½ × 11½ ft.   13.5 knots

Cadmus class Sloops
Fantome   Built at Sheerness Dockyard
Launched 23 Mar 1901, converted for surveying 1907, paid off for disposal
1925
Merlin   Built at Sheerness Dockyard
Launched 30 Nov 1901, converted for surveying 1906, paid off for disposal
1923
1070 tons.   185 × 33 × 11¼ ft.   13.25 knots

Converted Salvage Tug
Hearty   Built as *Indra* by Thomson, Dundee.
Launched 18 Apr 1885, converted for surveying 1910, paid off for disposal
1920
1300 tons.   212 × 30 ft

Daisy class Surveying Trawlers
Daisy   Built by Duthie, Torry.
Launched 1911, paid off for disposal 1920
Esther   Built by Duthie, Torry.
Launched 1912, paid off for disposal 1920
510 tons.   125 × 22½ ft

Surveying Ship
Endeavour   Built by Fairfields, Govan
Launched 1912, reduced to accommodation hulk 1943
1280 tons.   241 × 34 × 11¼ ft.   13 knots

Aberdare class Minesweepers
Beaufort   Built by Ailsa, Troon, original name *Ambleside*
Launched 21 Feb 1919, paid off 1935, sold for scrap 1938
Collinson   Built by Ailsa, Troon, original name *Amersham*
Launched 30 Apr 1919, commissioned for trials only, sold 1922

Crozier	Built by Simons & Co, original name *Ventnor*
	Launched 1 Jul 1919, became South African Navy's *Protea* 1921
Fitzroy	Built by Lobnitz, original name *Portreath*
	Launched 15 Apr 1919, paid off 1938, converted to minesweeper, **Sunk 1942**
Flinders	Built by Lobnitz, original name *Radley*
	Launched 27 Aug 1919, paid off 1938, scrapped 1945
Kellett	Built by Simons & Co, original name *Uppingham*
	Launched 31 May 1919, Paid off 1938, **converted to minesweeper, scrapped 1945.**
	800 tons. 231 × 28¾ × 7½ ft. 16 knots

'24' class Patrol Sloops

Herald	Built by Blyth Shipbuilding Co, original name *Merry Hampton*
	Launched 19 Dec 1918, converted for surveying 1923, scuttled, **Singapore** 1941, raised and taken into service by Japanese as *Heiyo*, sunk by **mine 1944.**
Iroquois	Built by Barclay Curle.
	Launched 24 Aug 1918, converted for surveying 1922, paid off 1931, scrapped 1937
Ormonde	Built by Blyth Shipbuilding Co.
	Launched 8 Jun 1918, converted for surveying 1923, paid off 1936, **scrapped 1937**
	1320 tons. 276½ × 35 × 12 ft. 17 knots

Surveying ship

Challenger	Built at Chatham Dockyard
	Launched 1 Jun 1931, paid off 1953, scrapped 1954
	1140 tons. 220 × 36 × 12½ ft. 12.5 knots

Bittern class Surveying Convoy Sloop

Stork	Built by Denny, Dumbarton
	Launched 21 Apr 1936, paid off 1939, converted to Convoy Escort Sloop, scrapped 1958
	1100 tons. 282 × 37 × 10 ft. 19 knots

Halcyon class Surveying Ships

Franklin	Built by Ailsa, Troon
	Launched 22 Dec 1936, paid off 1952, scrapped 1956
Scott	Built by Scott, Caledon, Dundee
	Launched 23 Aug 1938, paid off 1964, scrapped 1966

Halcyon class Survey Minesweeping Sloops

Gleaner	Built by Gray, Hartlepool
	Launched 10 Jun 1937, converted to Convoy Escort 1939, scrapped 1950
Jason	Built by Ailsa, Troon
	Launched 6 Oct 1937, converted to Convoy Escort 1939, sold for merchant conversion 1946

Halcyon class **Minesweepers**

Seagull   Built at Devonport Dockyard
                Launched 28 Oct 1937, converted for surveying 1945, paid off 1950,
                scrapped 1956
Sharpshooter Built at Devonport Dockyard
                Launched 10 Dec 1936, converted for surveying 1945, renamed *Shackleton*
                1953, paid off 1962, scrapped 1965

All *Halcyon* class :
                830 tons. $230 \times 33\frac{1}{2} \times 7$ ft.   17 knots

Hastings class **Sloops**

Folkestone   Built by Swan Hunter
                Launched 12 Feb 1930, taken in hand for conversion to survey ship May
                1939, but never completed, and reverted to Escort Sloop December 1939,
                scrapped 1947.
Scarborough   Built by Swan Hunter
                Launched 14 Mar 1930, converted for surveying 1938, rearmed 1939 as
                Escort Sloop, paid off 1944, scrapped 1947.
                1025 tons. $266\frac{1}{3} \times 34 \times 11\frac{1}{4}$ ft.   16.5 knots

Harbour Defence Motor Launches

72 feet long, 54 tons full load, with a speed of 12 knots, a number of these
launches were employed on surveying during and after World War II, their
designation changing and their numbers altering in consequence after the
war. The following are those known to have been so employed, with changes
of number where known.

    1001 (later SML 1)
    1053 (later SML 2, then 322)
    1081 (later SML 3, then 323)
    1085 (later SML 4, then 324)
    1091 (later SML 5, then 325)
    1248
    1254
    1301 (later SML 352, then *Meda*)
    1368
    1387 (later SDML 3516, then *Medusa*)
    1393 (later SML 6, then 326)
    1411 (later SML 7, then 327)

SMLs 585, 586 employed surveying 1946 to 1948 were probably an interim
numbering of 1091 and 1393.

Bay class Frigates

Cook   Built by Pickersgill, original name *Loch Mochrum*, then *Pegwell Bay*
                Launched 1 Sep 1945, completed for surveying 1950, paid off 1964,
                scrapped 1965

Dalrymple Built by Pickersgill, original name *Loch Glass*, then *Luce Bay*
            Launched 12 Apr 1945, completed for surveying 1947, paid off 1965, sold to
            become Portuguese *Afonso de Albuquerque* 1966.

Dampier   Built by Smiths Dock, Middlesborough, original name *Loch Eil*, then *Herne Bay*
            Launched 15 May 1945, completed for surveying 1948, paid off 1968,
            scrapped 1969.

Owen   Built by Hall Russell, Aberdeen, original name *Loch Muick*, then *Thurso Bay*.
            Launched 19 Oct 1945, completed for surveying 1949, paid off 1965,
            scrapped 1970.
            1,600 tons. 307⅓ × 38½ × 12¾ ft. 18 knots

Surveying Ship

Vidal   Built at Chatham Dockyard,
            Launched 31 Jul 1951, paid off 1971, scrapped 1976
            1940 tons. 315 × 40 × 13 ft. 16 knots

Echo class Inshore Survey Craft

Echo   Built by J S White, Cowes
            Launched 1 May 1957, paid off 1985

Egeria   Built by Weatherhead, Cockenzie
            Launched 1957, paid off 1985

Enterprise Built by Blackmore, Bideford.
              Launched 1958, paid off 1985
              160 tons. 106¾ × 22 × 6¾ ft. 14 knots

'Ton' class Coastal Minesweepers

Mermaid   Built by Doig, Grimsby, original name *Sullington*.
            Launched 7 Apr 1954, converted for surveying 1964, paid off 1968, scrapped
            1970

Myrmidon Built by Doig, Grimsby, original name *Edderton*.
            Launched 1 Nov 1952, converted for surveying 1964, paid off 1968, became
            Royal Malaysian Navy's *Perantau* 1969
            360 tons. 153 × 28¾ × 8¼ ft. 15 Knots

'Ham' class Inshore Minesweepers

Waterwitch Built by J.S.White, Cowes, original name *Powderham*.
              Launched 27 Nov 1958, converted for surveying 1964, paid off from surveys
              1981, sold for scrap 1986

Woodlark Built by J.S.White, Cowes, original name *Yaxham*.
            Launched 21 Jan 1958, converted for surveying 1964, paid off from surveys
            1980, expended as target 1986
            120 tons. 107 × 22 × 5½ ft. 14 knots

Hecla class Ocean Survey Ships

Hecla   Built by Yarrows, Blythswood
            Launched 21 Dec 1964 still in service 1994

Hecate	Built by Yarrows, Scotstoun
	Launched 31 Mar 1965, paid off 1990, scrapped 1993
Hydra	Built by Yarrows, Blythswood
	Launched 14 Jul 1965, became Indonesian *Dewa Kembar* 1986
	2,800 tons. $260 \times 40 \times 15\frac{1}{2}$ ft. 14 knots

Bulldog class **Coastal Survey Vessels**

Bulldog	Built by Brooke Marine, Lowestoft
	Launched 12 Jul 1967 still in service 1994
Beagle	Built by Brooke Marine, Lowestoft
	Launched 7 Sep 1967 still in service 1994
Fox	Built by Brooke Marine, Lowestoft
	Launched 6 Nov 1967, paid off 1988, sold for commercial surveying 1990.
Fawn	Built by Brooke Marine, Lowestoft
	Launched 29 Feb 1968, paid off 1991, sold for commercial use 1992.
	2080 tons, $189 \times 37\frac{1}{2} \times 12$ ft. 15 knots

Improved *Hecla* class **Ocean Survey Ship**

Herald	Built by Robb Caledon, Leith
	Launched 4 Oct 1973 still in service 1994
	2945 tons. $250 \times 60 \times 16$ ft. 14 knots

Hired and requisitioned Vessels

Melisande	367 ton yacht hired 1918-19
Astral	450 ton former Belgian Pilot Cutter requisitioned as Barrage Balloon Vessel, 1940; surveying 1944-45.
Arpha	600 ton pleasure steamer hired 1940-45 for FHO Mediterranean working from Alexandria.
Gulnare	54 ft launch purchased for SCES, in service 1938-48
Nguva	180 ton tug hired in East Africa for surveying 1942-46
Valesca	180 ton drifter requisitioned for SHO Yarmouth 1940-44
White Bear	1822 ton yacht *Iolanda,* purchased 1943, converted for survey in Far East with printing equipment. Paid off and sold 1947

APPENDIX 3

New Charts New Editions and Notices to Mariners

(figures in brackets denote Fleet products in each category)

Year	New Charts	New Editions	Notices to Mariners
1920	32 (2)	223 (8)	2,137
1921	44 (8)	197 (15)	2,229
1922	50 (3)	235 (3)	2,031
1923	31 (4)	175 (6)	2,086
1924	34 (8)	158 (31)	2,048
1925	25 (5)	143 (10)	2,106
1926	32 (6)	81 (5)	2,215
1927	63 (1)	79 (3)	2,329
1928	49 (2)	56 (4)	2,025
1929	45	73 (2)	2,167 (27)
1930	46	75 (4)	2,163 (26)
1931	38 (1)	69 (2)	2,400 (25)
1932	51 (13)	81 (1)	2,060 (19)
1933	43	63	2,063
1934	47	83	2,163
1935	37 (5)	52 (1)	2,244 (35)
1936	29	45	2,550
1937	63	49	2,472
1938	47	71	2,780
1939	38 (42)	32 (26)	2,720 (297)
1940	146	153	*
1941	242	56	3,103 *
1942	131	108	2,871 *
1943	783	333	2,941 *
1944	744	273	2,959 *
1945	209 (193)	46 (144)	3,131
1946	31 (52)	47 (131)	4,207
1947	57 (27)	44 (10)	3,374
1948	52 (12)	33 (33)	2,939

1949	32 (3)	42 (3)	2,713 (229)
1950	54 (1)	57 (3)	2,558 (190)
1951	62 (11)	51 (3)	2,427 (118)
1952	70 (17)	56 (3)	2,713
1953	69 (13)	56 (1)	3,101
1954	101 (5)	57 (3)	2,924 (128)
1955	108 (5)	46 (4)	3,193 (176)
1956	106 (4)	75 (48)	3,240 (126)
1957	108	52 (1)	3,121 (169)
1958	83 (1)	40 (2)	3,032 (120)
1959	91 (3)	42	3,208 (133)
1960	103 (2)	59 (2)	3,208 (124)
1961	74 (1)	67 (2)	2,802 (129)
1962	86 (1)	65 (2)	2,810
1963	61 (6)	65 (1)	2,750 (110)
1964	70 (2)	52 (1)	2,772 (79)
1965	58	51 (3)	2,844 (113)
1966	110	102	3,050
1967	149	134	2,987
1968	90	70	2,683
1969	90	122	2,387
1970	84	148	2,469

* for these years Fleet and unclassified charts are not differentiated. The bulk of both new charts and new editions would have been for the Fleet.

APPENDIX 4

Chart Sales and Issues

Year	Sales (sheets)	Receipts (£)	Issues to the Fleet and OGDs
1920	760,843	96,984	429,246
1921	488,598	90,085	253,883
1922	351,283	55,040	260,270
1923	257,425	41,903	199,088
1924	350,226	56,540	280,622
1925	290,239	25,296	344,163
1926	286,757	49,299	348,036
1927	340,500	59,720	357,350
1928	354,947	61,429	371,005
1929	336,305	56,960	313,724
1930	322,327	54,320	397,008
1931	253,395	42,292	339,870
1932	200,506	34,446	338,476
1933	244,666	43,084	176,754
1934	240,700	41,640	152,100
1935	289,390	47,072	293,500
1936	308,298	51,351	178,717
1937	412,934	67,727	269,362
1938	469,772	76,569	433,886
1939	520,993	96,417	1,893,509
1940	440,023	89,133	1,789,094
1941	321,576	76,308	2,139,434
1942		66,793	4,055,000*
1943		35,741	7,609,000*
1944		34,590	7,350,000*
1945	546,265	99,919	5,633,562
1946	1,222,765	231,371	2,478,731
1947	1,099,210	231,371?	1,158,148
1948	998,738	182,330	878,413
1949	942,471	166,823	834,162

1950	928,456	155,451	632,939
1951	1,029,798	232,991	663,836
1952	1,014,198	247,116	653,856
1953	1,065,105	250,117	676,314
1954	1,056,744	255,343	675,454
1955	1,199,575	293,634	786,115
1956	1,262,701	321,798	766,337
1957	1,404,450	368,980	588,193
1958	1,292,572	350,506	562,015
1959	1,215,276	338,434	659,105
1960	1,410,094	381,513	547,543
1961	1,429,819	398,970	620,158
1962	1,367,554	378,364	568,991
1963	1,425,267	419,107	552,318
1964	1,478,615	450,416	609,426
1965	1,451,608	465,412	490,634
1966	1,660,865	539,071	582,823
1967	1,965,027	637,364	580,979
1968	1,815,651	592,226	517,124
1969	1,901,625	672,745	579,982
1970	2,088,232	935,305	655,505

*for these years total sheetage only is recorded, though receipts brought
to account are also given in the annual reports.

APPENDIX 5

Manpower Statistics

Year	Afloat in Svy Ships	Whitehall	Chart Branch Cornwall Ho/ Bath/ Cricklewood	Taunton	Total in Dept.
1920	837	203			
1921	877	135			
1922	1034				131
1923	1029				118
1924	897				118
1925		15	104		147
1930		15	96		263
1933	843				
1934	843				
1935	843	14	94		245
1936	701				
1937	788				
1938	835				
1939	835	23	127		423
1942		104	158		1237
1943		46	150		1600
1944					1600
1946	618				
1947	503				
1948	594				
1949	1079				
1950	993		296	520	927
1951	1052				
1952	1058				
1953	926				
1954	986				
1955	963	13	285	534	939

Year	Afloat in Svy Ships	Whitehall	Chart Branch Cornwall Ho/ Bath/ Cricklewood	Taunton	Total in Dept.
1956	890				
1957	840				
1958	981				
1959	1050				
1960	904	12	233	487	817
1961	1052				
1962	1076				740
1963	1017	29	211	504	744
1964	908	29	221	506	756
1965	859	29	227	492	748
1966	788	40	213	489	761
1967	800	40	211	513	764
1968	743	35		704	739
1969	761	25		759	784
1970	737	23		789	812

Before the middle '60s personnel statistics, particularly for the shore establishment, are patchy, and not always consistent. Those given above are the best that can be extracted from sometimes conflicting data.

List of Place-Names
with modern equivalents

Name in Text	Modern Name
Abyssinia	Ethiopia
Batavia	Jakarta
Bathurst (Gambia)	Banjul
Belgian Congo	Zaire
British Guiana	Guyana
British North Borneo	Sabah
British Somaliland	part of Somalia
Burma	Myanmar
Ceylon	Sri Lanka
Ellice Islands	Tuvalu
Falkland Islands Dependencies	British Antarctic Territories
Gilbert Islands	Kiribati
Gold Coast	Ghana
Karamania	S. Coast of Turkey—no modern equivalent
Kingdom of the Serbs, Croats and Slovenes	Yugoslavia
Leningrad	St Petersburg
New Hebrides	Vanuatu
Port Swettenham	Port Kelang
Queenstown (Ireland)	Cobh
Saigon	Ho Chi Min City
Siam	Thailand
Singapore Old Strait	Selat Johor
Straits Settlements	part of Malaysia, Singapore
Sveaborg	Suomenlinna
Trucial Oman	United Arab Emirates
Zara	Zadar

INDEX

Note: Page numbers in **bold** indicate biographical details.

Drake 209
draughtsmen 17, 18
DUKWs 105, 143
Dunkirk 119, 123
Duty Officer, WWII 115
Dyde, Cdr B S **237**

East Coast of England Survey Unit 147, 167–72,
    201, 218
East India Company 5, 6
East Indies, 1945 surveys 134
Echo 282
    1958 surveys 147, 171
    1960–70 surveys 201, 218–28
    details 252
Echo class 147, 171
    Asdic trials 207
    details 252
echo–sounders 124, 126
    automatic 76
    deep 201, 208
    development 28, 31–2
    drawbacks 152
    dry–paper 205, 207
    metrication 215
    portable 105
Edderton (later *Myrmidon/Perantau*) 204
Edgell, Vice Adm. Sir John A 28, 30, 73–83, **92–3**
    Operation OVERLORD 123–41
    Second World War 102–22
EG&G sonar 207
Egeria 147
    1960–70 surveys 201, 218–28
    details 252
Egret class 77
Egypt
    1920–22 surveys 30, 38–40
    1935 surveys 75, 87
    WWI surveys 24
    WWII 120–1
electronic position fixing
    Decca development 150–2, 207
    latticed charts 110
    radar 144
    Tellurometer device 152
    training 149
Elizabeth II, Queen
    Coronation Review 166
    welcome home squadron 167

Ellice Islands, 1959 surveys 172
Ellinor 16
Elliot, Hon. George 11
Elliott Bros 208
Endeavour 18, 30
    1914–18 surveys 21, 25
    1919–31 surveys 37–49
    1932–39 surveys 73, 74, 75, 77, 79, 84–91
    1942–3 surveys 131–2
    chart production equipment 92
    details 249
    paid off 1939 102
    paid off 1943 105
    recommissioning 89
    replacement 77
Endurance (formerly *Anita Dan*)
    1968–70 surveys 226–8
    conversion 206
England
    see also Bristol Channel; English Channel
    East Coast
        1809 surveys 7
        1919 surveys 37
        1920 surveys 38
        1921 surveys 39
        1922 surveys 40
        1923 surveys 41
        1924 surveys 42
        1925 surveys 43
        1926 surveys 44
        1927 surveys 45
        1928 surveys 46
        1929 surveys 47
        1930 surveys 48
        1931 surveys 49
        1932 surveys 84
        1933 surveys 85
        1934 surveys 86
        1935 surveys 87
        1936 surveys 88
        1937 surveys 89
        1938 surveys 90
        1939 surveys 91
        1939–45 surveys 102–3
        1940 survey 129
        1941 surveys 130
        1942 surveys 131
        1943 surveys 132
        1945 surveys 134
        1946 surveys 143, 159

Gilbert Islands
   1957 surveys 170
   1959 surveys 172
   1961 surveys 219
   1962 surveys 220
   1963 surveys 221
Gleaner
   1938–9 surveys 77, 79, 90–1
   Asdic experiments 152
   details 250
   replacement 144
   WWII role 102
Glen, Cdr N C 125, **181–2**
Glennie, Vice Adm. R W **58**
Gordon, Cdr D L **182**
Grattan, Cdr J C 149, **182–3**
gravity surveys 201, 203, 208
Great Britain's Coasting Pilot 5
Green, Lt Cdr R G **183–4**
Griffiths, Cdr R H **184**
Gulnare 16
   1940–45 surveys 104, 127, 129–34
   1945–60 surveys 143, 147
   details 252

H–hour 124–9
Halcyon class 77
   Asdic 'Cockchafer' 152
   conversion 144
   details 250–1
Hales, Lt Cdr S J **184–5**
Hall, Rear Adm. G P D **185–6**
Hall, Miss Margaret 213
Halley, Edmond 5
Halliday, Cdr R I C **238**
Ham class, details 252
Harbour Defence Motor Launches
   see also HDML...; ML....; SML
   details 251
Hardy, Capt N A C **58–9**, 75
Harvey, Capt. J R **59**
Haselfoot, Capt. F E B **60**
Haslam, Rear Adm. Sir David **186–7**
Hastings class 78
   details 250
Hatfield, Cdr H R **187–8**
Hayter, Lt Cdr P J D **188**
HDML *see also* Harbour Defence Motor Launches

HDML 106 107
HDML 1001 126, 127, 128
HDML 1053 126, 127
Hearty 18
   1914–18 surveys 21, 25
   1919 surveys 37
   details 249
Hebe 202
Hecate 14, 204
   1966–70 surveys 224–8
   details 252
Hecla 12
Hecla class
   1965–70 surveys 202, 204–5
   automatic plotting machines 215–16
   details 252–3
   gravity surveys 208
Hecla, ocean survey ship
   1965–70 surveys 204–5, 223–8
   automatic data logging 208
   details 252
Heiyo (formerly *Herald*) 106
helicopters
   Hecla class 204
   Vidal 146, 203
Henderson, Cdr D A **60–1**, 143, 149
Hennessey, Capt S J 126, **136–7**
Henry Hughes & Co. 32
Herald (formerly *Merry Hampton*, later *Heiyo*) 30,
203
   1924–31 surveys 42–9
   1932–39 surveys 73, 75, 79, 84–91
   1939–45 surveys 102, 106
   commissioning 41
   details 206, 250, 252
   replacement 76–7
   sounding gear 32
Herne Bay see Dampier
Heron (later *Auckland*) 77
Hi–Fix equipment 205, 207, 208
Hoborough, – (cartographer) 121
Hong Kong 30
   1939 survey 75, 90
   1946–8 surveys 144, 145
   1962 surveys 220
Hope, Capt G L **238–9**
Hughes, Cdr A M **97**
Hughes, Kelvin 207
Hunt, Cdr F W 106, **188–9**
Hurd, Capt. Thomas 6, 7–9

Printed in the United Kingdom for HMSO
Dd296894 2/95 C12 G559 10170